910
REF

018654

GCSE
Geography
for WJEC B

Andy Owen, Colin Lancaster,
Andy Leeder & Jacqui Owen

D0709816

WITHDRAWN FROM LIBRARY On 27/4/21

THOMAS TALLIS SCHOOL LIBRARY

NOT TO BE
TAKEN AWAY

DYNAMIC
LEARNING

HODDER
EDUCATION
AN HACHETTE UK COMPANY

Acknowledgements The assessment boxes in this book have been evaluated and adapted by Stuart Currie. Stuart is an experienced Avery Hill paper setter.

Text extracts and screenshots
p.8 Percentage of households living in income poverty by region (updated June 2007), Department for Work and Pensions; **p.9** *b* Centre for Sustainable Energy, screenshot of fuel poverty in Staffordshire from *www.fuelpovertyindicator.org.uk*; **p.9** *t* Joseph Rowntree Foundation, data on income poverty in the UK by ethnic group from *www.jrf.org.uk*; **p.11** *r* Association of Public Health Observatories, map of regions of England with lower than average standard of living (2006); **p.12** Screenshot from a GIS displaying low-paid workers from *www.poverty.org.uk/summary/maps.shtml*, reproduced by permission of the New Policy Institute; **p.13** South East Public Health Observatory, screenshot from the Community Health Profiles GIS from *www.healthprofiles2008.info/instant_atlas/svg_template_with_maps/atlas.svgz*; **p.18** *b* Data on variations on standard of living and quality of life in Newcastle-under-Lyme from *2001 Census*; **p.24** Screenshots from interactive atlas maintained by Barcelona City Council from *www.bcn.es/guia/welcomea.htm*; **p.26** *b* Screenshot from interactive atlas maintained by Barcelona City Council from *www.bcn.es/guia/welcomea.htm*; **p.29** Screenshot from interactive atlas maintained by Barcelona City Council from *www.bcn.es/guia/welcomea.htm*; **p.33** Molly O'Meara Sheehan, 'Where the Sidewalks End: How the Poor Combat Poverty Daily' from *Worldwatch* (November/December 2002), © www.worldwatch.org; **p.36** *bl* Map of key areas for new homes, Department of Communities and Local Government; **p.36** *br* Graph of changing size of households in England, Department of Communities and Local Government; **p.41** The Peabody Trust, web extract from *www.peabody.org.uk*; **p.53** *r* The City of Johannesburg website from *www.joburg.org.za*; **p.58** *b* Google search engine, © Google 2007; **p.59** Ndaba Dlamini, 'Jo'burg advertises its successes' from *www.joburg.org.za* (February 15, 2006); **p.62** *b* Countryside Council for Wales, from *Ynyslas Visitor Survey* (1996); **p.63** Countryside Council for Wales, screenshots from CCW's protected sites and landscapes map from *www.ccw.gov.uk/interactive-maps/protected-sites-map.aspx* (2008); **p.66** *b* Population structures in rural and urban wards of Shropshire in the West Midlands from *2001 Census*; **p.67** *t* Data comparing occupations in Shrewsbury and Bishop's Castle from *2001 Census*; **b** Data comparing ethnic population of Bishop's Castle and the West Midlands from *2001 Census*; **pp.68-69** Commission for Rural Communities, data on rural services and housing from *Homes for Rural Communites* (Commission for Rural Communities, 2005); **p.70** An extract from the song 'Country Life', written by Steve Knightley and recorded by Show of Hands, reprinted by permission; **p.77** Eurostat, data on mobile phone subscriptions in Europe; **p.99** ASEAN, diet in the delta before and after the cyclone, and percentage of deaths by age and gender from *Post Nargis Joint Assessment by the Tripartite Core Group* (July 2008); **p.100** *b* BBC Springwatch, website screenshot of frogspawn sightings; **p.105** *tr* Environment Canada, Data on mean temperature in Churchill, Canada in April and May in selected years from *http://climate.weatheroffice.ec.gc.ca/climateData/canada_e.htmls*; **p.107** *t* Thomas R Knutson, US National Oceanic and Atmospheric Administration / GFDL; *m* Dr Malcolm Ramsay, © Jim Metzner Productions, Inc.; *b* Environment Agency, data on closures of the Thames Barrier, 1983 - 2007; **p.117** *tr* Robert Lawton, Department of Biological Sciences, University of Alabama, Rainforest Alliance Neotropics Communications Eco-Exchange; **p.119** *l* Earthlands, protected areas (including forest reserves) in Central America and Mexico, Institute for

Environmental Awareness; **p.122** Screenshot from *www.groundwateruk.org/html/basics/basics9.htm*; **p.126** *b* Table of climate data, The South African Weather Service; **p.127** *t* Center for Sustainability & the Global Environment, SAGE, Hydrographs (data) from *www.sage.wise.edu/riverdata/index.php?qual=256*; **p.132** *r* Rainfall and discharge data for R Llobregat, Barcelona (May 2007-May 2008) from *http://aca.gencat.net:2020/sdim/visor.co*; **p.158** Arctic Adventures, 'River Fun: RiverRafting on the Hvita river right next door to Geysir in Iceland' from *www.adventures.is*, reproduced by permission; **p.159** Icelandic Tourist Board, data on leisure activities of tourists from *www.visitIceland.com*; **p.163** Viewpoints taken from icWales website from *www.walesonline.co.uk*, © Western Mail & Echo Ltd 2007 and BBC Wales; **p.183** The World Bank, data on male employment in Mali, and changing employment structure by sector; **p.185** *m* Eurostat, percentage of the population of Europe with internet access (2007); **p.186** *b* West Midlands Regional Observatory, data on Jobs gained or lost in the West Midlands, 2000-05; **p.189** Daouda Ballow, 'Waste recycling; an example of informal work' from *www.oxfam.org.uk/coolplanet* (Oxfam, 2007); **p.191** *t* Extract from *Rural Women in the Sahel and their Access to Agricultural Extension: Overview of Five Country Studies*, 1994, World Bank Report; **p.203** *tl* Examples of India's interdependance with the world economy from *www.forbes.com/2008/04/01*; *bl* Mobile phone customers in the six largest mobile markets from *www.celluar-news.com*; **p.205** United Nations Human Development, data on the digital divide: percentage of population who have internet access; **p.207** *r* Data on average annual salaries for Indian health workers in India from *www.payscale.com/research* (2008); **p.215** *r* Data on cocoa supply and demand, 2007/2008 from *ICCO Quarterly Bulletin of Cocoa Statistics*, Vol. XXXIV, No. 2; **p.219** *t* The World Bank, data on GNI per person 2008 for the countries of West Africa (2008); *b* UNICEF, data on health indicators for Mali and Niger; **p.224** *b* 'A national issue' (extract) from *The Guardian* (23 June 2008); **p.228** BBC One logo, reproduced by permission; ITV 1 logo, reproduced by permission of ITV Network Ltd; **p.228** Redrawn maps of the increase / decrease in audiences of regional programmes, 1998-2003 from *www.ofcom.org.uk*; **p.229** James Purnell, extract from a speech to the Institute for Public Policy Research from *www.culture.gov.uk/reference_library/minister_speeches/2050.aspx*; **p.233** Nokia, data on Nokia's employees 2003-2007 and Nokia's sales 2003-2007; **p.235** *l* International Telecommunication Union, screenshot of mobile phone subscribers in Africa from *www.itu.int*, reproduced by kind permission of ITU; **p.240** *br* Eurostat, data on overfishing by European Union countries; **p.245** *t* UNICEF, website data on Pacific population and data on Pacific region development; **p.253** *tl* Galapagos National Park, data on tourist arrivals to the Galapagos; **p.256** International Galapagos Tour Operators Association, website extract (2007).

Crown copyright material is reproduced under Class Licence Number CO2P0000060 with the permission of the Controller of HMSO.

Maps on **pp.21, 39, 47, 162, 176, 227,** reproduced from Ordnance Survey mapping with the permission of the Controller of HMSO, © Crown copyright.

Every effort has been made to trace all copyright holders, but if any have been inadvertently overlooked the Publishers will be pleased to make the necessary arrangements at the first opportunity.

Although every effort has been made to ensure that website addresses are correct at time of going to press, Hodder Education cannot be held responsible for the content of any website mentioned in this book. It is sometimes possible to find a relocated web page by typing in the address of the home page for a website in the URL window of your browser.

Hachette Livre UK's policy is to use papers that are natural, renewable and recyclable products and made from wood grown in sustainable forests. The logging and manufacturing processes are expected to conform to the environmental regulations of the country of origin.

Orders: please contact Bookpoint Ltd, 130 Milton Park, Abingdon, Oxon OX14 4SB.
Telephone: (44) 01235 827720. Fax: (44) 01235 400454. Lines are open 9.00 – 5.00, Monday to Saturday, with a 24-hour message answering service. Visit our website at www.hoddereducation.co.uk

© Andy Owen, Colin Lancaster, Andy Leader and Jacqui Owen 2009
First published in 2009 by
Hodder Education,
An Hachette UK company
338 Euston Road
London NW1 3BH

Impression number   5 4 3 2

Year   2014 2011 2012 2011 2010 2009

All rights reserved. Apart from any use permitted under UK copyright law, no part of this publication may be reproduced or transmitted in any form or by any means, electronic or mechanical, including photocopying and recording, or held within any information storage and retrieval system, without permission in writing from the publisher or under licence from the Copyright Licensing Agency Limited. Further details of such licences (for reprographic reproduction) may be obtained from the Copyright Licensing Agency Limited, Saffron House, 6–10 Kirby Street, London EC1N 8TS.

Cover photo Women selling food at the market, Accra, Ghana © Sven Torfinn/Panos Pictures
Illustrations by Oxford Illustrators, Barking Dog and DC Graphic Design Ltd
Typeset in 11.5pt Times by DC Graphic Design Limited, Swanley Village, Kent
Printed in Italy

A catalogue record for this title is available from the British Library

ISBN: 978 0340 983737

Contents

018654

Introduction

About this book

The structure of the book

Your WJEC GCSE Geography course is divided into three themes. Each theme takes about a term and a half of your two-year course to complete. This book also has three sections: one for each theme of the course.

The main features of the book

This book includes the following features which have been designed to try to help you make the most of your course and prepare you for your examination.

Case studies

A case study is an example of a geographical concept or issue. For a good case study you will need to know:

- the name of the place and where in the world your case study is located
- what this is a good example of
- a few simple facts or figures.

To make you aware of these case studies we have used the above icon. The icon is used at the beginning of the case study.

Focus on ... case studies

The examiners have found that if you try to learn too many different case studies you might get them confused with each other! So we have used some places several times as examples of different aspects of geography. This will allow you to focus on a few places in much more detail, so we have called them Focus on ... case studies. The icon for these (shown above) is used in the same way as the case study icon.

Examiner's Tips

The examiner's tips sections are designed to help you prepare for standard questions that are asked in the examinations. They are spread throughout the book. When you are doing an activity in the book and an exam technique section could give you some help, this table will help you find them easily. The above icon will make them easy to find on the page.

Activities

The activities in the book are designed to get you doing a number of things:

- discussing geographical issues
- analysing data in the maps, graphs and photos
- understanding concepts and case studies
- practising examination type questions.

Internet

The internet is a useful geographical resource. It contains facts that you could use to extend your case study notes. It's also great for finding and explaining people's opinions. We've used the icon above wherever we think there is a useful website that could add extra detail to the book. This icon is also used in some internet research boxes. These boxes are designed to maximise your search skills when you are surfing the net for geographical information.

Going Further

Going Further sections cover some interesting issues that are not essential to your understanding of GCSE Geography, but might lead you into new areas of research. Geography is a popular choice at AS level. Going Further might just get you thinking about this next step.

Figure 1 The location of case studies (outside the UK) that are used in this book

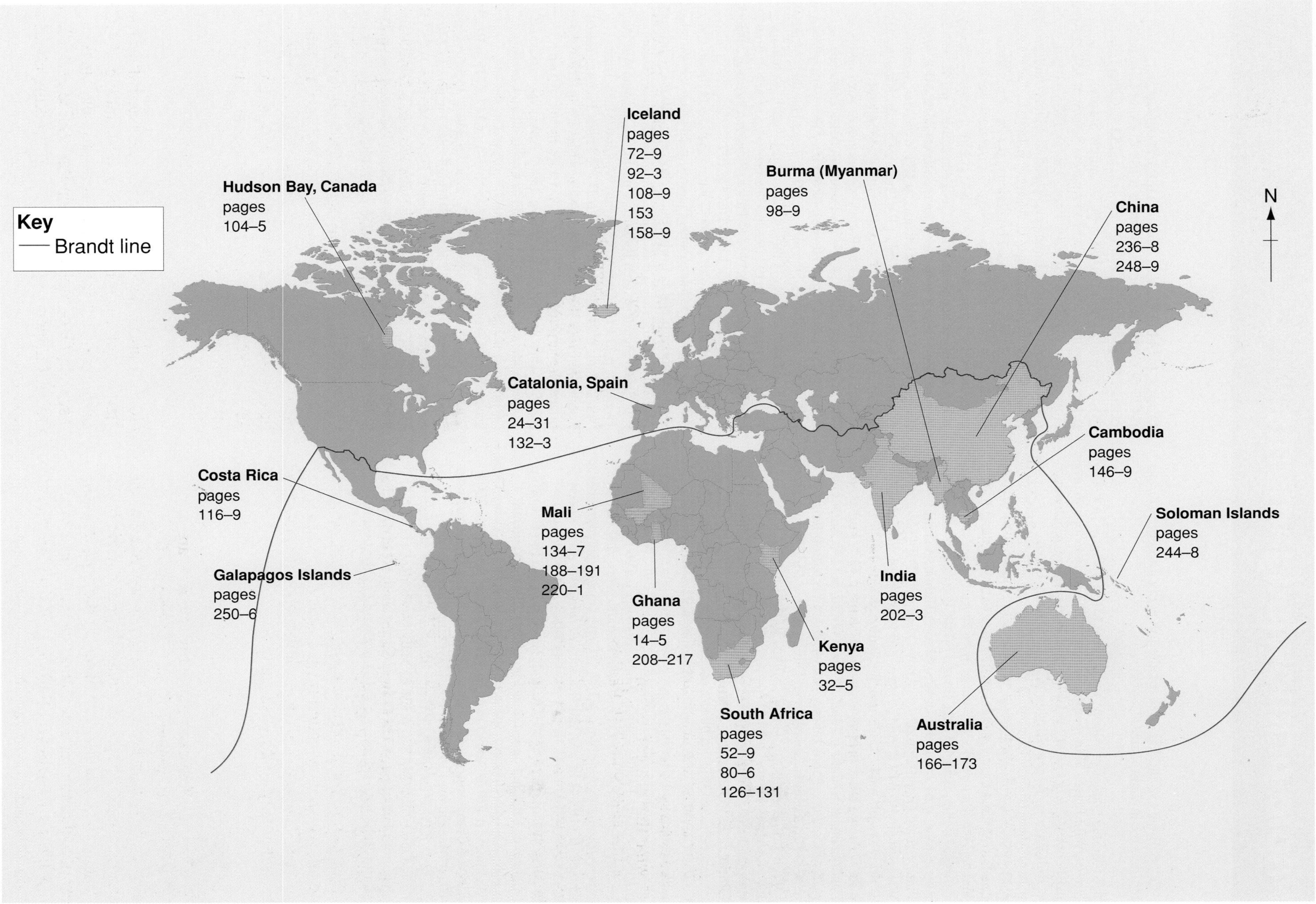

Key

— Brandt line

Hudson Bay, Canada
pages
104–5

Iceland
pages
72–9
92–3
108–9
153
158–9

China
pages
236–8
248–9

Burma (Myanmar)
pages
98–9

Cambodia
pages
146–9

Soloman Islands
pages
244–8

Catalonia, Spain
pages
24–31
132–3

India
pages
202–3

Australia
pages
166–173

Mali
pages
134–7
188–191
220–1

Kenya
pages
32–5

South Africa
pages
52–9
80–6
126–131

Costa Rica
pages
116–9

Ghana
pages
14–5
208–217

Galapagos Islands
pages
250–6

N

Photo acknowledgements

The publishers would like to thank the following for permission to reproduce copyright material.

p.7 *t* © Stan Gamester/Alamy, *tm* © Dave Ellison/Alamy, *tb* © Chris Howes/Wild Places Photography/Alamy, *b* © Ashley Cooper/Corbis; **p.10** *both* © Andy Owen; **p.14** *l* © Still Pictures/Jorgen Schytte, *r* © Still Pictures/Jorgen Schytte; **p.20** *all* © Andy Owen; **p.26** © Alamy/Tony Vilches; **p.32** © Photo by Adam Rogers, UNCDF; **p.34** © Sean Sprague/Alamy; **p.38** *all* © Andy Owen; **p.39** WWT London Wetland Centre/picture © Berkeley Homes; **p.40** © Raf Makda/View Pictures/Rex Features; **p.46** © Andy Leeder; **p.48** *all* © Andy Leeder; **p.58** © Getty Images/Mark Peters; **p.60** © Peter Bigglestone; **p.61** *l* © Getty Images/Maeers/Hulton, *r* © Still Pictures/Paul Glendell; **p.62** *l* © Andy Owen, *r* © The Photolibrary Wales/Alamy; **p.64** *l* © Andy Owen, *r* © Keith Burdett/Alamy, *b* © Andy Owen; **p.68** *l* © Christopher Furlong/Getty Images; **p.70** © Andy Owen; **p.71** © Peter Bigglestone; **p.72** © Ferðakort & Landmælingar Íslands; **p.73** *all* © Andy Owen; **p.74** © Andy Owen; **p.75** *t* © Science Photo Library/NASA, *b* © Corbis/Bob Krist; **p.78** © Rex Features/Splashdown Direct; **p.79** © Still Pictures/Nick Cobbing; **p.80** © Corbis/David Turnley; **p.81** © Jeremy Jowell/iAfrika Photos; **p.84** © Alamy/Stuart Abraham; **p.87** *t* © Still Pictures/Jacques Jangoux, *bl* © NASA Goddard Space Flight Centre, *br* © Rex Features; **p.88** © NASA/Image Courtesy GOES Project Science Office; **p.90** © Space Science and Engineering Center, University of Wisconsin, Madison; **p.92** © Andy Owen; **p.96** © http://visibleearth.nasa.gov/view_detail.php?id=6204; Jacques Descloitres, MODIS Rapid Response Team, NASA/GSFC; **p.105** © Nature Picture Library/Mats Forsberg; **p.106** *t* © Rex Features/Sipa Press, *c* © Corbis/Arko Datta/Reuters, *b* © Getty Images/Simmons Aerofilms; **p.108** © Getty Images/photographer's Choice; **p.110** *t* © FLPA/Paul Hobson, *all others* © Andy Owen; **p.112** © Webb Aviation; **p.113** *t* © Still Pictures/L.F. Postl, *b* © Andy Owen; **p.114** © NHPA/Jordi Bas Casas; **p.116** *t* © Corbis/Michael & Patricia Fogden, *b* © Photolibrary/Peter Weimann; **p.118** © NASA/Goddard Space Flight Centre; **p.119** © Alamy/Celia Mannings; **p.120** © Andy Owen; **p.121** © Simon Robinson, 2004; **p.129** © Transformation Resource Centre; **p.131** *t* © International Water Management Institute, *b* © PlayPumps International; **p.132** © JOSEP LAGO/AFP/Getty Images; **p.134** All © Jesse Allen, Earth Observatory/NASA; **p.136** © Mark Newham eye ubiquitous/hutchison; **p.138** © Steve Sant/Alamy; **p.141** © Richard Martin-Roberts/Getty Images; **p.142** © David Goddard/Getty Images; **p.144** © Richard Stanton/UPPA/Photoshot; **p.147** © Corbis/Richard T. Nowitz; **p.150** © Colin Lancaster; **p.151** *l* © Andy Owen, *r* © PA Photos; **p.152** © Colin Lancaster; **p.153** © Andy Owen; **p.154** *both* © Andrew Stacey; **p.155** © Andrew Stacey; **p.157** © Andrew Stacey; **p.158** © Arctic Adventures; **p.160** *t* © Science Photo Library/M-SAT Ltd, *b* © US Army Corps of Engineers; **p.165** © Alamy/Andrew Palmer; **p.166** © Rex Features/James D. Morgan; **p.168** *l* © Getty Images/Tim Graham, *r* © NHPA/A.N.T. Photolibrary; **p.170** *t* Australian Government Bureau of Meteorology © Commonwealth of Australia, reproduced by permission, *b* © NASA; **p.174** © Andrew Stacey; **p.176** © Robert Seago; **p.177** © GeoPerspectives; **p.181** *tl* © Still Pictures/Ron Giling, *tr* © Getty Images/Raveendran/AFP, *bl* © Getty Images, *br* © Corbis/Strauss/Curtis; **p.182** *tl* © Alamy/Jim West, *tr* © Alamy/David Pearson, *bl* © PA Photos/Thomas Kienzle/AP, *br* © PurestockX; **p.185** © Corbis/Pierre Vinet/Universal Pictures/ZUMA; **p.186** *t* © Potteries Museum & Art Gallery, *b* © Andy Owen; **p.188** *t* © Panos Pictures/Dieter Telemans, *bl* © Panos Pictures/Crispin Hughes, *br* © Getty Images/Seyllou/AFP; **p.189** © Alamy/James Hawkins; **p.191** © Janet Henshall Momsen (1991) Women and development in the third world_ Routledge_ Figure 3_2 page 39; **p.192** *l* © Jo Hale/Getty Images, *r* © Source Thin Black Lines, page 36; **p.194** *l* © Panos_Pictures/Christien Jaspars, *r* © page 24_ Thin Black Lines DEC; **p.197** © Panos Pictures/Giacomo Pirozzi; **p.199** © Panos Pictures/Alfredo Caliz; **p.203** © Stuart Freedman/Panos Pictures; **p.207** © PA Photos/Kirsty Wigglesworth; **p.208** © Corbis/Flip Schulke; **p.210** *tl* © Christian Aid/Austin Hargreaves, *tr* © Corbis/Reinhard Krause/Reuters, *b* © Panos Pictures/Karen Robinson; **p.212** © Christian Aid/Penny Tweedie; **p.213** *l* © Oxfam, *r* © Greg Williams/Make Trade Fair/Oxfam; **p.216** © Fairtrade®; **p.217** © Panos Pictures/Karen Robinson; **p.218** © Practical Action/Lucy Stevens; **p.220** © Getty Images/Issouf Sanogo/AFP; **p.221** © Panos Pictures/Crispin Hughes; **p.225** © Huw John/Rex Features; **p.230** © Nokia 2009; **p.232** © Corbis/Andreas Gebert/DPA; **p.233** © Corbis/Claro Cortes IV/Reuters; **p.235** © Corbis/Strauss/Curtis; **p.236** © Getty Images/Goh Chai Hin/AFP; **p.237** © NASA; **p.242** © Thin Black Lines (1988) ISBN 0-948838-02-7_ DEC; **p.244** © Jocelyn Carlin/Panos Pictures; **p.245** © Natalie Behring/Panos Pictures; **p.246** *t* © Natalie Behring/Panos Pictures, *m* © Forests Monitor, *b* © Forests Monitor; **p.247** © Natalie Behring/Panos Pictures; **p.250** © Heidi Snell/Visual Escapes; **p.253** © Corbis/Stuart Westmorland; **p.254** © Photolibrary/Mark Jones; **p.255** © Photolibrary/C. C. Lockwood.

The Big Picture

Most of the residents moving into our cities are young professionals or students. So do we still need to provide the facilities needed by young families such as schools and safe open space?

Rising house prices are a problem for first-time buyers. Do we need to build more new property to rent?
Can we learn from our neighbours in Europe, where renting from private landlords is a more popular option?

What should be done with the older terraced houses in our industrial cities? Their demolition is controversial.
Do the older parts of our cities need a makeover?

The suburban semi-detached houses built between the First and Second World Wars have provided popular homes for many families, but what should we build in the future for young families?

Chapter 1
Quality of life and standard of living

KEY QUESTIONS

- How is quality of life different from standard of living?
- How do quality of life and standard of living vary in urban and rural areas?

Measuring standard of living in the UK

One of the key concepts studied in this theme is inequality. Whether we are studying the UK or a developing country such as Ghana, it is a fact that some people are wealthier than others. Study of quite small areas (such as Newcastle-under-Lyme, the town featured in Chapter 2) shows that some districts have wealthy residents, whilst other communities have many people living in poverty. But how do we measure wealth and poverty, and is it simply our income that makes us happy with where we live?

Income, or lack of it, is the usual way to define someone's **standard of living**. Incomes depend on a variety of factors such as:

- local levels of unemployment and the availability of suitable work
- whether work is full-time or part-time
- the qualifications and level of skill required to do the job.

In the UK the government records both individual and household income. This is necessary to give a true picture of poverty: for example, someone might have a low-paid or part-time job but be living with a partner who has a much higher income. The household income for this couple is likely to be much higher than for a single parent who happens to have only part-time work. It is these household income figures that are used to define poverty in the UK. A household is said to be in **income poverty** if its income is less than 60 per cent of the contemporary UK median (average) household income. Using this definition the UK government estimates that:

- 3.9 million children in the UK live in poverty
- half of all lone parents live in poverty
- 22% of all UK households live in poverty
- 19% of all pensioners live in poverty.

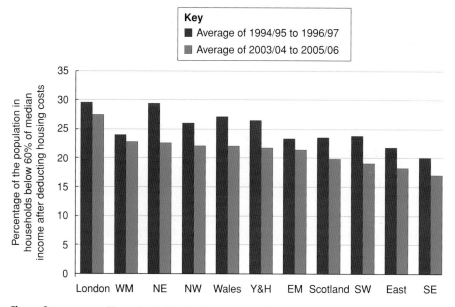

Figure 1 Percentage of households living in income poverty by region

The Joseph Rowntree Foundation is a UK charity that conducts research into the causes of social problems. Its research suggests that people living in poverty are unlikely to have a high-street bank account, have poor access to healthy food and are likely to spend more than 10 per cent of income on energy bills (the last is known as **fuel poverty**). Whilst the percentage of people living in income poverty has dropped slowly over the last ten years, it is thought that the number of people in fuel poverty has risen sharply as the cost of heating rose dramatically between 2007 and 2008.

Figure 2 Income poverty: the percentage of households living in poverty in the UK by ethnic group. Source: www.jrf.org.uk

Ethnic group	Percentage living in income poverty
Bangladeshi	67
Pakistani	55
Black African	46
Black Caribbean	30
Indian	28
White	19

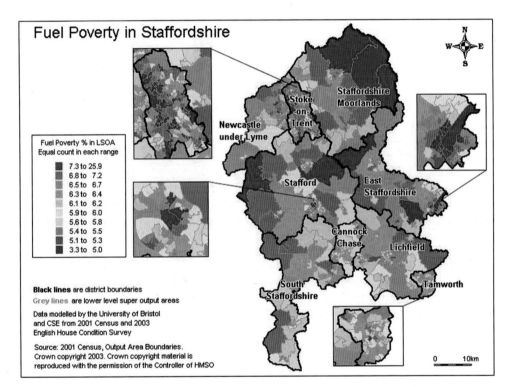

Figure 3 Fuel poverty in Staffordshire (percentage of households in each district that spend more than 10 per cent of their income on energy bills). Source: www.fuelpovertyindicator.org.uk

Activity

1 **a)** Make definitions for all the terms in bold on these two pages.
   b) Give three different reasons why a household might experience poverty.

2 Use Figure 1. Describe what has happened to poverty in different regions over time.

3 Suggest why it is important that the government is aware of the differences shown in Figure 2.

4 Study Figure 3.
   a) Describe the distribution (see page 25) of areas that have the highest percentage of fuel poverty.
   b) Would you expect people in rural or urban parts of the UK to have greater fuel poverty? Explain your answer.
   c) Using an atlas, or the internet, investigate whether fuel poverty is higher in urban or rural areas of Staffordshire.

How is quality of life different from standard of living?

Income isn't the only factor to influence how we feel about where we live. We might have a reasonable income but if our neighbourhood has a high crime rate, poor services (for example no leisure facilities or green spaces) and there's a busy road outside the front door, we might experience a relatively poor **quality of life**. Quality of life is a measure of the happiness or contentment that we feel and is influenced by factors such as:

- **Personal health** Long-term health-related problems such as asthma, heart disease, obesity or HIV can have serious impacts on our quality of life.
- **Environment** The environmental quality of the neighbourhood in which we live (traffic noise, congestion, air quality, vandalism) and its facilities (shops, transport, cinema, chemist, schools etc.) can create both positive and negative impacts on quality of life.

Figure 4 How do urban and rural settings influence quality of life?

THOMAS TALLIS SCHOOL LIBRARY   018654

How do we use quality of life and standard of living indicators?

Figure 5 provides evidence of variations in standard of living and quality of life that exist within England.

An understanding of these patterns is important so that the government can target those areas that need most support. For example, knowing that fewer people in the northern regions of England are successful in their attempt to stop smoking means that the National Health Service can target these areas with extra funds.

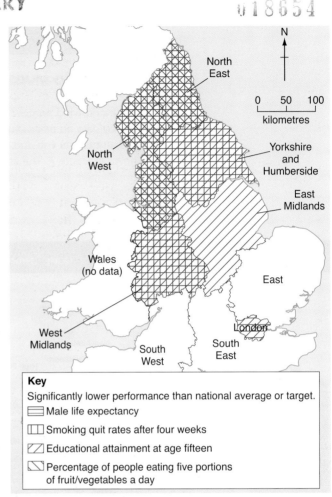

Key

Significantly lower performance than national average or target.

▤ Male life expectancy

▥ Smoking quit rates after four weeks

▨ Educational attainment at age fifteen

◺ Percentage of people eating five portions of fruit/vegetables a day

▲
Figure 5 Regions of England with lower than average standard of living and quality of life using four indicators. Source: Association of Public Health Observatories (2005)

◀ **Figure 6** Regional variations in quality of life and standard of living. Cells coloured red are significantly worse than the national average. Cells coloured blue are significantly better than the national average

	Infant mortality per 1,000 births	Adult male obesity (%)	Unemploy-ment (% 2005)
Average for England	5.4	20.8	4.6
North East	5.7	24.7	5.5
North West	5.8	20.3	4.8
Yorkshire & Humberside	6.4	22	4.2
East Midlands	5.3	23.2	4.3
West Midlands	6.6	22.2	4.6
East	4.4	19.5	3.9
London	5.7	18.2	6.7
South East	4.4	20.3	3.7
South West	4.8	18.9	3.5

Activity

5 Study Figure 4. Suggest how each of the following people might rate the quality of life in the urban and rural homes shown in the photo. Give reasons:
   a) a 15-year-old who is keen on sport, cinema and seeing his/her friends
   b) a young mother with a toddler and a child at primary school
   c) a recently retired couple.

6 **a)** Choose a suitable technique to either graph or map the data in Figure 6.
   b) Describe the regional patterns you see in Figures 5 and 6.

7 **a)** Summarise: which regions have the poorest and which the best quality of life?
   b) Evaluate: what data would be useful if you wanted to investigate regional variations in standard of living?

8 **a)** What connection, if any, exists between the unemployment figures in Figure 6 and the educational attainment indicator in Figure 5?
   b) Suggest reasons for this apparent connection.

Going Further

Using GIS to investigate standard of living in the UK

There is a growing number of online atlases that use Geographical Information Systems (GIS) to display data on maps. A GIS will allow you to interact with the data: you can select the data that interests you and display it in map or graph form. A screenshot from one such atlas is shown in Figure 7. The atlas displays standard of living indicators such as low pay, unemployment or benefit claimants, collected from local authorities in England, Scotland and Wales.

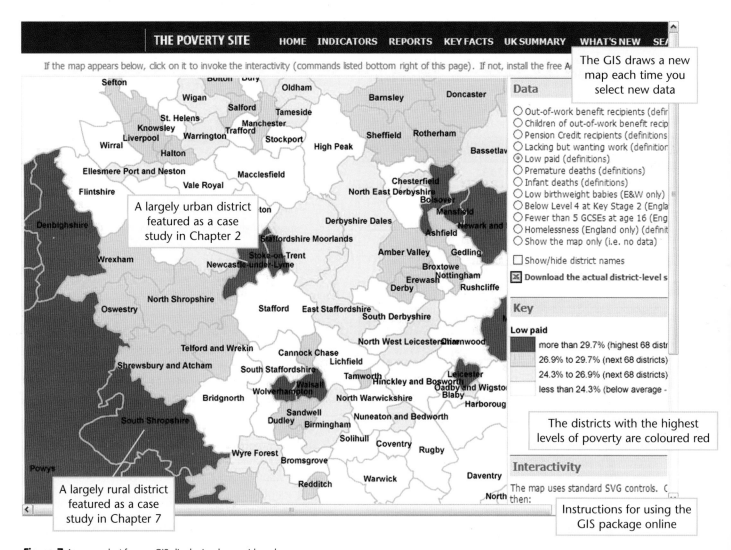

Figure 7 A screenshot from a GIS displaying low-paid workers

www.poverty.org.uk/summary/maps.shtml
This webpage explains the system requirements for the GIS featured in Figure 7. Follow the link to load the atlas.

Using GIS to investigate variations in quality of life

Standards in education, crime rates and health measures are all mapped in an interactive website created by England's health authorities (see the screenshot in Figure 8).

This chart displays data for the area selected on the map (in this case Easington). If the bars are to the left of centre then the region has data that is worse than the national average. You can see here that Easington scores badly for healthy eating and smoking, but is better than average for road injuries and deaths.

Use the drop-down menu to choose the quality of life data you wish to view.

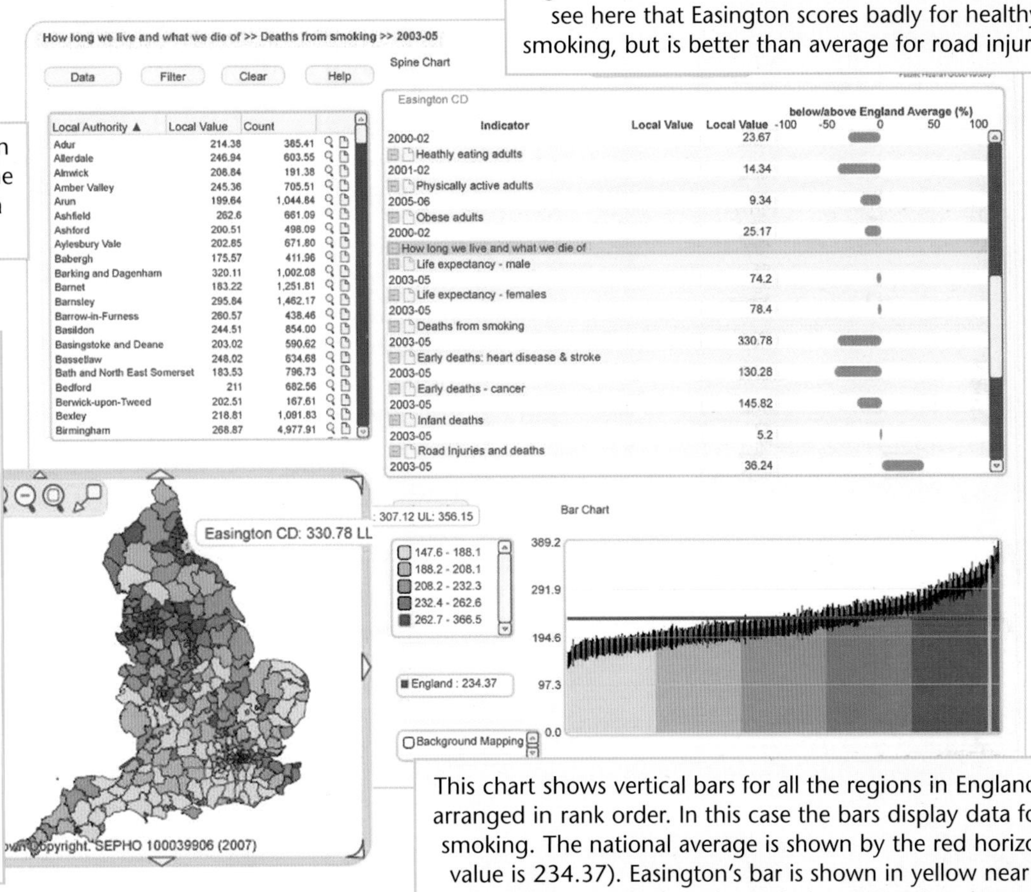

The map is automatically coloured using data stored in the GIS. On this map the darker shades are areas where deaths from smoking are highest. You can use the zoom button to view the map at a larger scale. As you hover over the map the name of the local authority is displayed.

This chart shows vertical bars for all the regions in England and they are arranged in rank order. In this case the bars display data for deaths from smoking. The national average is shown by the red horizontal line (the value is 234.37). Easington's bar is shown in yellow near the extreme right of the graph. The value (which is 330.78) is shown on the map.

Figure 8 A screenshot from the Community Health Profiles GIS

Activity

9 Use Figure 7 and an atlas.
   a) Describe the distribution (see page 25) of low-paid districts.
   b) What evidence is there that low pay is more or less common in rural districts?

10 Use the GIS weblink to investigate patterns of benefit recipients, low paid and premature deaths in your own region. Structure a short report around the following headings:

   • *Geographical patterns in the data*
   • *Possible connections between the data*

www.communityhealthprofiles.info
Follow the links from this home page to the interactive map to display a wide variety of quality of life maps and graphs for England.

11 Describe the distribution of smoking-related deaths shown in the map in Figure 8.

12 Use the GIS weblink to investigate the following statement:

   Rural counties such as Cornwall, Devon and Shropshire have significantly healthier populations than more urban areas of England.

 Ghana

Investigating standard of living in Ghana

Ghana is a **Less Economically Developed Country** (or **LEDC**) in West Africa. The average standard of living here is much lower than in the UK. The average Ghanaian earns about 30 times less than the average person in the UK even after the difference in the cost of living has been taken into account. Quality of life is different too. Families living in a city in either country might complain that noise, traffic or crime is affecting their quality of life. However, a Ghanaian household is much more likely to be affected by an unsafe water supply or lack of electricity or sewerage systems than a UK family. Such problems are particularly common in rural communities in Ghana where standards of living are less than half that of urban communities.

Not only is there a gap between rural and urban incomes, there is also a growing north–south divide in Ghana. Northern Ghana is very rural whereas the south of the country is more urban. Incomes in the more urban southern regions of the country are 2.4 times higher than in the more rural north. The reasons for this include:

- The south has more cities and better transport so industry has grown faster there.
- The south is more accessible to tourists and has benefited from the growth of tourism.
- The north has unreliable patterns of rainfall, which make farming more difficult than in the south.

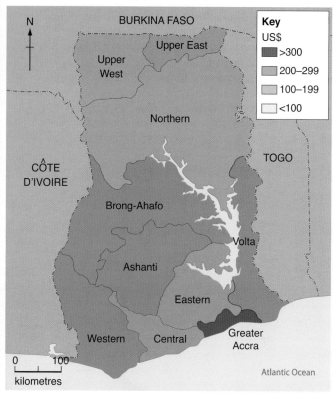

Figure 9 The regional pattern of income in Ghana (latest survey 2000)

Figure 10 A street market in Accra

Figure 11 Village life in rural Ghana

How do differences in quality of life affect people in Ghana?

The northern regions of Ghana face severe problems such as poverty, lack of job opportunities (especially for women), and lack of safe drinking water. The region has a harsh climate and farming is an unreliable way of making a living. The lack of decent roads and public transport makes it difficult for rural families to get to local towns to visit friends, go to the shops, or get medical attention. There is a severe shortage of teachers in the northern regions of Ghana. In rural northern Ghana, the **infant mortality rate (IMR)** is twice as high as in urban areas in the south. Malaria, acute respiratory infections, diarrhoea, malnutrition and measles are still the five main causes of death in young children.

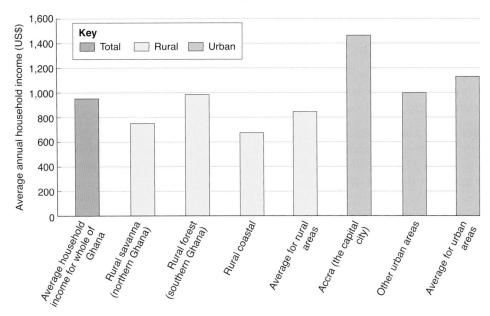

Figure 12 Average household incomes in urban and rural parts of Ghana (last survey 2000)

	Immunisation coverage (%)		
	1998	**2003**	**Difference**
National	62	69.4	7.4
Western	67.4	60.4	–7
Central	49.1	82.1	
Greater Accra	73.7	69.1	
Volta	59.8	82.3	
Eastern	52.1	65.6	
Ashanti	67.8	71.6	
Brong-Ahafo	66.6	79	
Northern	47.4	48	
Upper East	68	77	
Upper West	65.8	60.3	

Figure 13 Percentage of children immunised by region, Ghana

Activity

13 Describe the distribution (see page 25) of regions in Ghana where average incomes were above US$200 in 2000.

14 Use Figure 12 to compare the average household incomes:
  a) in Accra with those in other urban areas
  b) in Accra with rural areas.

15 Suggest how each of the following factors contributes to the high infant mortality rates in the north of Ghana:
  a) poor transport networks
  b) low family incomes.

16 a) Copy Figure 13 into your book and complete the final column (two rows have been done for you).
  b) Choose a suitable technique to map or graph the data in this column.
  c) Comment on the progress being made in Ghana to improve quality of life in rural areas.

Chapter 2
Investigating social patterns where we live

KEY QUESTIONS

- How and where are different types of housing provided?
- What opportunities and constraints determine access to housing?
- How and why do these opportunities and constraints lead to social patterns in where people live?
- What issues arise from the inequalities?

Understanding the housing market in the UK

Householders in the UK have three main options. They can choose to:

- own their home
- rent their home from a **social landlord** (the local council or housing association)
- rent from a private landlord.

These are the three main forms of **housing tenure**. There are currently 14.6 million owner-occupied households in the UK, 3.7 million **social housing** households and 2.6 million privately rented households.

The decision to buy or rent your home is complex. Home ownership is seen by many people as a long-term investment. Although house prices can go down as well as up, they have tended to rise faster than wages, as shown in Figure 2. In order to access this part of the housing market you either need a large lump sum of money (perhaps an inheritance) or a regular wage so that you can convince the mortgage lender that you will be able to make the regular repayments on your mortgage. If you fail to keep up with the repayments you can lose your home. This is known as **repossession**.

Renting from a private landlord is an option that suits a wide range of people as suggested in Figure 3. This sector of the housing market contains a range of properties from luxury penthouses to tiny bedsits. In many cases the landlord makes an agreement to let the property for only six months. This suits people who are expecting to move again soon, like a student or a young professional seeking a new job, but is less desirable for families wishing to settle down.

An alternative to renting from a private landlord is to rent from a not-for-profit organisation such as a housing association or the local authority. Most social landlords use a points system: everyone on their waiting list is allocated points depending on their need. People on a waiting list for social housing have relatively little choice about where they live as this decision is made by the housing officer.

Figure 1 Changing housing tenure in the UK

Housing tenure		% of all households			
		1981		2007	
Owner occupiers	Owned outright	25	57	31	70
	Buying with a mortgage or loan	32		39	
Tenants renting from a social landlord	Rented from local council	30	32	11	18
	Rented from housing association	2		7	
Tenants renting from a private landlord	Unfurnished	9	11	9	12
	Furnished	2		3	

www.communities.gov.uk/housing/housingresearch/housingstatistics/
This government website has many spreadsheets of data on UK housing that you can download.

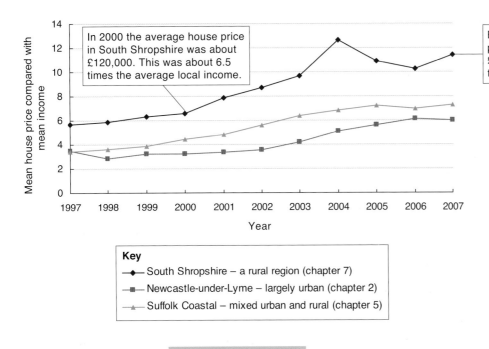

In 2000 the average house price in South Shropshire was about £120,000. This was about 6.5 times the average local income.

By 2007 the average house price in this region had risen to £260,000 which was 11.5 times the average local income.

Figure 2 How the average cost of housing compares with the average income in urban and rural case studies examined later in this theme

Key
—◆— South Shropshire – a rural region (chapter 7)
—■— Newcastle-under-Lyme – largely urban (chapter 2)
—▲— Suffolk Coastal – mixed urban and rural (chapter 5)

Figure 3 The private rented sector meets a variety of people's housing needs

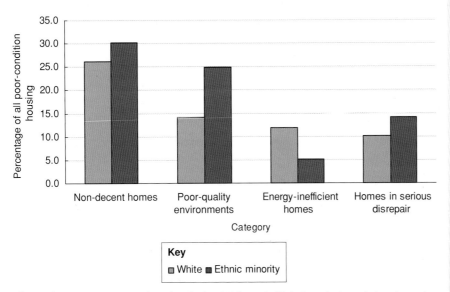

Figure 4 The UK government has identified 17,000 households in the private rented sector and nearly 4,000 in the social sector that are in poor condition

Activity

1 a) Choose a suitable technique to show the data in Figure 1 on a graph.
   b) Describe the changes in this data.

2 a) Compare the three trends shown in Figure 2.
   b) Suggest the impact of these trends on young people who live in rural areas.

3 Study Figure 3. Suggest the advantages and disadvantages of the private rented sector.

4 Use Figure 4 to compare the needs of white and ethnic minority households who live in poor housing in the private rented sector. Suggest what should be done to solve this problem.

 Newcastle-under-Lyme

Investigating social patterns and housing provision

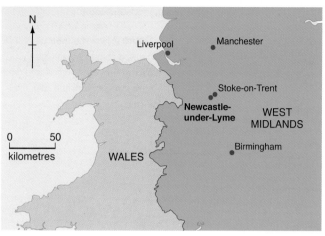

Figure 5 The location of Newcastle-under-Lyme

Newcastle-under-Lyme is a large town in Staffordshire in the West Midlands. It has a population of around 125,000 people. Our key enquiry questions are:

- How do quality of life and standard of living vary from one part of the urban area to another?
- How and why are different types of housing provided?
- How do opportunities and constraints lead to social patterns in where people live?

You can use similar enquiry questions to investigate inequality in your own local area.

Fact file based on Newcastle's Community Health Profile ▶

www.communityhealthprofiles.info/

This website describes quality of life in all local authorities in England. These Community Health Profiles describe key health data for each local authority commenting on whether the figures are above or below average.

Some key facts about standards of living and quality of life in Newcastle-under-Lyme compared with other urban areas in the West Midlands.

- Life expectancy varies considerably from one part of the town to another.
- GCSE examination results are significantly lower than the national average.
- There is a high rate of recorded violent crime, with nearly 3,000 incidents in a single year.
- The number of elderly people who are supported by family and voluntary organisations to live independently in their own home is significantly higher than the national average.
- It is estimated that less than 20 per cent of adults eat a healthy balance of fruit and vegetables, and a quarter of adults are obese.
- Deaths or serious injury due to traffic accidents are significantly lower than average.

| | Averages | | Wards of Newcastle-under-Lyme | | | | |
| | | | Inner urban areas | | | Suburban wards | Commuter village |
Percentages	England	Newcastle-under-Lyme	Cross Heath	Silverdale	Town	Westlands	Loggerheads
Unemployed people aged 16–24	26	31	41	32	31	22	23
People of working age with a limiting long-term illness	13	16	20	20	15	12	13
General health: good	69	66	60	60	62	72	72
General health: fairly good	22	23	26	26	24	20	20
General health: not good	9	11	14	13	14	8	8

Figure 6 Evidence of variations in standard of living and quality of life in Newcastle-under-Lyme. Source: 2001 Census

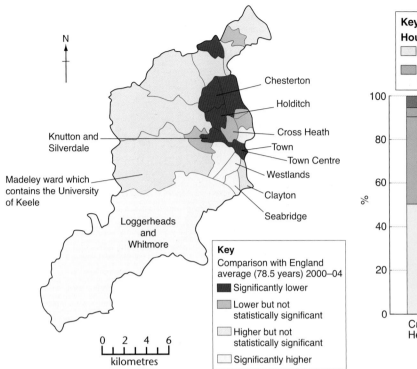

Figure 7 Variations in life expectancy in Newcastle-under-Lyme

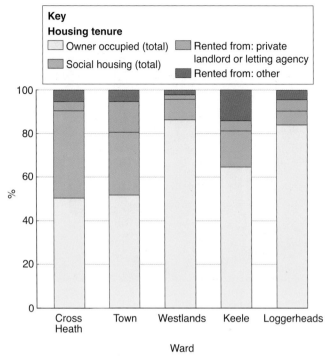

Figure 8 Housing tenure in five wards of Newcastle-under-Lyme

Activity

5 Study the Fact file on page 18. Use it to make:
  a) two positive statements about quality of life in Newcastle-under-Lyme
  b) two negative statements about quality of life in Newcastle-under-Lyme.

6 Use Figure 7 to describe the distribution (see page 25) of wards with:
  a) significantly lower life expectancy
  b) significantly higher life expectancy.

7 Use Figures 6 and 7 to complete the table below which compares local averages to averages for England.

8 Using Figure 8, compare the housing tenure in Cross Heath (an inner urban ward) with Westlands (a suburban ward).

9 a) Choose suitable techniques to produce a series of graphs to illustrate the data in Figure 6.
  b) Summarise the main differences in quality of life between the inner urban, suburban and commuter village areas of Newcastle-under-Lyme.

	Cross Heath (inner urban)	Westlands (suburban)	Loggerheads (commuter village)
Life expectancy		Significantly higher	
Unemployed people (aged 16–24)	Significantly higher		
People of working age with a limiting long-term illness		Slightly lower	
General health: good			Slightly higher

Figure 9 Town ward in Newcastle-under-Lyme's inner urban zone. OS map ref: 848456

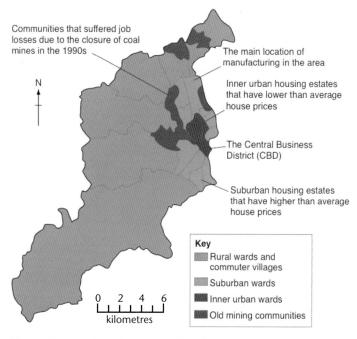

Communities that suffered job losses due to the closure of coal mines in the 1990s

The main location of manufacturing in the area

Inner urban housing estates that have lower than average house prices

The Central Business District (CBD)

Suburban housing estates that have higher than average house prices

N

0 2 4 6
kilometres

Key
- Rural wards and commuter villages
- Suburban wards
- Inner urban wards
- Old mining communities

Figure 11 A map of wards in Newcastle-under-Lyme

Figure 10 Baldwin's Gate is part of Loggerheads ward. This is a commuter village on the western edge of Newcastle-under-Lyme's suburbs. OS map ref: 793402

Figure 12 Westlands ward is one of Newcastle-under-Lyme's suburban zones. OS map ref: 843448

Activity

10 Describe the housing in each photograph (Figures 9, 10 and 12) using these headings:
- Type (terraced, semi-detached, detached)
- Density
- Age.

11 Study Figure 13.
   a) Give a four-figure grid reference for Westlands.

b) What is the straight-line distance from the town centre (grid ref: 849459) to the suburban wards of:
   i) Westlands   ii) Seabridge   iii) Clayton?

12 Give map evidence (see page 21) that suggests that quality of life in Clayton (grid square 8543) is better than in Cross Heath (grid square 8447).

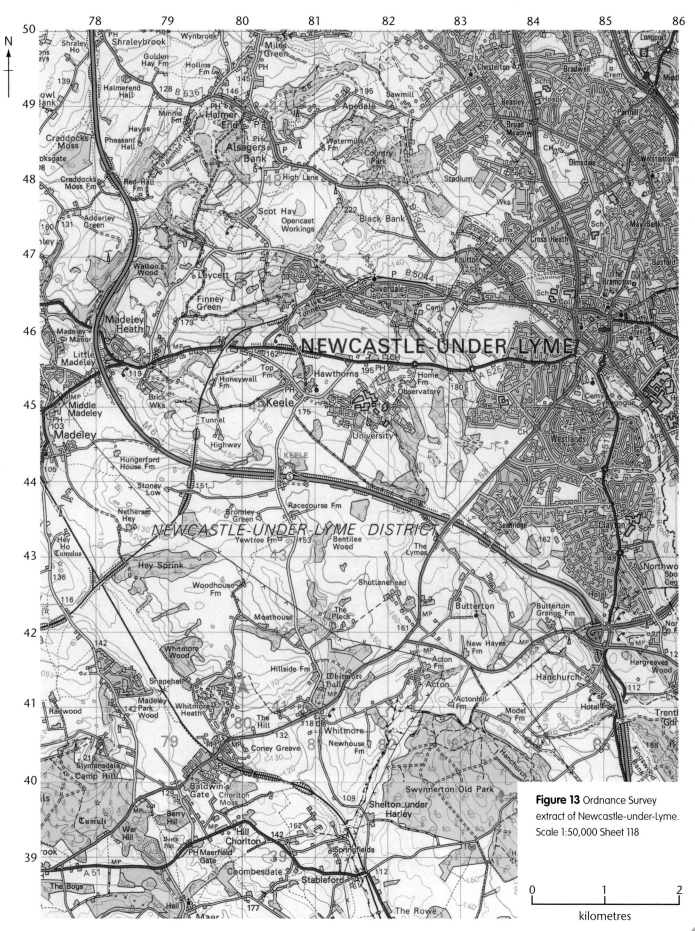

Figure 13 Ordnance Survey extract of Newcastle-under-Lyme. Scale 1:50,000 Sheet 118

Who lives where in Newcastle-under-Lyme?

Do different groups of people live in different parts of Newcastle? Do some parts of the town have:

- more highly qualified residents (which would indicate a higher standard of living, as people with higher qualifications usually have better-paid jobs)?
- more families or more elderly residents than average?

 www.statistics. gov.uk This is the official website of the UK National Census. Use the Neighbourhood Statistics link on the homepage to search the site using postcodes. The data in Figure 14 is available on this site.

	Newcastle-under-Lyme	Inner urban wards		Suburban wards	Rural wards	
	Average (%)	Cross Heath	Town	Westlands	Keele	Logger-heads
Age groups						
0–4 years	5.25	6.42	3.95	5.12	1.03	4.86
5–15 years	13.37	14.13	7.57	13.78	2.91	12.90
16–19 years	5.33	5.80	5.03	4.37	24.78	4.33
20–44 years	34.07	33.39	41.63	27.11	60.89	27.19
45–64 years	25.08	23.10	19.85	28.05	6.43	33.37
65 years and over	16.91	17.17	21.96	21.58	3.95	17.35
People aged 16–74 with:						
No qualifications	34.32	46.15	28.95	21.97	3.05	22.93
Highest qualification attained level 3 (equal to A level)	8.81	5.92	13.22	8.06	67.39	7.83
Highest qualification attained level 4/5 (equal to a degree)	15.49	9.57	22.16	32.16	19.47	25.67

Figure 14 Age structure and qualifications in five wards in Newcastle-under-Lyme

Activity

13 Use Figure 14 to complete the following table:

Compared with Newcastle-under-Lyme average	Cross Heath	Town	Westlands	Keele
% of population of school age (5–15)	Similar			
% of population younger adults (20–44)				Significantly higher
% of population aged 65 and over	Slightly higher		Significantly higher	
% of adults with no qualifications	Significantly higher			
% of population with a degree				

14 Use evidence from Figures 8 and 14 to compare Cross Heath (an inner urban ward) and Westlands (a suburban ward).

15 Choose three pieces of evidence from Figures 8 and 14 that suggest that Keele ward contains a university.

Going Further

How education standards shape our cities

Parental choice over education for their children has become a significant factor that determines who lives where in the modern UK city. For many parents the standard of local education is an important factor when choosing the location of their family home. The **catchment areas** of successful primary or secondary schools become desirable areas in which to live. As more parents try to buy houses in the catchments of these schools, house prices begin to rise. The opposite trend may also be true: the catchments of less successful schools are less desirable to parents, and house prices in these areas remain at lower levels.

www.upmystreet.com
You can use this website to find data such as the school performance statistics and average house prices shown in Figure 15 in your own urban area.

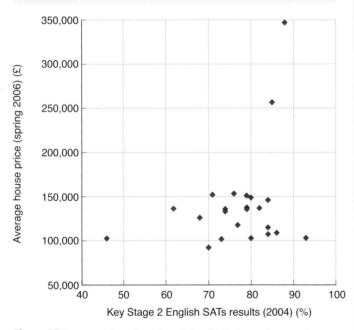

Figure 15 Scattergraph to show the relationship between house prices and Key Stage 2 English SATs results in Newcastle-under-Lyme

Activity

16 Study Figures 15 and 16. Working in groups:
  a) Investigate the links between:
    • house price and deprivation score
    • house price and primary school score.
  b) Suggest reasons for the links you have found. Remember that this region was affected by the loss of jobs in coal mining and manufacturing during the 1980s and 1990s.

Ward	Average house price (£) (spring 2006)	KS2 English SATs results (2004)
Talke	92,563	70
Knutton and Silverdale	93,568	38
Holditch	101,815	73
Bradwell	103,062	93
Chesterton	103,464	46
Silverdale and Parksite	103,529	80
May Bank	108,046	84
Ravenscliffe	108,956	86
Wolstanton	115,033	84
Porthill	117,686	77
Cross Heath	126,467	68
Audley and Bignall End	133,906	74
Clayton	135,658	74
Kidsgrove	136,502	62
Butt Lane	136,502	79
Madeley (Keele community)	137,205	82
Town	138,079	79
Thistleberry	146,335	84
Newchapel	148,826	80
Westlands	151,168	79
Halmerend	152,082	71
Seabridge	153,184	76
Loggerheads	256,000	85
Baldwin's Gate	346,000	88

Key

Lowest quality of life		Significantly higher levels of deprivation
		Slightly higher levels
		Slightly lower levels
Highest quality of life		Significantly lower levels of deprivation

Figure 16 House prices and Key Stage 2 English results in Newcastle-under-Lyme

KEY QUESTIONS

- ⊙ What is meant by access to services?
- ⊙ How are different services distributed in urban and rural areas?
- ⊙ How and why does access to services in urban and rural areas vary between different groups of people?

Barcelona

What do we mean by urban services?

One advantage of living in a large urban area is that you can get access to a range of useful services:

- Leisure and sports facilities such as swimming pools or tennis courts.
- Cultural venues such as museums, galleries and theatres.
- Health services such as clinics and hospitals.
- A range of schools, colleges and universities providing parents with choice.
- Places of worship for a variety of faiths.
- Specialist shops and services such as travel agents and solicitors.
- A variety of public transport services including bus, train and underground.

This case study examines the distribution of some services in the city of Barcelona, Spain. It also investigates why some groups of people in Barcelona have better access to these services than others.

Figure 1 The location of Barcelona

Figure 2 This is a screenshot from an interactive atlas maintained by Barcelona City Council. This Geographic Information System (GIS) allows the user to select layers which can be added to a base map of the city. The layers show features useful to local people, such as youth centres (shown here), or to tourists, such as hotels and museums

Barcelona

Barcelona, Spain – Does everyone have equal access to urban services?

People living in larger cities such as Barcelona have more choice of services than people living in the countryside: but do all city dwellers have equal access to urban services? In this case study we will see that some groups of people have better access to urban services than others. This may be for one of two reasons:

• The services are not distributed evenly through the urban area. So, for example, people living in a central district may have better access to theatres and museums than people living in a distant suburb of the city.
• Some services are more expensive than others, and not all groups of people can afford them.

Activity

1 Suggest two reasons why some districts have more youth centres than others.

2 Use Figure 2 to complete this description of the distribution of youth centres in Barcelona:

There is a .... pattern in the city centre with a large group of youth centres in .... The rest of the youth centres have a .... pattern with very few centres in districts such as .... and .... whereas districts such as .... have more.

3 a) Match the following services to their likely distribution pattern:
   • motorway service stations
   • clustered
   • high-street banks in a town
   • regular linear
   • primary schools in a large town
   • regular

   b) Suggest reasons why these services are distributed in this way.

EXAMINER'S TIPS

Describing distributions

To describe a distribution is to describe how similar features are spread across a map. Geographers are interested in the distribution of natural features such as forests or other habitats, as well as human features such as settlements, hospitals or sporting facilities.

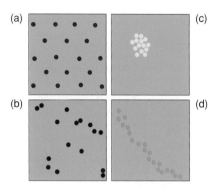

Figure 3 Distribution patterns

Describing a distribution requires you to do two things.

1 You need to describe where on the map the features are located. For example, a lot of the youth centres marked on Figure 2 are in the Ciutat Vella (or old city of Barcelona), whereas there are very few in Sants-Montjuïc.

2 You need to describe any pattern the features might make. These distribution patterns are shown in Figure 3:

• **Regular**, where the features are more or less equally spaced.
• **Random**, where the features are scattered across the map at irregular distances from each other.
• **Clustered**, where the features are grouped together into only one part of the map.
• **Linear**, where the features all fall along a line.

Activity

4 Match the four distribution patterns shown in Figure 3 to the following terms:
   • random   • regular
   • linear   • clustered

Barcelona

Multicultural Barcelona and the distribution of services for ethnic groups

Barcelona is a large city with a population of more than 1.5 million people. The surrounding districts are also urban, so its overall size is greater than 4 million people. The city grew rapidly during the 1970s and 1980s, attracting migrants from Spain and abroad. Like many large European cities, it has a diverse multicultural population, and the city has sizeable populations of people descended from:

- Mexico and other Spanish-speaking Central and South American countries
- parts of Asia, especially Pakistan and China
- various African countries, but especially Morocco
- other European countries.

Figure 4 Halal butchers in El Raval provide a service for the Muslim population of the district

Barcelona's ethnic groups tend to be concentrated in the **inner urban** districts of the city. The district of El Raval, in the Ciutat Vella (the old city centre), has a sizeable immigrant population: 27.6 per cent of the population are foreign migrants compared with 7.2 per cent for Barcelona as a whole. Muslims from Morocco and Pakistan may choose to live here because they have better access to particular services that are also clustered in this part of Barcelona. For example, Ciutat Vella has ten of Barcelona's sixteen mosques, and three of these are in El Raval. The district also has many shops catering for the Muslim population such as halal butchers and stores offering internet or telephone connections to all parts of the globe. It also has video rental stores that specialise in Asian films.

However, an alternative explanation for the concentration of Moroccans and Pakistanis in El Raval is that this is one of the cheapest districts of Barcelona in which to live. Many immigrants from these countries do poorly paid work and cannot afford to live in other, more expensive, parts of the city.

Activity

5 Describe the distribution (see page 25) of mosques in Figure 5. Make sure you use the relevant words from the following list:
- regular
- random
- linear
- clustered
- distribution.

Figure 5 The distribution of mosques in Barcelona

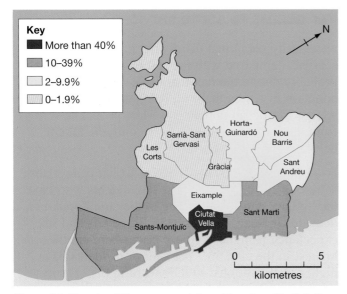

Figure 6 Pakistani and Moroccan population of Barcelona (% of total in each district)

Key
- More than 40%
- 10–39%
- 2–9.9%
- 0–1.9%

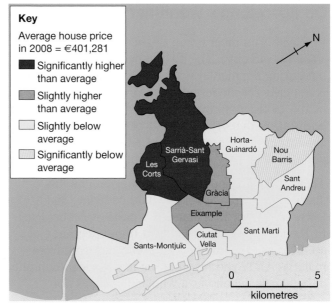

Figure 7 Average house prices (euros) 2008

Key
Average house price in 2008 = €401,281
- Significantly higher than average
- Slightly higher than average
- Slightly below average
- Significantly below average

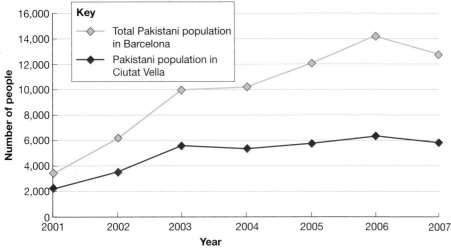

Key
- Total Pakistani population in Barcelona
- Pakistani population in Ciutat Vella

Figure 8 The Pakistani population of Barcelona

	Moroccan population in Ciutat Vella	Total Moroccan population in Barcelona
2001	3,019	7,165
2002	3,645	9,751
2003	4,061	11,985
2004	4,247	13,594
2005	4,390	14,508
2006	4,468	15,522
2007	3,887	12,816

Figure 9 The Moroccan population of Barcelona

Activity

6 Explain why there are so many mosques in Ciutat Vella.

7 Give three reasons why Pakistani and Moroccan immigrants might choose to live in El Raval.

8 Use Figures 6 and 7.
  a) Compare the distribution of Barcelona's Muslim population with the pattern of house prices.
  b) What does this suggest about the income of Pakistani and Moroccan immigrants?

9 Study Figure 8.
  a) Describe the trend shown on both lines.
  b) Use the graph to explain whether Barcelona's Pakistani population is getting more or less concentrated into Ciutat Vella.

10 a) Use the data in Figure 9 to draw another pair of lines on a line graph.
  b) Compare this graph with Figure 8. What are the main similarities and differences?

Do Barcelona's wealthier districts have better access to some services?

El Raval is an inner urban district within the Ciutat Vella (or old city). The district has narrow streets set out during the medieval development of the city, so it is not easy for modern traffic. Most of the housing is in six- to eight-storey apartment buildings. The **population density**, at 34,445 people per km², is about four times greater than London's average population density of 8,860 people per km².

There are many indicators that suggest that this district has both a lower standard of living, and a lower quality of life, than other parts of Barcelona. El Raval has the second-lowest **life expectancy** of all districts. The number of people suffering from malaria, AIDS and tuberculosis is significantly higher here than in the city as a whole. This does not

necessarily mean that the district has poor healthcare services compared with the rest of Barcelona. It is probably due to the fact that these diseases are more common in Africa than in Spain, and the district has a large Moroccan population. Most people suffering from these diseases would have contracted them before migrating to Spain.

By contrast, Sarrià-Sant Gervasi, which is a western suburb of Barcelona, is home to residents who have the highest standard of living in the city. Population densities here are the lowest in Barcelona and life expectancy is highest. House prices here are the highest in the city. 36.7 per cent of residents have higher qualifications, so they work in better-paid jobs.

	Density (persons per km²) 2004	Life expectancy 2006	Persons with higher qualifications (%) 2006	Immigrant population (%) 2007	Average house price (euros) 2008
Ciutat Vella	23,943	73.2	11.4	44.1	331,346
Eixample	34,863	79.7	23.9	16.3	459,624
Sants-Montjuïc	8,246	78.4	11.1	17.9	315,813
Les Corts	13,718	80.4	26.9	10.9	566,689
Sarrià-Sant Gervasi	6,900	80.5	36.7	11.0	832,854
Gràcia	28,477	79.2	21.6	14.1	409,216
Horta-Guinardó	14,197	79.0	12.1	11.8	333,214
Nou Barris	20,572	78.2	6.2	15.2	267,952
Sant Andreu	21,504	79.1	10.5	12.0	328,427
Sant Marti	20,192	78.9	10.6	13.8	359,966
Barcelona	15,635	78.5	16.5	100*	401,281

Figure 10 Standard of living and quality of life indicators for Barcelona's main districts

* 100% of the immigrants living in the city live in Barcelona. This includes 4.6 per cent who have no fixed address

Activity

11 Study Figure 10. Choose one column that shows standard of living and one that shows quality of life. Explain the difference between these two concepts.

12 Use Figures 10 and 12.
   a) Compare the quality of life in Les Corts with Sarrià-Sant Gervasi.
   b) Compare the standard of living in Eixample with Nou Barris.

Making comparisons

'Compare' is a common command word in the WJEC B Geography examination. You could be asked to compare two climate charts or two hydrographs in Theme 2. In Theme 1 you could be asked to compare two contrasting districts of a city, such as El Raval and Sarrià-Sant Gervasi.

Figure 10 shows some of the indicators that give Ciutat Vella district a lower standard of living, such as lower life expectancy and a low percentage of persons with higher qualifications. It also shows how figures for the same indicators suggest a higher standard of living in Sarrià-Sant Gervasi district.

In order to compare these two places successfully you must link a statement about one to the other with a connective in the same sentence. Connectives are words such as 'however', 'whereas' and 'similarly' (more are given in Figure 12). For example:

Ciutat Vella has an average life expectancy of 73.2 years, which is the lowest in Barcelona, *whereas* life expectancy in Sarrià-Sant Gervasi is 7.3 years higher and is the highest in the city.

Connectives to highlight difference
… unlike …
… whereas …
… though …
… conversely …
… is much greater than …
… is much smaller than …
… is significantly larger than …

Connectives to highlight similarity
… like …
… similarly …
… equally …
… identically …
… likewise …
… in common with …

Figure 12
Connectives that can be used for comparison

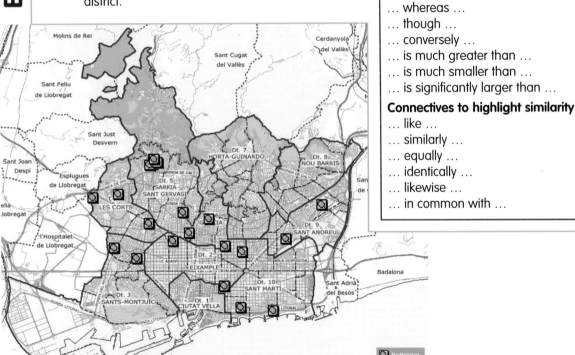

Figure 11 Distribution of badminton courts in Barcelona

Activity

13 Use Figure 11.
  a) Describe the distribution (see page 25) of badminton courts in Barcelona.
  b) List the districts which have no badminton courts. Using Figure 10, state whether each of these districts has house prices that are above or below Barcelona's average.
  c) Assuming that customers have to pay a membership or court fee to play badminton, explain why the badminton courts are located only in certain districts.
  d) What groups of people have poor access to these sports facilities?

Going Further

Using scattergraphs to make connections

Figure 15 divides each of the main districts of Barcelona into smaller statistical zones (rather like wards in a UK city). It provides four pieces of evidence that could be used to investigate inequality within the city.

Geographers are interested in the way in which factors such as immigration, education, healthcare and housing density are interconnected. Is it true, for example, that districts with a higher percentage of people with higher qualifications also have longer life expectancies? This might be because people who have experienced higher education have:
- higher incomes and can therefore afford private healthcare

- better understanding of healthcare issues such as the need for a balanced diet and to moderate smoking and drinking.

Geographers usually express such ideas as a **hypothesis**: a statement that can be proved or disproved using the available evidence. In this case our hypothesis might be: **Districts with a higher percentage of people with higher qualifications also have longer life expectancies.**

This hypothesis can be tested in several ways using the data in Figure 15. One of the most effective ways is to draw a scattergraph where two sets of data that might be connected are plotted on the same graph, as in Figures 13 and 14.

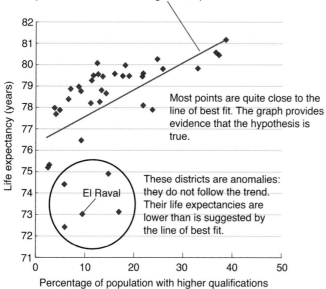

Figure 13 Scattergraph showing the positive relationship between life expectancy and percentage of the population with higher qualifications

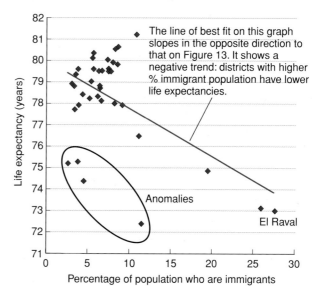

Figure 14 Scattergraph showing the negative relationship between life expectancy and the percentage of the population who are immigrants

Activity

14 Define the terms hypothesis and anomaly.

15 Study Figure 14.
   a) What hypothesis is tested by this scattergraph?
   b) Does the graph provide better or worse proof of a connection than Figure 13?
   c) Explain why four districts are shown as anomalies.

16 Study Figure 15.
   a) Suggest another hypothesis.
   b) Test your hypothesis by drawing a scattergraph.
   c) What conclusion do you reach?

District		Statistical zone	Foreign born (%)	Life expectancy (years)	Density per km²	Higher qualifications (%)
Ciutat Vella	1	Barceloneta	11.5	72.4	10,308	5.8
	2	Parc	19.5	74.9	17,854	14.6
	3	Gòtic	26.0	73.1	19,714	16.9
	4	El Raval	27.6	73.0	34,445	9.4
Eixample	5	Sant Antoni	7.8	79.5	45,038	17.8
	6	Esquerra Eixample	8.6	79.8	36,605	25.8
	7	Dreta Eixample	8.1	79.9	18,811	32.9
	8	Estació Nord	7.6	79.6	30,787	21.7
	9	Sagrada Familia	7.6	79.5	47,642	18.9
Sants-Montjuïc	10	Poble Sec	11.2	76.5	45,948	9.2
	11	Montjuïc	4.7	74.4	143	5.7
	12	Zona Franca-Port	4.5	78.4	2,344	6.4
	13	Font de la Guatlla	6.5	78.7	21,586	14.1
	14	Bordeta-Hostafrancs	6.9	79.5	30,603	11.6
	15	Sants	6.5	78.8	39,805	13.2
Les Corts	16	Les Corts	5.8	80.3	22,161	24.6
	17	Pedralbes	10.9	81.2	4,606	38.4
Sarrià-Sant Gervasi	18	Sant Gervasi	8.3	80.5	18,297	37.1
	19	Sarrià	8.7	80.6	7,809	36.5
	20	Vallvidrera-Les Planes	9.2	77.9	286	23.6
Gràcia	21	Gràcia	6.8	79.5	40,751	21.5
	22	Vallcarca	6.7	78.1	14,315	21.8
Horta-Guinardó	23	Guinardó	5.8	79.6	32,067	15.8
	24	Horta	3.5	78.8	17,924	9.0
	25	Vall d'Hebron	5.3	78.2	4,860	10.9
Nou Barris	26	Vilapicina-Turó de la Peira	5.5	79.0	33,712	8.7
	27	Roquetes-Verdum	4.0	77.9	29,140	4.8
	28	Ciutat Meridiana-Vallbona	3.9	75.3	4,014	2.7
Sant Andreu	29	Sagrera	5.6	80.1	35,620	12.4
	30	Congrés	3.9	79.6	33,166	12.5
	31	Sant Andreu	3.7	79.3	28,486	11.2
	32	Bon Pastor	2.8	75.2	5,727	2.4
	33	Trinitat Vella	8.3	78.0	9,836	3.7
Sant Marti	34	Fort Pius	7.5	80.0	26,364	18.0
	35	Poblenou	6.3	78.3	8,364	12.8
	36	Barris Besòs	3.6	77.7	25,675	3.9
	37	Clot	6.4	79.5	42,986	13.5
	38	Verneda	3.2	78.9	30,907	7.0

Figure 15 Investigating inequality in Barcelona

Chapter 4
Changing the city

KEY QUESTIONS

- ❂ What changes are taking place in housing and social provision?
- ❂ Why are these changes taking place?
- ❂ How and why might these changes benefit or disadvantage groups of people?
- ❂ How might these changes affect local built and natural environments?
- ❂ How might sustainable residential places be planned?

How are urban areas changing?

Cities are growing and changing fastest in Less Economically Developed Countries (LEDCs). The process by which the population of a country becomes more urban and less rural is known as urbanisation. Urbanisation causes the physical and human growth of towns and cities. The pace of urban growth in many LEDC cities is so fast that the city's **infrastructure** cannot keep pace with the demand from new residents. As a consequence many LEDC cities fail to provide an adequate quality of life with many city dwellers lacking:

- suitable housing
- a piped water supply
- sewers and safe levels of **sanitation**
- paved roads or street lighting
- electricity connected to the home.

In many places city dwellers live in homes that have not been planned by the city council. This may be a shelter on the pavement of an Indian city, or a corrugated iron shack in Nairobi, Kenya. In either case, the house was not planned so it has no sewer or connection to the water supply. It does not formally exist and in most cases the land on which it was built does not belong to the resident. That is why these properties are often referred to as:

- squatter settlements or shanty towns
- **informal settlements**
- spontaneous settlements.

Are these women making bricks, laying them or both?

If they are building homes, do they have permission to build here?

Are these labourers paid for this work?

Figure 1 Cities in LEDCs are growing fast. Many are being improved using self-help projects. This project is in Madagascar

Self-help

The residents of informal settlements usually have no **security of tenure**. In other words, they have no legal right to live there and could be evicted at any time. It is this insecurity, as well as poverty, that prevents people from improving their homes. However, after they have been established for some years, and the threat of eviction has gone, informal settlements are gradually improved. These improvements are often made by the residents themselves with advice and practical support from the local council or a **Non-Governmental Organisation (NGO)**. This type of urban change is called a **self-help** project.

WHERE THE SIDEWALKS END:
HOW THE POOR COMBAT POVERTY DAILY

Molly O' Meara Sheehan

On city maps, the location of this settlement – called 'Mtumba' by the 6,000 people who live there – shows up as prime habitat for rhino and giraffe. That's because this unsanctioned community lies on the edge of Nairobi National Park. Mtumba is only one of the many slums around Nairobi. In fact, more than half of the residents of Kenya's capital city cannot afford to live in 'formal' housing, and have been forced to find shelter in slums like this one.

'We can't depend on the government for anything,' says Castro as we walk through the settlement. He points out a water tap – one of two small spigots that supply water for the entire settlement. But no city water is piped here. Instead, these taps are fed by private companies that truck in tanks. And they sell their water at a premium. As of yet, no company has seen fit to establish any sort of business setting up toilets or sewers. Instead the 6,000 people who live here share three flimsy pit latrines.

Informal communities have certain advantages. Rents are lower than in formal housing. There are no property taxes. Residents can skirt cumbersome zoning laws that separate housing from businesses, and set up shop inside their homes or just outside. Mtumba's commercial strip boasts rows of brightly painted storefronts, each about one metre wide. There are produce stands, coffee shops, a 'movie house' showing videos, a barber shop, and an outfit that collects old newspapers.

But … slums are often located in a city's least-desirable locations – situated on steep hillsides, on flood plains, or downstream from industrial polluters – leaving residents vulnerable to disease and natural disasters.

'Land is the key to implement any project for development,' says a Mtumba woman who is involved in the community's self-run school. She explains that the people of her community have difficulty convincing themselves – let alone anyone else – to invest in water, toilets, or any sort of improvement. Why bother if the neighbourhood could be bulldozed the next day? Indeed, a central obstacle to any sort of 'self-help' in many slums is that in the eyes of the law the residents do not belong on the land where they live.

Figure 2 Extract from *Global Urban Development* magazine, describing the Mtumba informal settlement in Nairobi, Kenya

Activity

1 Define the terms **informal settlement** and **self-help project**.

2 Discuss Figure 1. If you were designing an enquiry into this settlement what other questions would you want to ask?

3 Read Figure 2 carefully.
   a) Explain two advantages of informal settlements.
   b) Explain why the location of informal settlements is often hazardous.

4 Who is making decisions about Mtumba informal settlement? Use Figure 2 to explain what each of the following groups is doing:
   a) The residents.
   b) Officials of the city authority such as planners.
   c) Local businesses.

5 Explain why insecurity of tenure is likely to reduce quality of life for urban dwellers.

Kenya

Contrasting approaches to urban poverty in Kenya

We have seen that various groups make decisions about Kenya's informal settlements. Sometimes these groups have different ideas about how urban areas should change, and this can lead to conflict.

Amnesty International is an international NGO. It has accused the Kenyan government of the forcible eviction of people from informal settlements in both Mombassa and Nairobi. Amnesty International claims that shanty homes have been bulldozed. Possessions have then been burned to prevent people from rebuilding shanty housing elsewhere. There may be a number of reasons for this controversial action:

- Property developers want the land to build planned houses which can be sold for a profit.
- Government officials are concerned that informal settlements look untidy and prevent foreign tourists visiting the country.
- Police believe that shanty towns protect criminals such as drug dealers.

Figure 3 Shanty homes in Kibera

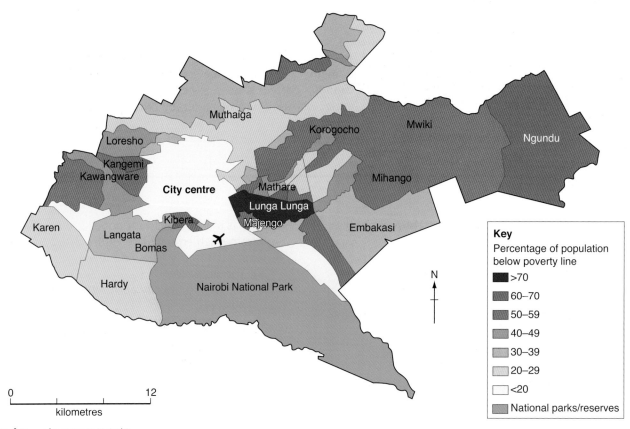

Figure 4 Map of poverty in Nairobi

Self-help through micro-credit schemes

The Population Council is an international, not-for-profit NGO. In Kenya the Population Council decided to introduce a **micro-credit** scheme for young women. The scheme is called TRY.

If you earn less than US$1 a day, how can you save even small amounts of money so that you can start your own business? Traditional banks are unlikely to lend you any money because you do not own a house or have some other guarantee that you can repay the loan. So micro-credit loans are now being used to support new businesses in the world's poorest communities. Micro-credit is where small loans are given to entrepreneurs who are too poor to qualify for traditional bank loans.

The TRY micro-credit scheme provides small loans to young women living in the squatter settlements of Nairobi. The girls receive basic financial training and are then grouped into teams of five. Each girl agrees to save a minimum of 50 Kenyan shillings (about US$0.65) each week.

The girls meet once a week. At these meetings they collect and record their savings and are given business advice. Many of these young women become great friends and use the meeting as an opportunity to share concerns about their relationships with partners or parents as well as their money worries. After saving for eight weeks, each team of five girls decides which two of its members are going to receive the first loan. These loans are in the order of 10,000 Kenyan shillings (US$130). Making this decision can be difficult, but it is based on the strength of each girl's business plan. Other members of the group can only receive their loans after the first two loans have been paid back. This arrangement creates a strong sense of responsibility: none of the girls wants to let down other members of the group.

The young women have used their loans in all sorts of businesses such as hairstyling, tailoring or running a market stall. Other girls have taken up jobs in welding or as mechanics. Some create new businesses, others expand existing businesses.

Not only has the scheme helped poor young women to set up businesses and earn money, it has also helped them to save. Before joining the scheme each girl had average savings of just US$43. After three years each member has average savings of US$95.

Activity

6 Use Figure 4 to describe the distribution (see page 25) of districts where:
  a) more than 50 per cent of the population lives below the poverty line.
  b) more than 70 per cent of the population lives below the poverty line.

7 If shanty homes are bulldozed, suggest what will happen to the residents.

8 Define the term **micro-credit**.

9 Suggest why micro-credit schemes loan money to women and the poorest members of society.

Going Further

The Grameen Bank

The Grameen Bank (which means 'Bank of the Villages') was founded in 1983 by Muhammad Yunus. It makes micro-credit loans to the poorest people of Bangladesh. It has been so successful that it has inspired the development of micro-credit schemes in many other developing countries, including Kenya. Muhammad Yunus was awarded the Nobel Peace Prize in 2006.

www.grameen-info.org/
The official Grameen Bank website gives more information about micro-credit loans in Bangladesh.

www.grameenfoundation.org/
The website of a non-profit making organisation set up to reproduce the success of the Bangladesh Grameen Bank in other countries.

Activity

10 From the homepage www.grameen-info.org/ click on the link to the Grameen Bank and click the drop-down menu under 'Methodology' in the top bar to find the link to 'Ten Indicators'. What do these indicators tell you about the way in which poverty is measured in Bangladesh compared to the UK?

11 Use the Grameen Foundation website to produce a map of countries in which micro-credit schemes are supported by the Foundation. Explain why micro-credit schemes are necessary in relatively wealthy countries such as the USA.

Is the UK suffering a housing crisis?

The UK is experiencing a housing crisis. It is estimated that at least an extra 223,000 new houses or flats are needed every year to meet demand. The government has set the building industry a target: by the year 2016 it wants to see 240,000 homes being built every year. That's an extra 3 million homes between 2007 and 2020. But where should these new homes be built? The greatest demand is in the South East of England. The economy is strongest in the South East, so this is an area where many younger people are moving to from other parts of the UK and from other EU countries.

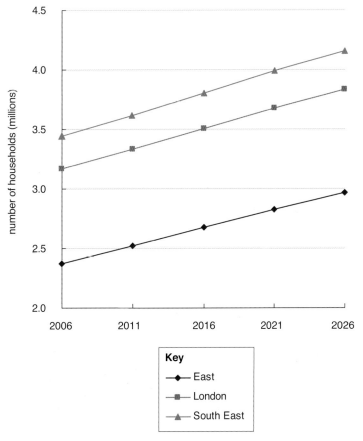

Key
- East
- London
- South East

Figure 5 Future number of households in London, East and South East England

Brownfield or greenfield?

A lot of new house building took place after the Second World War. New suburban homes were built on the edges of UK cities and the term **urban sprawl** was used to describe the resulting uncontrolled growth. UK planners at the time were so concerned about the loss of countryside that they prevented further loss by creating **green belts**: wide zones around many UK cities within which new developments were restricted. Green belts currently occupy 13 per cent of total land area in England. Many people living in smaller towns and rural areas of the South East are reluctant to see new housing development on any **greenfield site** whether it is on existing green belt land or any other farmland. An alternative is to use a **brownfield site**. In other words, new homes could be built on derelict sites within cities. Apart from preventing the loss of green spaces this has other advantages which make this a more sustainable option:

- Residents will use existing services such as public transport, schools and shops, which helps to maintain demand for these services and keeps them running.
- The city remains compact rather than sprawling outwards. This reduces commuting distances from home to work.

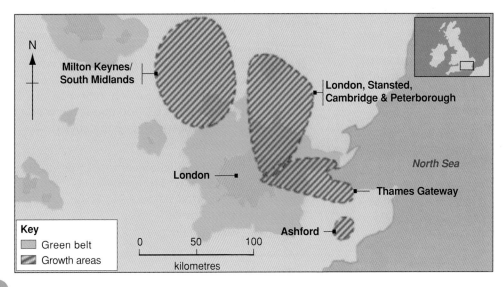

Key
- Green belt
- Growth areas

Figure 6 The key areas for new homes

Figure 7 Why do we need so many new houses in the East and South East regions?

We are living longer: In 2003, the population over 65 was 11 million people: by 2026 it is estimated that this will increase to 13 million people. With better health, more elderly people are staying in their home, which means property is not freed up for the next generation.

Population increase: With a combination of natural increase (more births than deaths), migration into the region from other parts of the UK and immigration (e.g. economic migrants from Eastern Europe), the population of the East is expected to grow by 10 per cent (compared with the UK growth rate of 6.7 per cent).

Increasing number of people living alone: A lot of young adults choose to live alone. Also more marriages are breaking up, so there is a need for more homes to accommodate the split families (the divorce rate has actually slowed in recent years).

Why do we need so many new houses in the East and South East?

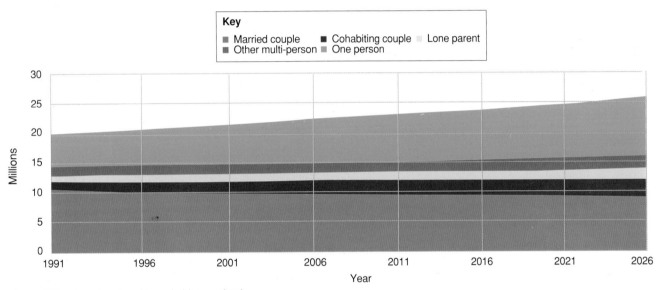

Figure 8 The changing size of households in England

Activity

12 Describe the trend shown in Figure 5.

13 a) List five groups who might oppose plans for new housing and five who might benefit from it.
b) Explain why many people will be concerned that new homes are being planned for green belt areas.

14 Use Figure 8.
a) Roughly how many households were in each category in 1991 and how many will there be in 2026?
b) Compare the trend in married couples with one-person households over this period.
c) Use Figure 7 to explain the trends you can see in Figure 8.

15 Write a short article for your local newspaper explaining why new homes are needed. Keep your article factual and between 300 and 500 words long.

 London

Barnes Reservoir: a case study of the redevelopment of a brownfield site

In 1995 a huge project began in Barnes, southwest London, to redevelop a brownfield site occupied by four disused reservoirs. The old concrete structures of the reservoirs were an eyesore and were too dangerous for use by local people for recreation. However, they were being used by waterfowl for feeding and nesting. So a project was devised with three main partners:

- The Wildfowl and Wetlands Trust: a conservation charity that manages nine wetland sites around the UK. They have created a 40-hectare wetland ecosystem on part of the site by bulldozing the old concrete walls of the reservoir and creating bodies of water of different size and depths to suit different birds.
- Thames Water: the company that owned the reservoirs.
- Berkeley Homes: a property developer that helped to finance the project by building and selling homes on part of the site.

 www.wwt.org.uk
is the official website of the Wildfowl and Wetlands Trust and has information about all nine WWT visitor centres in the UK. Why not see if there is one near you?

Green spaces act like the lungs of a city. They help to control pollution levels.

More than 130 species of wild bird are recorded at the site each year.

Bodies of water in a city help to reduce summer air temperatures. It may be desirable to create more urban wetlands to make cities more sustainable in the face of climate change.

Figure 9 Some of the benefits of the new wetlands ecosystem

Figure 10 An aerial view of the Berkeley Homes housing (bottom right) and WWT London Wetland Centre (centre of photo)

Activity

16 Use Figure 11.
  a) Describe the location of the Wetland Centre.
  b) When Figure 10 was taken, in which direction was the camera pointing?
  c) Identify local services that could be used by residents of the new development. Use these headings for the services and give six-figure grid references:
    i) Health facilities
    ii) Transport
    iii) Leisure and recreational services.

17 Use Figures 9 and 11. Suggest five factors that might give residents of the new housing (grid reference 228774) a high quality of life.

18 **a)** Explain three advantages of developing brownfield sites rather than greenfield sites.
   b) Do you think this particular project is a good example of sustainable urban development? Explain your answer carefully.

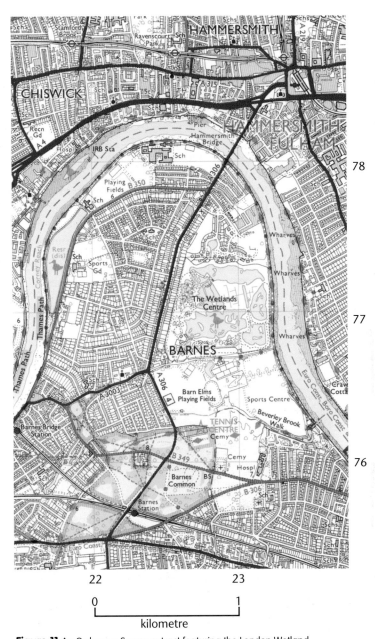

Figure 11 An Ordnance Survey extract featuring the London Wetland Centre. Scale 1:25,000 Sheet 161

London Wetland Centre facts and figures

- The site contains more than 30 different wetlands.
- There are 600 m of boardwalk and 3.4 km of pathway.
- More than 170 species of wild bird are recorded annually.
- 24 species of butterfly and 500 moth species have been recorded.
- 21 dragon and damselfly species have been recorded.
- Four species of amphibian are recorded annually.

What is a sustainable community?

The BedZED community shown in Figure 12 is a **sustainable community** of 82 homes built in Beddington, Surrey by a housing association called the Peabody Trust. The homes use green technologies to reduce their energy consumption. The development only uses renewable energy sources: solar energy and woodchips. A boiler uses waste woodchips to create both heat and power for all the homes. The Trust claim that BedZED is a **carbon-neutral development** – in other words, the homes do not add any extra carbon dioxide emissions to the atmosphere.

The houses have created a lot of media interest and the residents are proud of their 'green' homes. The UK needs many more new homes and, because of problems created by **climate change**, the government wants many more carbon-neutral schemes to be built. In fact, the government says 3 million new homes will be needed in the UK by 2020. But building so many new houses is bound to create conflict as local residents often object to new housing being built close to their homes. A priority for both the government and the developers is that any new housing developments are seen by local communities as sustainable. They should:

- create a better quality of life for people living there today
- use resources in such a way that future generations can also have a decent quality of life.

The buildings have 300 mm of insulation in the walls (most modern houses have 50 mm). This conserves heat energy so well that the homes need to be kept cool. These funnels direct fresh cool air into the buildings.

Large windows on the south side of the building collect heat energy from the sun – a technique known as passive solar gain.

Slate and tile roofs shed water quickly into storm drains. This can lead to problems of flash flooding. Roof gardens use up some rainwater and slow down the flow of run-off into the storm drains.

Figure 12 The Beddington Zero Energy Development (BedZED) is the UK's largest carbon-neutral eco-community – the first of its kind in the UK

www.peabody.org.uk/
The Peabody Trust is a Housing Association providing social housing at a fair rent to its tenants. It is responsible for the BedZED development shown in Figure 12. Follow the links to new developments to read more.

www.eco-schools.org.uk/
This site describes how to audit your own school so that you can see how green it is.

Figure 13 Web extract from the Peabody Trust

What are the features of BedZED?

The design is to a very high standard and is used to enhance the environmental dimensions, with strong emphasis on roof gardens, sunlight, solar energy, reduction of energy consumption and waste water recycling.

BedZED provides 82 residential homes with a mixture of tenures, 34 for outright sale, 23 for shared ownership, 10 for key workers and 15 at affordable rent for social housing – with a further 14 galleried apartments for outright sale.

The homes are a mixture of sizes and the project also includes buildings for commercial use, an exhibition centre, a children's nursery and a show flat so that visitors may see what it is like to live at BedZED.

Using renewable materials

Where possible, BedZED is built from natural, recycled or reclaimed materials. All the wood used has been approved by the Forest Stewardship Council or comparable internationally recognised environmental organisations, to ensure that it comes from a sustainable source.

Space heating

Through the innovative design and construction, heat from the sun and heat generated by occupants and everyday activities such as cooking are sufficient to heat BedZED homes to a comfortable temperature. The need for space heating, which accounts for a significant part of the energy demand in conventional buildings, is therefore reduced or completely eliminated.

Green transport plan

Transport energy accounts for a large proportion of the energy consumption of any development.

A green transport plan promotes walking, cycling and use of public transport. A car pool for residents has been established, and all these initiatives have helped to provide a strategic and integrated approach to transport issues.

The BedZED project shows that it is possible to reduce reliance on cars and it introduced the first legally binding Green Transport Plan as a condition of planning permission.

BedZED's target is a 50 per cent reduction in fossil-fuel consumption by private car use over the next ten years compared with a conventional development.

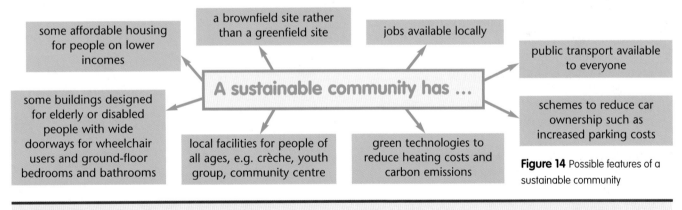

Figure 14 Possible features of a sustainable community

Activity

19 Discuss the features in Figure 12. Use this and the eco-schools website (www.eco-schools.org.uk/) to audit (list the good and bad features of) your own school. How could your community be more sustainable?

20 Study Figure 13. Explain how the BedZED development:
  a) caters for at least three different groups of people
  b) reduces carbon emissions in three different ways
  c) reduces people's use of cars.

21 Discuss Figure 14.
  a) For each feature in the diagram, suggest how it might be sustainable.
  b) Suggest at least two of the features that might be controversial. Which groups of people might come into conflict over these suggestions?
  c) Suggest at least two more features that you think are necessary in a new sustainable community.

Chapter 5
Planning issues in urban and rural environments

KEY QUESTIONS

- Who is involved in planning decisions in residential places?
- How and why do conflicts occur?
- Why do some people have more power than others to influence planning decisions?
- How might sustainable residential places be planned?

Understanding the planning system in England and Wales

The planning system in England and Wales involves three tiers of decision making. The national government sets overall targets for things such as housing, new schools and transport. Each Regional Assembly then has to produce a **Regional Spatial Strategy** (in Wales this document is called the Wales Spatial Plan). The planners need to consider the impact that the need for new housing will have on other elements of the plan, such as new roads, schools, better waste management or conservation projects. Finally, the detailed plans for each local area are produced by local authorities. They must plan within the guidelines provided by the Regional Spatial Strategy. They consult local people in order to produce a **Local Development Framework (LDF)**. These three tiers of decision making are illustrated in Figure 1.

Who is involved in planning decisions?

The answer is all of us! We are all **stakeholders** – in other words, everyone has a view on the planning issues that affect their community. A key element of the planning process is that all stakeholders can become involved. They can respond to the ideas being put forward by the three tiers of the planning process, i.e. national government, Regional Assemblies and local authorities. The aim is that all individuals and groups who may be touched by planning decisions will feel that they can contribute to the policy and help to shape it. Stakeholders come in all shapes and sizes, they might be:

- an individual householder who is concerned that a proposed new road will disturb their peaceful home
- a parish council that is keen to see an increase in playground facilities in its area
- a pressure group that is lobbying to protect a specific area of countryside
- development consultants working on behalf of a large landowner who hopes to build a large sports complex.

We can all play a part in the planning process, sometimes promoting new developments, sometimes trying to stop planning proposals.

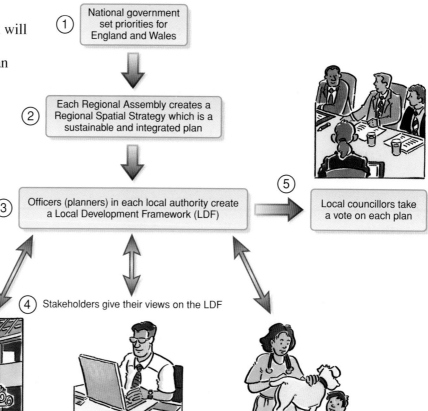

① National government set priorities for England and Wales

② Each Regional Assembly creates a Regional Spatial Strategy which is a sustainable and integrated plan

③ Officers (planners) in each local authority create a Local Development Framework (LDF)

⑤ Local councillors take a vote on each plan

④ Stakeholders give their views on the LDF

Figure 1 The three tiers of decision making in the planning process

Figure 2 Number of new households needed by 2026 in each of the Regional Assemblies in England

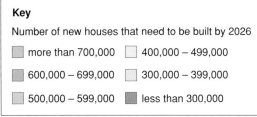

Key

Number of new houses that need to be built by 2026

- ▓ more than 700,000
- ▓ 600,000 – 699,000
- ░ 500,000 – 599,000
- ░ 400,000 – 499,000
- ░ 300,000 – 399,000
- ▓ less than 300,000

Activity

1 a) Work in pairs. Discuss the photos and their captions on page 7. Which of these planning issues most affects your local community?

b) Join with another pair. Discuss the solutions that you think would help solve the planning issues you have identified for your local community.

2 Give three different examples of stakeholders. Do you think the views of all stakeholders carry equal weight in the planning process? Explain your answer.

3 Use Figure 2.

a) Describe the pattern in England. Which regions will need to provide most new housing?

b) Suggest why some regions need more new homes than others.

4 Use Figure 3.

a) Draw a line graph that shows the percentage of affordable homes built in your region of England. Describe the trend and suggest how this will have affected first-time buyers.

b) Draw an outline of Figure 2 (or use the internet to find a similar outline map). Use your outline to draw a density shaded map of the data for 2005 in Figure 3.

c) Describe the pattern on your map. Which regions have been most and least successful? Suggest why the national government has brought in guidelines for each region.

Figure 3 Percentage of all new houses completed each year that are 'affordable'; that is, where the rent is controlled by a local authority or where ownership of the property is shared between the occupier and the developer.

	1998	1999	2000	2001	2002	2003	2004	2005
North East	15	13	11	9	12	5	8	9
North West	16	18	13	13	13	13	8	9
Yorkshire & Humberside	14	12	10	10	9	7	8	7
East Midlands	12	11	9	10	9	7	9	9
West Midlands	17	16	17	14	13	16	12	15
East	13	15	10	12	12	11	12	13
London	32	31	31	30	24	26	30	24
South East	19	19	15	15	14	16	18	18
South West	16	15	15	13	14	13	16	15
England (average)	17	17	14	15	14	13	14	14

Suffolk Coastal District

Recognising conflicting viewpoints – a planning dilemma

In 2004 the draft East of England Plan recognised the need for nearly 500,000 new homes to be built in the East of England by the year 2021. The plan required 58,000 of these to be built in Suffolk with a minimum of 10,000 to be constructed in Suffolk Coastal District.

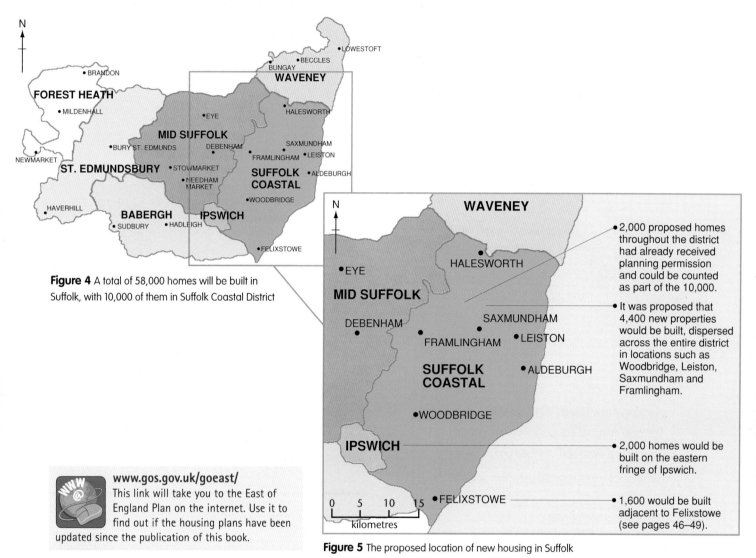

Figure 4 A total of 58,000 homes will be built in Suffolk, with 10,000 of them in Suffolk Coastal District

Figure 5 The proposed location of new housing in Suffolk

www.gos.gov.uk/goeast/
This link will take you to the East of England Plan on the internet. Use it to find out if the housing plans have been updated since the publication of this book.

Activity

5 Copy and complete the following description:

Suffolk Coastal District is west/east of Ipswich. It is one of six/seven rural districts in the county of Suffolk. The largest settlement in SCDC is Felixstowe which is approx ...... km to the north/north-west/south-east of Ipswich.

6 **a)** Describe the distribution of proposed new housing in Figure 5.
   b) Suggest reasons why the largest clusters are close to Ipswich and Felixstowe.
   c) Suggest why so many houses will be dispersed across the district.
   d) Suggest who might object to building these new houses, and who might support their construction.

How influential are the views of stakeholders?

Stakeholders are invited to participate in this planning process. They can attempt to persuade local authorities to change their plans. Sometimes they offer new, alternative ideas. After the consultation period is over, the planners will state their preferred options and publish definite plans. Even at this point, stakeholders can comment in the hope of affecting decisions. After all the stakeholder views are taken into account, the final decision is made by the elected council.

You will recognise that the views of some stakeholders might be taken more seriously than others. Some people try to prevent change because of the effect it will have on their own home or quality of life. They have what is called a 'not-in-my-back-yard' (**NIMBY**) attitude. Planners listen to such viewpoints but they must balance any negative social, economic or environmental impacts of a scheme against the needs identified in the LDF. In fact, most of the power is in the hands of two groups:

*   the officers employed by the Planning Authorities who prepare the LDF
*   the local councillors who vote on each plan.

However, if the councillors make unpopular decisions, anyone aged 18 or over can vote against them next time there is a local election.

Figure 6 Examples of views of different stakeholders considering change in South Suffolk

Councillor
I am a parish councillor and I speak on behalf of the village community. We are keen to increase the number of play facilities in our growing village. We want a small park for the younger children with swings and slides, and a floodlit all-weather football pitch for the teenagers. We have to persuade the council to build on the old derelict recreation ground.

Business owner – haulier
I own a large fleet of lorries taking goods in and out of the port. My drivers complain that there is a lack of rest places along the feeder roads. The authority needs to create lorry parks that have toilet and refreshment facilities.

Elderly lady
I've lived in this quiet village for 50 years and now I hear that they want to build 30 affordable houses. It will change the character of the village. I must try to stop the plans.

Environmentalist
I've no objection to new housing, not least the building of affordable homes for local people. However, they must select a brownfield site, not an area of green belt where we stand to lose more countryside.

Activity

7 Discuss the views expressed in Figure 6.
  a) Identify one NIMBY point of view.
  b) Identify one view that is considering a sustainable future.
  c) Of the four views, which views would you take more seriously, and why?

8 Using the search engine of your local newspaper, find examples of pressure groups, individuals and stakeholders who have participated in the consultation process outlined in a local LDF.

Investigating the options around Felixstowe

Suffolk Coastal District Council (SCDC) needed to consider the views of stakeholders in the communities where houses might be built. To do this they produced sketch maps showing the possible location of the new housing. Figure 7 is an example of one of these sketch maps. It shows the five potential sites that could be used to accommodate 1,600 homes and the associated community facilities close to Felixstowe. SCDC says that the proposals in their Local Development Framework:

- are for sustainable housing communities
- guarantee that one third of the houses will be 'affordable'
- are sensitive to reducing any social, economic and environmental impacts.

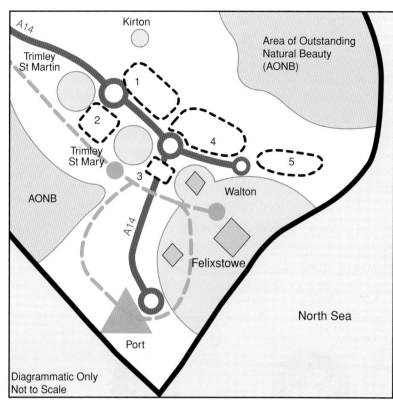

▲ **Figure 7** Planners' sketch map of five possible sites for the housing near Felixstowe

▼ **Figure 8** The fields at site 2 between the two Trimley communities

Activity

9 Study Figures 7, 8 and 9.
  a) Suggest three possible reasons why people living in Trimley St Mary and Trimley St Martin might object to sites 2 or 3.
  b) Explain what is meant by a **sustainable housing community**.

EXAMINER'S TIPS

Using evidence from OS map extracts I

Your exam may include an OS map extract at a scale of 1:25,000 like Figure 9. Questions may ask you to 'use evidence' from this map. If so, the examiner expects you to pick out features from the map and locate them with a four- or six-figure grid reference. For example:

Question
Use evidence from Figure 9 that suggests that this is a sustainable community.

Answer
A sustainable community has local services, job opportunities and a good transport network. On the map extract, there are schools, sports facilities and hospitals. The train station at 302351 means that commuters can reduce their carbon emissions. Jobs are available in the port, south of this extract. The port is shown in Figure 7.

Figure 9 Ordnance Survey extract of the Trimley area, showing the areas where development is possible. Scale 1: 25,000, Sheet 197.

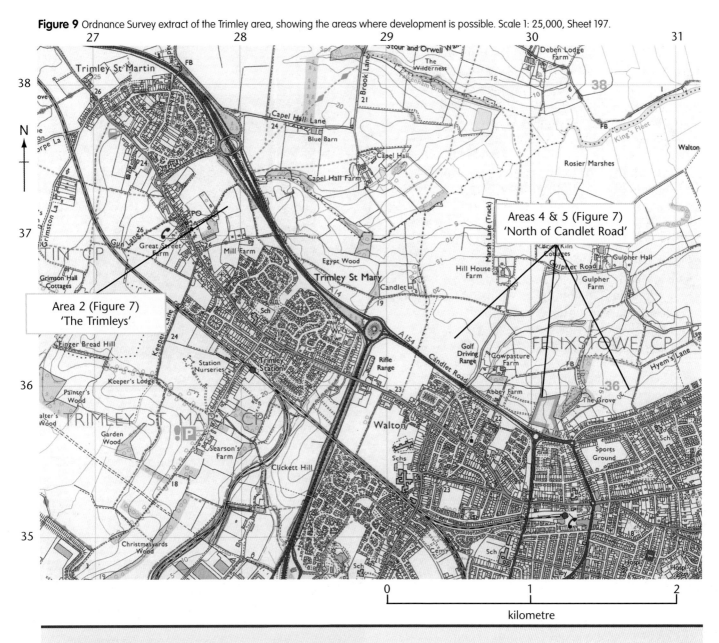

Activity

10 a) Use Figures 8 and 9 to choose adjectives that describe this landscape from the following pairs:

peaceful _ _ _ _ _ busy
natural _ _ _ _ _ artificial
modern _ _ _ _ _ traditional
friendly _ _ _ _ hostile

b) Use these and other adjectives to write a 200-word document that summarises a sense of place for this part of Suffolk.

11 a) Describe the feature found at each of the following six-figure grid references:

281361	296362	305355
291354	271377	277357

b) Use this and other evidence to write a 300-word document supporting the view that this area has sufficient transport, education and leisure facilities to be described as a sustainable community.

c) If 1,600 extra homes are built here, what additional services or transport links do you think will be needed. Justify your choice using evidence from the map.

What do the stakeholders think of the proposed development?

Figure 10 Stakeholder concerns about the development of Area 2

STAG is an informal group of like-minded villagers (from Trimley St Martin and Trimley St Mary). They have used the consultation period to voice their concerns about developing land between the two existing villages. The main fear is that the 'village-style life', enjoyed by both communities, will be lost when the area becomes a suburban landscape linked to Felixstowe and possibly to Ipswich in future years.

- We will lose our village lifestyle.
- Eventually there will be a Felixstowe–Ipswich continuum. We don't want to live in the suburbs.
- We will suffer building chaos for 20 years.
- The value of our properties will go down.
- The High Road, linking the two villages, will become jammed every morning and evening.
- There are not enough local services such as doctors, dentists and primary schools as it is.
- Who will build the new services? Will our community charges go up in order to pay for them?
- There will be disruption to local roads when they put in new power, water and telephone services.
- The A14 is already crowded and dangerous. Most of the new people will commute into Ipswich.
- They should build on brownfield sites or disperse the houses, not build them in one place.

Figure 11 Stakeholder concerns about the development of Areas 4 & 5

The 'Save Felixstowe Countryside' group is made up of a range of individuals, from all walks of life, who live in the Felixstowe area. Their single aim is to preserve the remaining countryside around Felixstowe for the benefit of local people, tourists and future generations.

- This is a high-quality rural landscape. It is valuable for walking, cycling and birdwatching. Local people and visitors alike enjoy it.
- It is a natural barrier between the Area of Outstanding Beauty and the town.
- Buildings will create light pollution that will disturb precious birds like kingfishers, marsh harriers and spotted woodpeckers.
- Further wildlife disturbance to brown hares and otters will be caused by noise and the presence of domestic cats and dogs.
- Most of the land is valuable Grade 2 agricultural land. We need this land for growing food for future generations.

- The Council talks about the need to include services and amenities as well as houses. How large will this area eventually be?
- Who will pay for the new power and drainage systems required – the hard-pressed ratepayers?
- Where will the allotment holders go?

Your decision

You have joined the planning team at SCDC for two weeks as part of your school's work experience programme. The senior manager wants you to have a taste of the problems and issues faced by planners who work for local authorities.

You are only working for two weeks at the planning office, so the planners have not given you the thousands of responses they have received following the draft proposals published in the LDF. They want you just to focus on the responses received about areas 2, 4 and 5. If the planning issue were this simple, which of the two sites would you recommend as a way of moving forward?

Make a copy of the matrix and use it to organise your initial ideas. On the matrix you should select a maximum of five issues from Figures 10 and 11. Try to select a range as some of the concerns overlap. Suggest if the issue relates to a social (SO), economic (EC) or environmental (EN) concern. Some of the issues may overlap these concerns. State why you think the issue relates to sustainability. Two rows have been completed for you.

Group	Issue selected from Figures 10 and 11	Social (SO)? Economic (EC)? Environmental (EN)?	Why is this a concern in terms of a sustainable future?
STAG (Save Trimley Against Growth)	We will suffer building chaos for 20 years	SO + EC	Villagers might decide to leave the area, splitting up friends and neighbours and forcing them to sell their houses cheaply.
SFC (Save Felixstowe Countryside)	We will lose an area of high-quality rural landscape	EN + EC	People need places for leisure as well as houses. If we build here local people have nowhere to walk dogs, and tourists will stop coming to Felixstowe, causing job losses.

Chapter 6
Urbanisation

Global patterns of urban development

The United Nations estimates that by 2008 more than half of the world's population will be living in **urban** areas: larger towns and cities. The **urban population**, which is the percentage of people living in towns and cities, has grown steadily since the 1950s:

- 30 per cent in 1950.
- 47 per cent in 2000.
- It is estimated that it will reach 60 per cent by 2030.

The process by which the population of a country becomes more urban and less rural is known as **urbanisation**. Urbanisation causes the physical and human growth of towns and cities. Urbanisation is caused by a combination of two factors:

- The migration of people from rural to urban areas.
- The **natural increase** of the urban population due to there being more births than deaths.

Urbanisation is currently much more rapid in the Less Economically Developed Countries (LEDCs) than in **More Economically Developed Countries (MEDCs)**. LEDCs tend to have faster-growing populations than MEDCs and they also have a larger number of people moving from rural to urban areas.

KEY QUESTIONS

- ✪ Where and why are people migrating into urban areas?
- ✪ What are the impacts?
- ✪ Can the consequences be managed in a sustainable way?

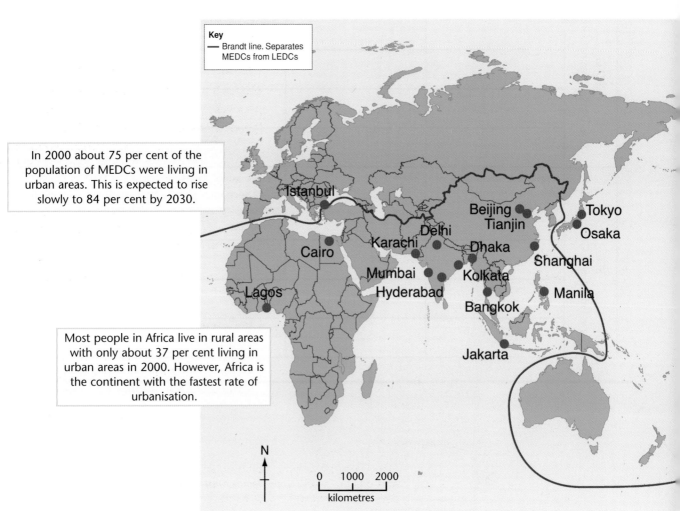

Key
— Brandt line. Separates MEDCs from LEDCs

In 2000 about 75 per cent of the population of MEDCs were living in urban areas. This is expected to rise slowly to 84 per cent by 2030.

Most people in Africa live in rural areas with only about 37 per cent living in urban areas in 2000. However, Africa is the continent with the fastest rate of urbanisation.

Figure 1 Map showing the location of those cities that are forecast to be mega-cities by 2015

People move for a variety of reasons. Conflicts and natural disasters may force people to move, in which case the migrants may be described as **refugees**. However, in most cases people migrate out of choice rather than because of violence or disaster. People generally move because they want to improve their standard of living by finding a better-paid job. A migrant who moves in order to find work is described as an **economic migrant**. Many migrants also expect that moving to the city will improve their quality of life, perhaps by giving them better access to clean water or healthcare facilities.

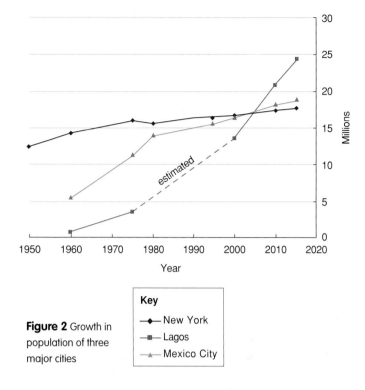

Figure 2 Growth in population of three major cities

Key
- New York
- Lagos
- Mexico City

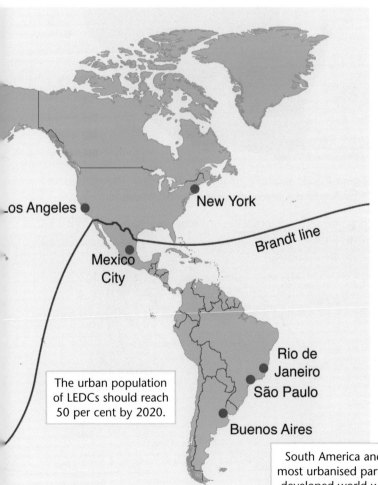

The urban population of LEDCs should reach 50 per cent by 2020.

South America and the Caribbean are the most urbanised part of the less economically developed world with about 75 per cent of the population living in urban areas.

Activity

1 Use Figure 1 to complete the following:

MEDCs have a *larger / smaller* proportion of people living in urban areas than LEDCs. Of the less economically developed regions:

- .... is the most urbanised
- .... is experiencing the most rapid urbanisation.

2 Use the text on these pages to make your own definitions for **urbanisation**, **refugees** and **economic migrant**.

3 Explain the two factors that led to the more rapid urbanisation in LEDCs.

4 Use Figure 1.
   a) Describe the likely distribution (see page 25) of the world's mega-cities in 2015.
   b) Use Figure 2 to describe and explain the trend of each graph.

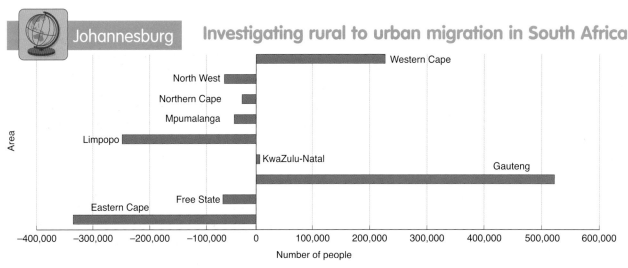

Johannesburg   **Investigating rural to urban migration in South Africa**

Figure 3 Total population gains and losses due to migration in 2005

Gauteng is South Africa's most urban province and contains three major cities of more than one million people: Johannesburg, Pretoria and Soweto. By contrast, the largest city in the neighbouring province of Limpopo has only 90,000 people and more than 90 per cent of the population lives in rural areas. In this case study we will investigate the reasons for migration between Limpopo and Gauteng, and also examine the effects of this migration on rural communities.

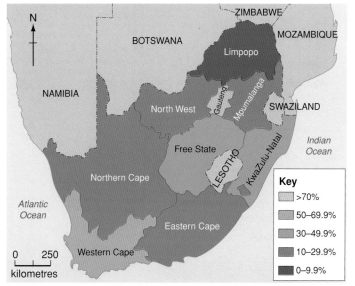

Figure 4 Urban population in South Africa's provinces (estimate based on population living in settlements greater than 20,000 people)

Activity

5 Use Figures 3 and 4 to complete the following:

The two most urban provinces are:

i) .... which gained .... migrants during 2005 and;

ii) .... which gained .... migrants in 2005.

The more rural provinces, such as ...., gained / lost population during the year.

6 Study Figure 5. Choose from the following phrases to describe the flow of migrants from Limpopo:

Most migrants migrate short / long distances. Most / all migrants move to provinces that are less rural than Limpopo. Some / many migrants move to the most urban provinces of South Africa.

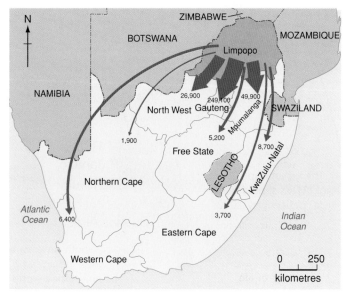

Figure 5 Migration from Limpopo province during 2005

What are the push/pull factors for rural to urban migration in South Africa?

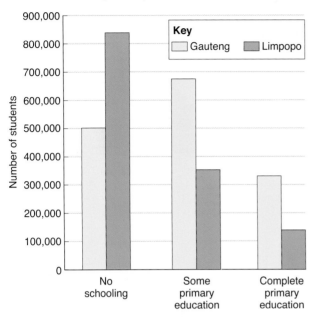

Figure 6 Comparing education in Limpopo with Gauteng

People living in rural areas such as Limpopo are attracted by the jobs and better opportunities available in cities such as Johannesburg. The possibility of better healthcare and schools for their children are **pull factors** that encourage migrants to leave their rural homes. At the same time, migrants are often dissatisfied with life in the countryside. Few rural houses have a connection to the national electricity grid. Most people do not own an electric cooker, let alone a computer or television. Lack of money, poor job opportunities and relatively low quality of life are all **push factors** that can force people to move away from rural areas.

People living in the province of Limpopo rely on either farming or tourism for their income. The region has a seasonal wet/dry tropical **climate** and a **savanna ecosystem**. Rural population densities are relatively high and farm sizes small.

Most households in Limpopo earn a little less than 1,000 Rand a month, whereas average household income in Johannesburg is 7,175 Rand a month. The **poverty line** in South Africa is defined at 1,100 Rand (about US$150) a month. Of people in Limpopo, 60 per cent live below this poverty line compared with only 20 per cent of people in Gauteng province.

Activity

7 Based on the evidence in Figures 3, 4 and 5:
   a) suggest why so few migrants move from Limpopo to Western Cape
   b) suggest which regions are losing migrants to Western Cape and give reasons for your answer.

8 Use Figure 6. How many students in each province:
   a) have no schooling
   b) complete primary education?

9 Explain how each of the following might be push factors that contribute to migration from rural areas of Limpopo.
   • The rural areas are densely populated.
   • Rainfall is low and unpredictable.
   • Rural communities are isolated from services such as schools and healthcare.

10 List the reasons for rural to urban migration using this table:

	Push factors	**Pull factors**
Economic reasons		
Education		
Quality of life		

The percentage of Johannesburg residents who:
• own an electric stove in the home: 77.86 per cent
• own a fridge or freezer: 87.26 per cent
• own a dishwasher: 5.24 per cent
• own a vacuum cleaner: 31.35 per cent
• own a television: 89.53 per cent
• own a hi-fi or music centre: 73.61 per cent
• own a personal computer: 17.86 per cent
• have a telephone connection: 57.65 per cent
• have eaten in a restaurant in the last month: 44.1 per cent
• bought a take-away meal in the last month (from a permanent establishment, not a street hawker): 55.26 per cent
• hired a video or DVD in the last month: 13.65 per cent.

Figure 7 Some lifestyle statistics for Johannesburg, drawn from the annual All Media Products Survey (AMPS)

11 Study Figure 7 taken from a South African website. Suggest how the internet and advertising might accidentally encourage further migration into Johannesburg.

What are the consequences of rural to urban migration?

What effect does migration have on the rural areas that the migrants leave behind? Does the loss of so many people cause economic and social problems in the countryside? Or does migration create benefits for rural areas? Research suggests that the consequences of migration are very complex. They include:

- **Brain drain** – the loss of some of the most skilled workers.
- **Remittances** – the money sent back by workers to support their families.
- Information and ideas – new technologies and skills learned in the city flow back into the country where they are used to support local businesses.

www.statssa.gov.za/census2001/digiatlas/index.html

This site uses **Geographical Information Systems (GIS)** to display an online atlas of South Africa. It uses data from the most recent census which can be displayed in either map or graph form.

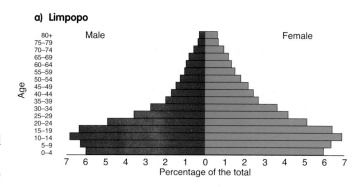

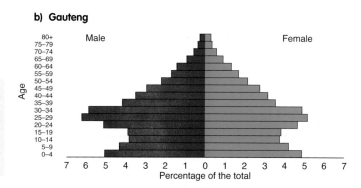

Figure 8 Population pyramids for a) Limpopo (a rural province) and b) Gauteng (a neighbouring urban province)

Activity

12 Compare the population pyramids in Figure 8. Focus on the differences/similarities in the following parts of each graph:
   a) The percentage of the population aged 0 to 19.
   b) The percentage of the population aged 25 to 34.
   c) The balance between males and females.

13 Use Figure 9 to suggest reasons for the differences you noticed between the population pyramids.

14 Explain whether each of the following is an advantage or disadvantage to a rural area that is losing migrants:
   a) brain drain
   b) remittances
   c) information and ideas.

Studies in South Africa show that:
- those aged between 15 and 35 are the most likely to migrate
- more males migrate than females, but an increasing number of females are migrating
- female migrants are slightly younger than male migrants
- circular migration (see page 55) is more common than permanent migration
- some rural migrants move to large urban areas such as Johannesburg, but many rural migrants move to smaller towns
- an increasing number of rural migrants move to other rural areas.

Figure 9 Key points of migration in South Africa

Circular migration

Many migrants do not make a permanent move to the city. It is common for people to leave the countryside when there are few farming jobs and return at busier times of the year, for example, at harvest. This temporary form of rural to urban migration is known as **circular migration**.

Circular migration brings both benefits and problems to rural communities. Migrants earn money which can be sent to the rural family and invested in improving the farm: repairing terraces and in tree-planting schemes. Circular migrants also reduce demand on village food and water supplies. This is particularly helpful in Limpopo which has a long dry season.

However, circular migration is almost certainly one of the reasons for the spread of AIDS and other sexually transmitted diseases. Studies in South Africa suggest that migrants are three times more likely to be infected with HIV than non-migrants. A returning migrant who is unaware that he or she is HIV positive could then infect a partner in the rural home. It is more difficult to treat rural AIDS sufferers because of their isolation from health clinics.

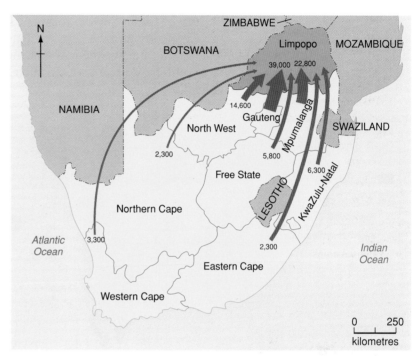

Figure 10 Migration into Limpopo, 2005

Activity

15 Define **circular migration**.

16 Use Figure 10.
   a) How many migrants returned from provinces that are mostly urban?
   b) Compare this map with Figure 5 on page 52. What are the similarities and differences?

17 Use the text and your own ideas to complete the following table about the advantages and disadvantages of circular migration:

	Advantages to the rural area	Disadvantages to the rural area
Economic		
Social		

18 Explain why circular migration is likely to be more beneficial to rural areas than permanent migration.

Investigating urban change in Johannesburg

Johannesburg is South Africa's biggest city. It has a population of more than 1.5 million. On the edge of the city is the settlement of Soweto. Soweto is a black township with another 1 million people. It grew up during the apartheid era when black Africans were forced to live in locations separate from white South Africans. Approximately 12 per cent of the housing in Soweto is informal.

Quality of life in Soweto for many residents is poor. The population has grown quickly and the housing density is very high. There is little space for leisure activities for the half a million children who live here. The township lacks sufficient basic services such as piped water, sanitation and waste collection.

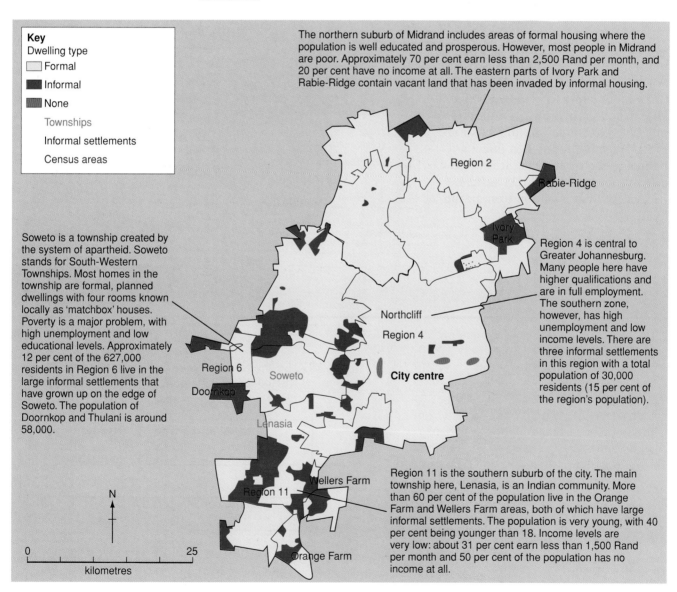

Figure 11 The distribution of informal housing in Johannesburg

Figure 12a Racial structure of the population

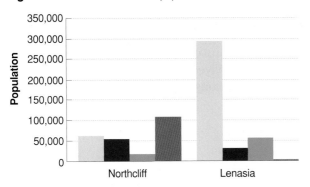

Districts of Johannesburg

Key		Northcliff	Lenasia
	African	59,484	292,880
	Mixed race	53,363	30,760
	Indian	17,238	54,457
	White	107,514	443

Figure 12b Occupations (number of people employed)

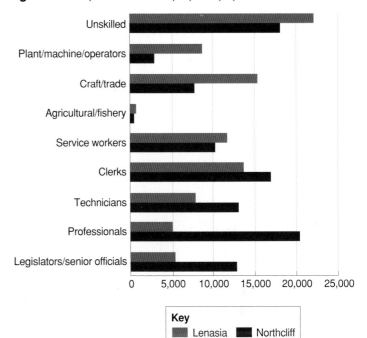

Key

Lenasia   Northcliff

Figure 12c Housing type

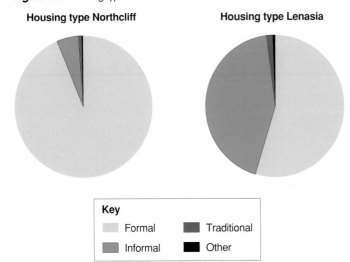

	Northcliff		**Lenasia**	
Households	number of houses	%	number of houses	%
Formal	75,603	94.0	60,093	54.8
Informal	3,726	4.6	47,499	43.3
Traditional	924	1.1	1,587	1.4
Other	141	0.2	444	0.4
Total households	80,394		109,623	

Activity

19 Using evidence from the graphs, compare the human geography of Lenasia with Northcliff. Use the following headings as a structure for three short paragraphs:
Racial structure   **Occupations**   **Housing type**

20 Using evidence from the graphs, suggest which of the two regions has the higher standard of living. Give at least two reasons for your answer.

21 Use Figure 11 to describe the location (see page 56) of Soweto.

22 Use Figure 11 to describe the distribution (see page 56) of informal settlements in Johannesburg.

Improving quality of life in Soweto

In the 1980s water supply in Soweto was very poor. The iron pipes carrying water were rusted and between 50 and 60 per cent of water was wasted in leaks. Many districts were able to have water only at night. Obviously, this was a major health concern. Gradually the situation has improved. Many new water pipes have been laid, and township roads have been paved. The local authority employed local people to do the work, so Sowetans benefited from extra jobs as well as improved services.

Figure 13 The township of Soweto is home to 1 million people

Activity

23 Explain how each of the following would affect quality of life:
a) High population density
b) Irregular water supply
c) Unpaved roads.

24 If you have access to a computer, use the internet to research and find definitions for the following terms:
a) socio-economic group   c) apartheid
b) housing tenure   d) township.
Read the advice that follows on how to find definitions.

 ## Using the internet to find definitions of geographical terms

Using the internet to research the meaning of a term is easy.

1 Use a search engine such as Google™.
2 Type in 'define': in the dialog box, and the word you want to define (see example on the right).
3 View the sites that are returned in your web search (see below). Some sites are more reliable than others. For example, university and government sites tend to be factual and accurate, whereas weblogs often contain opinions that may not be factually correct.

define: quality of life

Google Search   I'm Feeling Lucky

Search: ⦿ the web ○ pages from the UK

Advanced Search
Preferences
Language Tools

Definitions of **quality of life** on the Web:

- The overall enjoyment of life. Many clinical trials measure aspects of a patient's sense of well-being and ability to perform various tasks to assess the effects that cancer and its treatment have on the patient.
nydailynews.healthology.com/nydailynews/15836.htm

- The level of enjoyment and fulfillment derived by humans from the life they live within their local economic, cultural, social, and environmental conditions. The Jacksonville Community Council defines quality of life as the "feeling of wellbeing, fulfillment, or satisfaction resulting from factors in the external environments." Quality of life, in this sense, is most directly measured using subjective indicators. ...
indicators.top10by2010.org/glossary.cfm

 Johannesburg

Will Johannesburg meet its target?

The South African government has the aim of replacing all informal housing with low-cost social housing by 2014. The United Nations (UN) estimates that, in 2001, 33 per cent of South Africans were living in slum housing. This is a term not usually used by geographers, but it obviously means that this housing is inadequate. The UN does not believe that South Africa can achieve its target. Despite building 200,000 low-cost houses every year, they estimate that another 2.4 million will still be needed in 2014.

The Johannesburg City Authority is much more positive about progress. They claim that residents of Johannesburg (or Jo'burg) already have the highest standard of living in South Africa. Their report on change in the city (see Figure 14) makes very positive reading.

Jo'burg advertises its successes
February 15, 2006 By Ndaba Dlamini

The City is drawing attention to successes attained over the past five years through a media campaign currently under way.

THE City of Johannesburg has made positive strides over the past five years in its efforts to deliver quality services to its citizens. To highlight some of these achievements, it is running an advertising campaign in various media.

It focuses on:

- The tarring of roads, in particular in Soweto, where 232 km of roads were tarred over the past three years at a cost of Rand 74 million. In addition, the city maintains 30,000 km of roads annually.

- The upgrading of the water supply, namely that through Operation Gcin'amanzi the City has delivered water to and upgraded water supplies to 98 per cent of its households.

- Increasing the number of street lights – in the past five years the City has installed and upgraded 16,427 street lights, making it a safer place for all its citizens.

- Job creation, namely that in the past eight years more than 316,000 jobs have been created in Jo'burg, which is more than in any other major city in South Africa. In addition, while South Africa's economy has grown by 2.9 per cent since 1996, Jo'burg's has grown by an exceptional 4.5 per cent. Jo'burg is booming!

- The building of new and upgrading of existing parks – in the last five years Jo'burg has spent Rand 31 million on its parks. With more than 6 million trees, it is now the biggest man-made forest in the world, and the City employs more than 2,000 people to maintain these trees and parks every day.

- Increased metro police presence, which has risen by 331 per cent in the past five years.

- Housing – in the past five years the City has facilitated housing for 8,000 families.

Figure 14 Extract from the official Johannesburg website (www.joburg.org.za)

Activity

25 Study Figure 14. Explain how each of the initiatives described in the article has affected quality of life.

26 Explain why the Johannesburg City Council has done much more than just provide low-cost housing.

27 Write a 250-word newspaper article about urban improvement in South Africa. The article must have a positive point of view.

Chapter 7
Conflicting demands on Europe's countryside

KEY QUESTIONS

- Where and why are people migrating into rural areas?

- Why do urban dwellers seek increased access to rural areas? What conflicts arise?

- How has technology increased access to rural areas?

- How can rural environments under pressure from visitors be managed to ensure a sustainable environmental and social future?

How do urban and rural areas interact?

The migration of people from larger cities into towns and villages in the countryside is a process known as **counter-urbanisation**. This process has created enormous change in the rural areas of many More Economically Developed Countries (MEDCs), especially in western Europe. This chapter focuses on rural areas in the UK where change is causing conflict between established residents and incomers.

Figure 1 Types of interaction between rural and urban places in the UK

Leisure	Rural and coastal areas are increasingly used for day trips, adventure activities and short holidays by people who live in urban areas.
Commuting	Many people who live in small rural towns commute to jobs in larger cities.
Retirement	Some rural areas, for example parts of North Wales, Dorset and Cornwall, attract retired people who spent their lives working in urban areas.
Resources	The countryside produces food and most of the UK's renewable energy from wind farms. Since 93 per cent of the UK's population live in urban areas, most of this consumption is in towns and cities.
Waste	Most landfill sites are in rural locations but take waste from our cities.

Why do people want to move to the country?

Cities are often seen as stressful places in which to live and work. The cost and difficulty of commuting through rush-hour traffic, the lack of open space and places for children to play in safety, the noise, pollution and rising crime are all given as reasons for leaving the city. These negative views about city life are known as push factors. By contrast, life in a smaller town or village has many attractions. People are attracted to the peace and quiet, access to open countryside can reduce stress and tension, and lower numbers of cars may seem safer for parents who have young children. These positive features are known as pull factors and they attract people to move to rural areas.

Figure 2 Positive images of rural life tend to attract families with young children and retired people to move into the countryside. Country traditions such as Morris dancing (these are the Shropshire Bedlams) help to create supportive communities. Outsiders might view this as evidence that rural life is lived at a slower pace than the urban 'rat-race'

How has technology contributed to change in the countryside?

The move from town to country first became popular in the UK in the 1960s and 1970s. This was a period of rising car ownership and expansion of the motorway network. It became possible to **commute** from a home in the country to a job in the city. Since then, massive changes in communication technology have made it possible for increasing numbers of people to work from a home in the country. Writers, researchers and business consultants can spend most of the working week at a computer at home and need to commute to the office only for the occasional meeting. This type of work is known as **tele-working** or tele-cottaging.

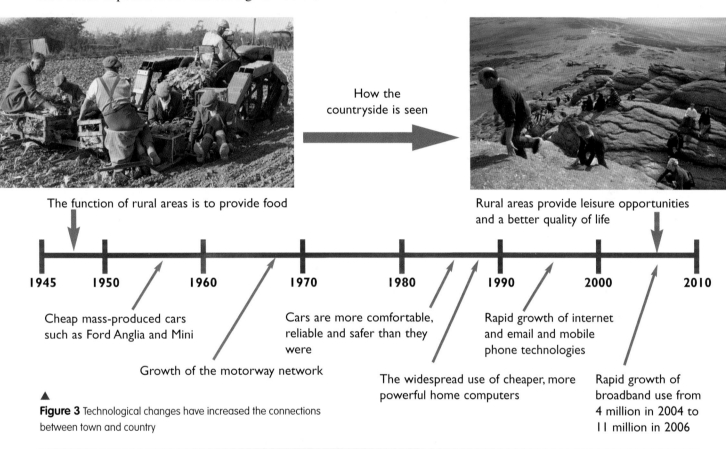

How the countryside is seen

The function of rural areas is to provide food

Rural areas provide leisure opportunities and a better quality of life

1945   1950   1960   1970   1980   1990   2000   2010

Cheap mass-produced cars such as Ford Anglia and Mini

Cars are more comfortable, reliable and safer than they were

Rapid growth of internet and email and mobile phone technologies

Growth of the motorway network

The widespread use of cheaper, more powerful home computers

Rapid growth of broadband use from 4 million in 2004 to 11 million in 2006

▲ **Figure 3** Technological changes have increased the connections between town and country

Activity

1 Study Figure 1. Working in pairs, list all the ways that the connections between urban and rural places might benefit:
   a) rural areas
   b) urban areas.

2 a) Explain what is meant by push factors and pull factors.
   b) Suggest the push and pull factors that might be considered by each of the following groups of people:
      i) Someone who has just retired from a job in the city.
      ii) A student who has just completed A levels in a rural school.

3 Study Figure 3. Use it to explain how technology has allowed:
   a) greater commuting
   b) greater use of the countryside for leisure
   c) more opportunities to move to the country and work from home.

4 Using Figure 3, suggest how you imagine the countryside might change 20 years from now.

Ynyslas National Nature Reserve

How can rural environments under pressure from visitors be managed?

Figure 4 A view across the Ynyshir nature reserve looking north-west over the estuary towards Aberdyfi

Figure 5 The Countryside Council for Wales says the dunes have a strong sense of place. The 'everchanging landforms as well as distinct vegetation patterns provide constant interest. Views in all directions from higher dunes provide constant drama'

The Dyfi estuary is a beautiful rural environment that attracts many visitors each year. People visit this part of West Wales for relaxation on the beach or in the dunes or to enjoy a number of leisure activities that include walking, riding, sailing and birdwatching.

The Dyfi estuary was classed as a Site of Special Scientific Interest (SSSI) in the 1950s. This was because the Dyfi was seen to be one of the best, most unspoilt estuaries in the west of Britain. Much of the estuary, including the sand dunes at Ynyslas at the mouth of the estuary, became a National Nature

Reserve (NNR) in 1969. An OS map that includes this part of the Reserve can be seen on page 162. The area is managed by the Countryside Council for Wales (CCW). This organisation has two main aims:

- 'to protect, maintain and, if possible, to enhance the wildlife of the reserves and their outstanding physical features'
- 'to allow as much public access as is compatible with the primary aims of conservation and research'.

There is a natural tension between these two aims. If too many people visit a site such as Ynyslas they could disturb wildlife or even damage fragile physical features such as the sand dunes themselves.

Figure 6 Results of a survey of 224 visitors to Ynyslas sand dunes

Trip purpose	Number
Informal visit to relax	94
To walk dog	56
Walk	49
Landscape appreciation	36
Family outing	25
Active sport	18
Nature watching	13
Picnic	11
Educational visit	9
Specialist interest	2
Other	18

Activity

5 a) The CCW describes the sand dunes as 'attractive, exposed and wild'. Discuss and choose three words to sum up the landscape in Figure 4.

 b) Read the caption to Figure 5. What would you say are the distinctive characteristics of the estuary as a whole?

6 a) Choose a suitable graphical technique to represent the data in Figure 6.

 b) Suggest which, if any, of these reasons for visiting the reserve might conflict with the aim of:
 i) conserving wildlife
 ii) conserving landscape features.

Source: Ynyslas Visitor Survey 1996

Using GIS to investigate conservation in Wales

The Countryside Council for Wales uses two interactive atlases to display information about the conservation of landscapes and wildlife in Wales. The screenshots in Figures 7a and b demonstrate how you might use some of the tools on one of these atlases.

Figure 7 Two screenshots from CCW's Protected Sites and Landscapes map

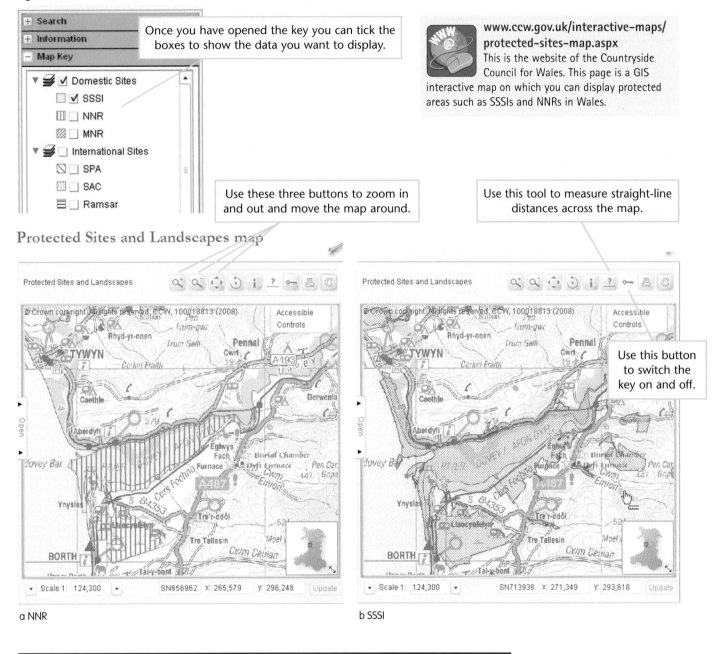

a NNR

b SSSI

Activity

7 Suggest environmental and economic reasons why it is necessary to conserve areas such as the Dyfi estuary.

8 Using Figures 7a and b, compare the location and area covered by the NNR and SSSI.

Ynyslas National Nature Reserve

Changing styles of management

Conservation management of the sand dunes at Ynyslas began in 1969 when the area was designated as a National Nature Reserve. During the 1960s some parts of the dune system had been damaged by off-road vehicles. In some places the marram grass, the roots of which help to bind the loose sand, had been destroyed by people driving into and parking in the dunes. The wind had then eroded huge hollows in the **windward** slopes of the dune system creating ugly scars known as **blow-outs**. The management strategies used by wardens at Ynyslas have gradually changed since 1969. These changes are summarised in Figure 8.

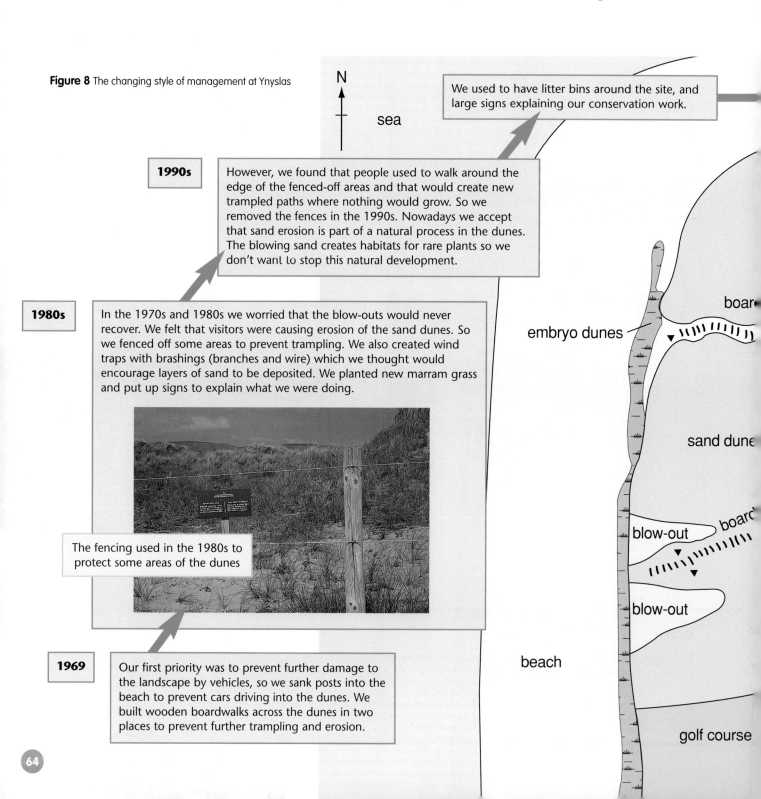

Figure 8 The changing style of management at Ynyslas

N

sea

1990s

We used to have litter bins around the site, and large signs explaining our conservation work.

However, we found that people used to walk around the edge of the fenced-off areas and that would create new trampled paths where nothing would grow. So we removed the fences in the 1990s. Nowadays we accept that sand erosion is part of a natural process in the dunes. The blowing sand creates habitats for rare plants so we don't want to stop this natural development.

1980s

In the 1970s and 1980s we worried that the blow-outs would never recover. We felt that visitors were causing erosion of the sand dunes. So we fenced off some areas to prevent trampling. We also created wind traps with brashings (branches and wire) which we thought would encourage layers of sand to be deposited. We planted new marram grass and put up signs to explain what we were doing.

The fencing used in the 1980s to protect some areas of the dunes

embryo dunes

boar

sand dune

blow-out

boar

blow-out

1969

Our first priority was to prevent further damage to the landscape by vehicles, so we sank posts into the beach to prevent cars driving into the dunes. We built wooden boardwalks across the dunes in two places to prevent further trampling and erosion.

beach

golf course

Activity

9 Study Figure 8. Use it to complete the following table. You should be able to identify at least four issues.

Issue	Management strategy	Evaluation of strategy
1		
2		

10 Produce a short report on management at Ynyslas. In it you must identify:
  a) why people visit
  b) the two main aims of the wardens
  c) how and why management strategies have changed
  d) how you think management of the dunes should change in future.

We found that the litter bins used to overflow and rubbish blew about, so we got rid of all the bins.

2000s

A lot of rabbits live in the dunes. They keep the grass short and stop it from choking the less competitive flowering plants. The rabbit dung makes the soil much more fertile and as many as 40 different species of flowering plants can grow in just 1 square metre. Also some birds nest in the abandoned rabbit burrows. So we like to have a healthy population of rabbits. However, our neighbour is the golf course. They don't want too many rabbits burrowing into the putting greens and creating damage. So we erected a rabbit-proof fence along our southern boundary. The problem is that this fence now has holes in it and will be costly to maintain.

Lots of song birds live in the dunes including linnet, stonechat, skylark and meadow pipit. We have one area where ringed plovers breed. These small birds nest on the ground and are easily disturbed. So we have fenced off the shingle area where they nest.

out

parking area

posts to prevent cars driving into the dunes

In recent years we have enlarged and improved the visitor centre and the boardwalks. Now anyone can easily cross the site to get to the beach. Wheelchair users can access the visitor centre along the boardwalks.

visitor centre

The boardwalk and visitor centre

road

caravan park

One of our biggest management problems today is dog fouling. People are banned from walking their dogs in the summer months on Borth beach to the south. So they come up to Ynyslas to walk their dogs. The problem is that there are very few bacteria in the sandy soil so the dog excrement does not bio-degrade. It lies around for ages and is a nuisance for other visitors.

2009

Pyramidal orchids

65

Shropshire

How are rural populations changing in South Shropshire?

Many wealthier families are moving out of big cities and into smaller towns. Local people complain their towns are turning into dormitories – in other words, commuters sleep there but they do not use local services. Roads are getting more congested as people drive ever further to work, schools and shops. What will our smaller towns be like to live in in the future?

In South Shropshire, in the West Midlands, the number of people moving into rural areas is balanced by a similar number of people moving out. The total population of rural South Shropshire is not changing much. However, newcomers to rural life often have social and economic (or **socio-economic**) backgrounds that are different from the local people they replace, so the socio-economic character of South Shropshire is gradually changing. As we shall see later, this socio-economic change can lead to conflict as newcomers clash with established residents.

Who is moving into South Shropshire and who is moving out?

The relatively high quality of life in the countryside appeals to a wide range of people from young professionals through families to the retired. What these people have in common is the ability to pay the relatively high prices of rural homes.

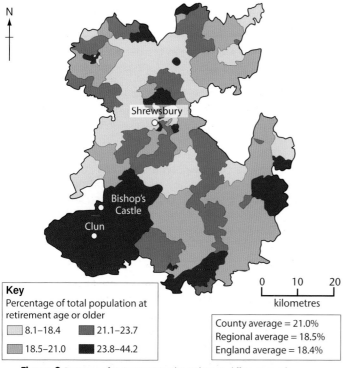

Key
Percentage of total population at retirement age or older

▨ 8.1–18.4	▨ 21.1–23.7		
▨ 18.5–21.0	■ 23.8–44.2		

County average = 21.0%
Regional average = 18.5%
England average = 18.4%

Figure 9 Patterns of retirement in Shropshire in different wards

The countryside doesn't appeal to everyone. Many teenagers living in the countryside move into urban areas when they leave school. The lack of jobs, leisure facilities, shops, theatres and cinemas in the countryside are push factors, while the chance to go to university and the greater choice of jobs are pull factors for moving to a city. In addition, the cost of buying a house in the countryside is likely to prevent young people on lower incomes from staying in a rural area.

	Age	Clun %	Bishop's Castle %	Shrewsbury %	West Midlands %
▨ Rural communities in South Shropshire.	0 to 9	9.2	10.3	11.7	12.6
	10 to 19	9.4	11.2	13.1	13.3
▨ An urban community of 96,000 in central Shropshire.	20 to 29	5.1	8.8	10.3	12.1
	30 to 44	19.4	19.5	22.0	21.9
▨ This large region includes South Shropshire and Shrewsbury. However, more than 90 per cent of the region is classed as urban.	45 to 59	24.6	22.9	20.3	19.1
	60 to 74	22.1	17.5	14.3	13.6
	75 +	10.0	9.8	8.4	7.4

Figure 10 Population structures in rural and urban wards of Shropshire in the West Midlands (Source: 2001 Census)

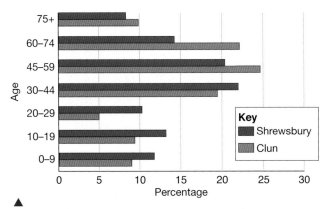

Figure 11 Comparing population structures in Shrewsbury and Clun

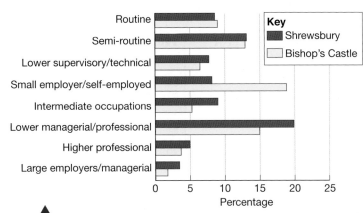

Figure 12 Comparing occupations in Shrewsbury and Bishop's Castle (Source: 2001 Census)

	Bishop's Castle	West Midlands
Total population	2,474	5,276,308
Percentage white	99.8	88.7
Percentage mixed – white and Asian, white and black African or black Caribbean	0.2	1.4
Percentage Asian or Asian British	0	7.3
Percentage black or black British	0	2.0
Percentage Chinese or other ethnic group	0	0.6

Figure 13 Comparing ethnic population of Bishop's Castle and the West Midlands (Source: 2001 Census)

Activity

11 Use Figure 9 to describe the location (see page 66) of
a) Bishop's Castle
b) Shrewsbury.

12 Use Figure 9 to describe the distribution (see page 66) of wards that have more than 23.8 per cent retired population.

13 Use Figure 11.
a) Compare the population structure of Clun with that of Shrewsbury.
b) Suggest two reasons for the differences you have noticed.

14 Use Figure 12.
a) Compare occupations in Bishop's Castle with Shrewsbury.
b) Use this evidence to explain why some younger adults are leaving South Shropshire.

15 Draw up a table like the one below. Add to the push and pull factors that cause movements in and out of rural areas like Shropshire.

Retired professionals moving out of larger towns and into the countryside		Young adults moving out of the countryside and into larger towns	
Push factors	Pull factors	Push factors	Pull factors
	Peace and quiet	Few full-time jobs	

16 Study Figure 13.
a) Explain what this data tells us about the ethnic origin of people who migrate into Bishop's Castle.
b) Suggest why so few Asian and black Afro-Caribbean people move into the countryside.
c) Suggest why this might cause problems for the UK's multicultural society unless things change.

Change can lead to conflict: the lack of affordable homes

- Is it true that many young rural people can no longer afford to stay in the countryside because there is a lack of **affordable homes**?
- Is it true that too little new social housing is being built and that the sale of owner-occupied housing to newcomers is forcing up the price of rural homes?

Newcomers to a rural area often commute to a full-time job outside the rural area, whereas local residents may work locally. Commuters may do their shopping in a large retail park on the edge of the city where they work because by the time they get home the village shops have closed for the day. The result is that, as a village attracts more commuters, its shops may get fewer customers. Village pubs close and are converted to homes, bus services are axed, and local shops and banks may also close. The rise of internet banking has also badly affected small rural branches.

Percentage of the rural population with access to:	2000	2004	2005
Banks and building societies (within 4 km)	66	64	60
Cashpoints (within 4 km)	85	85	90
Post offices (within 2 km)	90	85	85
Primary schools (within 2 km)	88	85	87

Figure 15 Changing rural services (Source: Commission for Rural Communities report 2005)

Figure 14 This primary school in South Shropshire is likely to merge with another school several kilometres away. The local community are opposing the planned closure of this building

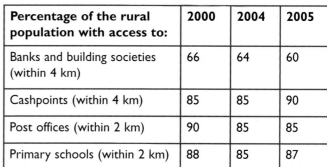
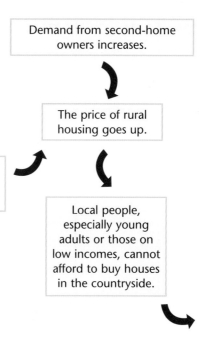

Very few new houses are built because planners do not want houses built in the countryside on greenfield sites.

Demand from second-home owners increases.

There are few council houses left in rural areas because of the Right-to-Buy schemes introduced in the 1980s.

The price of rural housing goes up.

The supply of houses for sale is low.

Local people, especially young adults or those on low incomes, cannot afford to buy houses in the countryside.

Too little social housing for people on lowest incomes.

People on lowest incomes move out.

Figure 16 Rural housing issues

Activity

17 Use Figure 15.
   a) Produce a graph to show what is happening to rural services.
   b) Give two different reasons for the closure of some rural banks and building societies.

18 Study Figure 16. Identify two main causes for the lack of affordable housing in rural areas.

	Rural areas			Urban areas		
	Private sector	Social housing	All new housing	Private sector	Social housing	All new housing
2003	37,600	2,400	40,100	47,200	7,100	54,300
2004	36,000	2,400	38,400	50,900	7,300	58,200
2005	36,700	2,800	38,500	55,900	9,000	64,800
	Change* −3.90%			Change* +19.40%		

Figure 17 New houses built in England. * = the percentage change (between 2003 and 2005) in the total number of new housing built. A minus number indicates fewer new houses were built in 2005 than in 2003

Average rural house prices in West Midlands (£s)		
Location of houses	2000	2004
Hamlets and isolated houses	190,856	302,657
Villages	160,331	247,712
Rural suburbs	107,551	173,598
Urban, up to population of 10,000	80,176	134,983

Figure 18 The rising cost of buying houses in the country is pricing many locals out of the market

Sparsity (population density)	Settlement type	Owned (%)	Social rented (%)	Private rented (%)
Less sparse	Small rural towns <10,000	67	21	10
	Rural suburbs	77	15	7
	Villages	78	10	9
	Hamlets and isolated dwellings	78	5	13
Sparse (most rural parts of England)	Small rural towns <10,000	70	16	12
	Rural suburbs	68	18	12
	Villages	73	11	13
	Hamlets and isolated dwellings	71	5	19

Figure 19 Housing tenure in rural England

Activity

19 Study Figures 17 and 19.
  a) Compare the amount of social housing built in rural areas with that built in urban areas.
  b) Compare the percentage of social housing available in hamlets with that in small rural towns.

20 Use Figures 17, 18 and 19 to produce a short report on the rural housing issue. Include:
  a) three graphs
  b) evidence that supports or rejects the view that there is a lack of affordable rural housing.

The second homes issue

The lack of affordable housing in rural areas is often linked to the sale of rural houses as **second homes** or holiday cottages. When a rural house is sold to be used as a second home at weekends or during holidays there are two effects:

1 One less house is available to local people. As we have seen, increasing demand for rural homes forces up rural house prices.
2 Even more village services are likely to close. Owners of second homes may spend only a few weeks of each year in their village home, so have little use for village services.

Which parts of England and Wales are affected by the second homes issue?

Figure 21 suggests that there are many different views about the function of the UK's countryside. This is partly because rural areas in the UK are so varied:

• Many small towns in the south-east have become commuter villages.

• Large parts of the south-east and east are used for growing cereal crops.
• Many coastal areas in the south-west are used for tourism.

Most second homes tend to be in the most scenic parts of England, especially in Devon, Cornwall, Cumbria and parts of Yorkshire. These areas are shown in Figure 22 on page 71.

Within these large regions there is huge variation. The average number of second homes for England is 0.6 per cent, but this rises to as much as 12.6 per cent among isolated homes and tiny hamlets in north-west England. The Lake District National Park has an unusually high number of second homes. In the area surrounding the village of Hawkshead, seen in the centre of Figure 21, it is estimated that 40 per cent of all homes are second homes or holiday cottages.

Figure 20 An extract from the lyrics of *Country Life* by folk group Show of Hands ▶

> *And the red brick cottage where I was born*
> *Is the empty shell of a holiday home.*
> *Most of the year there's no one there,*
> *The village is dead and they don't care.*
> *Now we live on the edge of town.*
> *Haven't been back since the pub closed down.*
> *One man's family pays the price*
> *For another man's vision of country life.*

A safe place for wildlife?

A place to retire?

Homes for commuters?

Farming and food production?

A holiday retreat?

Somewhere to go walking, riding and fishing?

Figure 21 What is the countryside for?

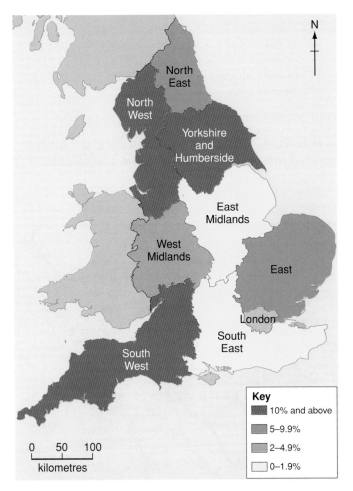

Figure 22 The percentage of homes in hamlets and isolated villages that are unoccupied because they are either second homes or rented out as holiday homes

Key
- 10% and above
- 5–9.9%
- 2–4.9%
- 0–1.9%

Dealing with the second homes issue

All homeowners have to pay Council Tax on their main home: this is a tax that pays for a range of local services such as police, waste collection and local community facilities such as sports centres. However, many second homeowners get a substantial discount from their Council Tax bill for their second home. This is often a 50 per cent reduction in the bill, meaning a saving of £400 or more a year.

In 2007 there were estimated to be 100,000 second homes in rural parts of England. If the owners of these second homes were made to pay the full Council Tax it would raise an extra £400 million.

In Shropshire, a decision was made in 2003 to reduce the discount on the Council Tax for second homeowners from 50 per cent to 10 per cent. During the period 2004–2007 this raised an extra £500,000 a year which was spent on local services. In South Shropshire, in which 2.6 per cent of the houses are second homes, this raised an additional £226,185 a year. The money has been spent on 80 different projects in South Shropshire, with payments of a few hundred pounds to several thousand pounds a year being made. The scheme is considered to be so successful that the project is being extended from 2007–2010. One of the projects to benefit most has been the SpArC project in Bishop's Castle. The SpArC project houses a small theatre space and a modern gym complex. It means that local people no longer have to travel to places such as Shrewsbury, which is 40 km away, to access local sports and leisure services.

Activity

21 Describe and explain the point of view expressed in the song lyrics in Figure 20.

22 Suggest why some rural areas have more second homes than others. Consider the effect of:
a) distance from larger cities
b) the attractiveness of the countryside.

23 Use an atlas or the internet to find a map of England's National Parks. Compare this map with Figure 22.

24 Discuss Shropshire's strategy to deal with second homes. Suggest:
a) Why a discount might be fair.
b) Reasons why the discount should be removed.

Figure 23 Students from the local college work with professional actors in the Sports and Arts in the Community (SpArC) project

 Iceland   Impacts of migration

In this case study we will investigate patterns of migration in Iceland. Most rural areas in Iceland are losing population, a process known as **depopulation**. How can isolated rural communities be given a sustainable future?

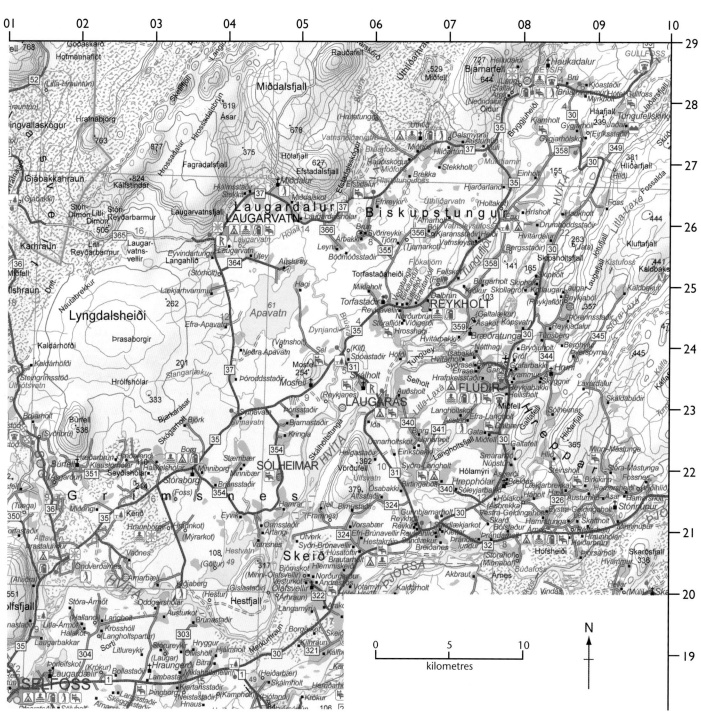

Figure 1 The Golden Circle region, east of Reykjavik. Grimsnes is in the south-west portion of the map (Scale 1:250,000)

How is counter-urbanisation affecting Iceland?

Iceland has only one major city, the capital Reykjavik. Many wealthy residents of Reykjavik own second homes in the countryside so they can get away from the city at the weekend. This is a form of counter-urbanisation. Most second homes are located in the 'Golden Circle' region: a rural area about one hour's drive to the east of Reykjavik. This area contains many of Iceland's most popular attractions such as Geysir and Gullfoss (see page 153).

The construction of second homes and the growth of tourism are changing this rural community and these changes could create conflict. Locals could feel swamped by newcomers: Grimsnes, just one housing development in the Golden Circle, has more than 1,500 holiday homes but has only 356 permanent residents.

The recreational use of rural areas by visitors from Reykjavik is also causing conflict. Off-road driving in the rural regions of Iceland is popular, but the tyre tracks and deep ruts are scarring the landscape. The Environment and Food Agency of Iceland is so concerned about this damage that most off-road driving has been banned since 1999.

Figure 2 There are more than 1,500 holiday homes like this in Grimsnes

Figure 3 The construction of new holiday homes in Selfoss (grid ref: 0120 in Figure 1) creates valuable local employment

Activity

1 Use Figure 1.
   a) Give a four-figure grid reference for Geysir (north-east corner of the map).
   b) Use the map to give directions and approximate distances to travel from Grimsnes to Geysir.
   c) Give four pieces of evidence that the area is heavily used by tourists.

2 Describe two ways in which counter-urbanisation could create conflict in Iceland's rural regions.

3 Suggest the arguments for and against the building of more second homes and holiday homes in Grimsnes.

4 Study Figure 4. Give three reasons why soils in Iceland are at great risk of erosion.

5 Suggest why it is necessary to protect Iceland's **wilderness** regions.

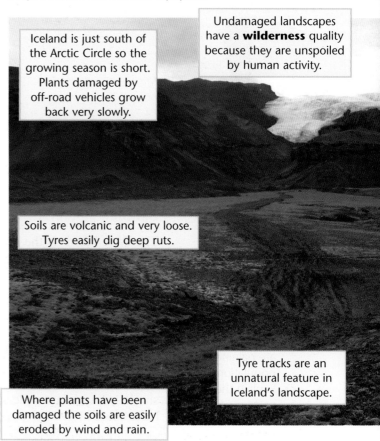

Iceland is just south of the Arctic Circle so the growing season is short. Plants damaged by off-road vehicles grow back very slowly.

Undamaged landscapes have a **wilderness** quality because they are unspoiled by human activity.

Soils are volcanic and very loose. Tyres easily dig deep ruts.

Tyre tracks are an unnatural feature in Iceland's landscape.

Where plants have been damaged the soils are easily eroded by wind and rain.

Figure 4 Illegal off-road driving in Skaftafell National Park has left these tyre tracks

Iceland

Rural depopulation

Reykjavik's population is 120,000 and a further 76,000 people live within its outer suburbs. Two-thirds of all Iceland's population (300,000 people) lives within 40 km of Reykjavik's city centre. This number continues to grow as migrants leave the remote rural regions of Iceland. The pull factors include better jobs and much better urban services.

Other regions of Iceland have no large cities. The sparsely populated rural areas in the north-west, north and east are too isolated from Reykjavik to be affected by counter-urbanisation and commuting. Each year the rural regions of Iceland receive some migrants and lose others. In some regions more people leave the region than move in, a situation known as **net out-migration**. The loss of people by migration, combined with low birth rates, is causing **rural depopulation**.

Activity

6 Define **pull factors**.

7 Give two reasons for the loss of population in remote rural areas.

Figure 5 A derelict trawler in the West Fjords

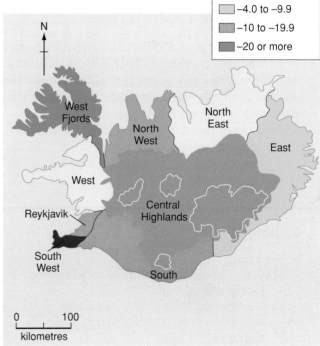

Figure 6 Regional population and migration (gains or losses) for the regions of Iceland (average figures for 2001–2005)

Key
Population change, gain or loss per year for every 1000 people:
Increase
■ 4.0 or more
▨ 0 to 3.9
Decrease
□ 0 to −3.9
▨ −4.0 to −9.9
▨ −10 to −19.9
▨ −20 or more

0 ——— 100
kilometres

Activity

8 Study Figure 6.
  a) Describe the distribution (see page 25) of regions which have lost most people.
  b) Describe which parts of Iceland are gaining population.
  c) Explain the pattern you have identified in answers a) and b).

Depopulation in the West Fjords

The West Fjords is the rural region of Iceland that has been hardest hit by depopulation. In the period from 1986 to 2003 net out-migration from the West Fjords averaged 27 people per 1,000 population. More women than men are leaving these regions, especially in the age range 20 to 49.

The West Fjords is the most remote part of Iceland from Reykjavik. The region covers an area of more than 12,000 km^2 (similar in size to the West Midlands, England) but has a total population of only 7,299 (the population of the West Midlands is 2.69 million). The many sea inlets or **fjords** make the coastline very long and inland it is mountainous. In addition the roads are poor, with many single-track and unmade surfaces, so journey times are slow. The weather can be hazardous; in 1995 two separate avalanches of snow killed 34 people.

The traditional economy of the West Fjords is in decline. Fishing has always been the biggest employer, but the government has cut the number of fish that can be caught in order to conserve fish stocks in the sea. Sheep farming is the second-biggest employer, but it is unprofitable and unpopular among the young.

Isafjordur is 457 km by road from Reykjavik but has an airport and good fishing harbour.

These mountains are more than 800 m high.

The road follows the edge of the fjord, so journeys by road are long and tedious.

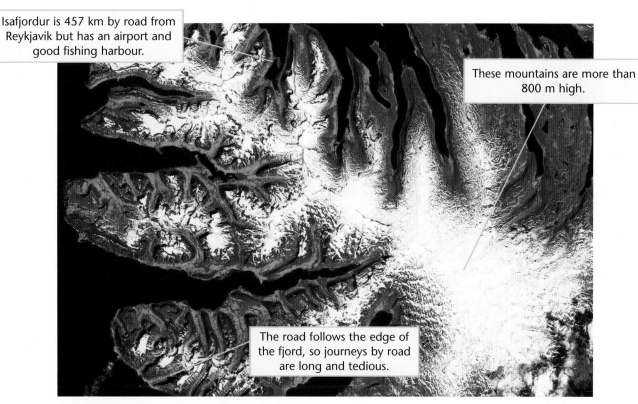

Figure 7 A satellite image of the inaccessible West Fjords

Figure 8 Isafjordur is the West Fjords region's largest settlement. It has a population of 2,700 people

Employment	West Fjords	Reykjavik
Agriculture, fishing and mining	15	1
Manufacturing	33	19
Services	52	80

Figure 9 Employment (percentages) in West Fjords compared to Reykjavik (2005)

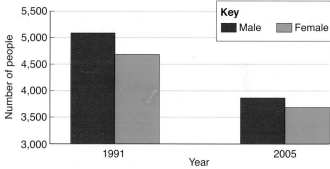

Figure 10 Population decline in the West Fjords (1991 and 2005)

Activity

9 Use the text on page 74 and Figures 7 and 8 to create a list of the push factors that might be causing migration from the West Fjords.

10 Use Figure 9.
   a) Compare the employment pattern in West Fjords with that in Reykjavik.
   b) Explain how this could be further evidence of push and pull factors.

11 Use Figure 10 to compare the population of West Fjords in 2005 with that in 1991.

Are Iceland's remote rural communities sustainable?

The migration of people from rural areas to Reykjavik is causing serious concern. If rural populations become too small then essential services such as schools and doctors' clinics become increasingly inefficient and expensive to sustain. If a doctor's surgery closes, local people find that they are further and further away from healthcare. Rural communities could become **unsustainable** and have no future.

A similar process has been happening in rural communities in other regions of the Arctic, such as Alaska, Greenland and Norway. As in Iceland, most migrants are young adults and more women than men migrate. In some of these regions the young men who remain in the rural area are experiencing severe social problems such as alcoholism and relatively high suicide rates.

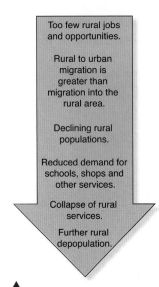

Figure 11 How rural depopulation creates unsustainable communities

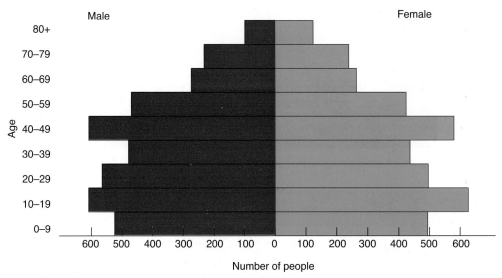

Figure 13 A population pyramid for the West Fjords in 2005

1986	14.1
1987	17.8
1988	31.1
1989	27.7
1990	18.4
1991	23.4
1992	9.8
1993	16.0
1994	28.6
1995	47.9
1996	40.7
1997	44.6
1998	39.4
1999	43.5
2000	29.1
2001	21.2
2002	23.0
2003	16.7
2004	27.6
2005	39.2
2006	33.4

Figure 12 Net out-migration from West Fjords 1986 to 2006. Figures are per thousand population

Activity

12 Study Figure 11.
  a) Identify the main cause of rural depopulation.
  b) Explain how closure of services can be both a cause and an effect of depopulation.

13 a) Choose a suitable technique to graphically represent the data in Figure 12.
  b) Is the depopulation issue getting worse? Describe the pattern shown on your graph.

14 Suggest what you think could be done to reduce the impacts of depopulation.

15 From what you have learned about the West Fjords, suggest why more women than men migrate from rural areas of the Arctic.

16 a) Describe the main features of the population pyramid, Figure 13.
  b) Explain how Figure 13 provides evidence of the age and sex of migrants who have left the West Fjords.

Going Further

How can new technology help rural communities?

The growth of the mobile phone network and greater use of the internet have allowed rural communities better access to information and services such as education courses from their home. This will help to reverse the negative impacts that have been made by the closure of rural services such as schools, libraries and shops. Mobile phone coverage in Iceland is excellent, even in the most isolated areas, and internet connection is actively encouraged by the government. As a result, the number of students using distant learning methods, such as web-based courses and video-conferencing, almost trebled between 1998 and 2001. The government believes that these technologies will reduce rural isolation and depopulation.

Activity

17 Use Figure 14 to compare Iceland's mobile phone subscriptions with:
a) Romania
b) Finland.

18 Use the data in Figure 14 to suggest how mobile phone subscription might be an indicator of both quality of life and standard of living.

19 Investigate the following hypothesis: *The Scandinavian countries, which have the most rural and isolated populations in Europe, were the quickest European countries to develop their mobile networks.* To structure this investigation you could:
a) put the countries in Figure 14 into rank order, starting with the country with the highest mobile subscriptions in 2000
b) use an atlas to identify which parts of Europe have the highest subscriptions
c) consider alternative explanations for any pattern you discover. This might include researching the Gross National Income for the countries in Figure 14.

Selected EU members	2000	2001	2002	2003
Austria	76	82	84	88
Bulgaria	9	20	32	45
Czech Republic	42	68	84	95
Denmark	63	74	83	89
Finland	72	81	87	91
Germany	59	68	72	79
Greece	54	73	85	81
Hungary	30	49	68	78
Italy	73	89	93	98
Latvia	17	26	39	52
Lithuania	14	29	47	62
Luxembourg	70	93	107	120
Poland	17	25	36	46
Portugal	65	81	83	90
Romania	9	20	23	32
Slovakia	21	41	56	68
Slovenia	57	76	77	87
Spain	61	73	82	90
Sweden	72	81	89	98
Non EU members				
Iceland	77	88	91	97
Norway	75	84	86	91

Figure 14 The rise of mobile phone subscriptions in Europe. Figures refer to number of subscriptions per 100 people. Source: Eurostat

 Iceland

Creating sustainable rural communities

Iceland's government wants to create sustainable rural communities. They believe that new industries such as tourism must be encouraged in order to **diversify** the rural economy. They are encouraging both Icelandic and **multi-national companies (MNCs)** to invest in rural communities. Foreign investors locating in a rural region of Iceland will experience a number of advantages:

- Business taxes in Iceland are lower than almost anywhere else in Europe.
- Energy is also cheap because Iceland uses **renewable resources** such as **hydro-electric power (HEP)** and geothermal (heat from the ground) rather than oil.
- Foreign film-makers who want to shoot their new film in Iceland are offered a refund of 12 per cent of all production costs.

Regional Development Agencies promote development in each of Iceland's rural areas. Their aim is to reduce inequalities between the rural areas and Reykjavik. The West Fjords Development Agency is attempting to attract **high-tech industries** such as data-processing or specialised food-processing or fishing-related industries. One example is an Irish company which has located a seaweed processing factory in West Fjords, employing ten full-time staff.

Can sustainable futures be created from tourism?

Iceland has a fast-growing tourist industry based on its natural resources and wildlife. Farmers are diversifying their income by converting farms and outbuildings into holiday accommodation. Bed-and-breakfast type accommodation is now widespread in rural Iceland, but the tourist season is short because of the climate.

The West Fjords has much to offer tourists interested in the natural environment:

- sea or river fishing
- birdwatching
- whale-watching from the harbour at Isafjordur
- kayaking, horse riding and hiking in the summer and skiing in winter.

Iceland has a long tradition of whale-hunting, but a television and radio poll in 2003 showed that 71 per cent of Icelanders would support an end to whaling if jobs could be created in nature-based tourism instead. A number of whalers and fishermen have switched from whaling to taking tourists on whale-watching trips. Whale-watching creates jobs and can continue without damaging the environment, so it is an example of a **sustainable development** for rural communities in Iceland.

Figure 15 Whale-watching could help to sustain rural communities

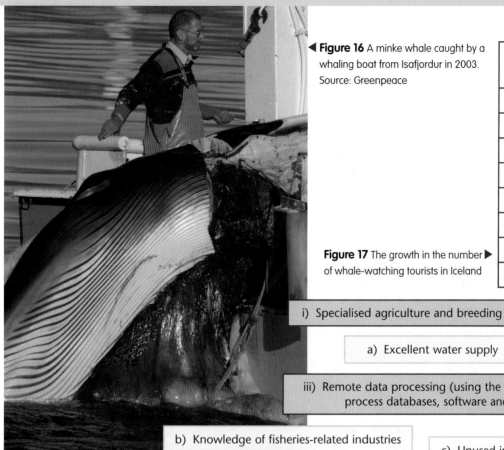

◀ **Figure 16** A minke whale caught by a whaling boat from Isafjordur in 2003. Source: Greenpeace

Year	Number of tourists
1995	2,200
1996	9,700
1997	20,540
1998	30,330
1999	32,250
2000	45,400
2001	60,550
2002	62,050

Figure 17 The growth in the number ▶ of whale-watching tourists in Iceland

i) Specialised agriculture and breeding

ii) Ecotourism

a) Excellent water supply

iii) Remote data processing (using the internet to transfer and process databases, software and spreadsheets)

b) Knowledge of fisheries-related industries

c) Unused industrial and farm buildings

iv) Film production

d) Relatively cheap, renewable sources of electricity

e) Long coastline with sheltered fjords

v) Production of fresh water and marine foods (e.g. fish farming)

vi) Industry that requires up to 30 megawatts of power

f) Highly educated and skilled workforce

g) Magnificent and clean environment

vii) Fisheries-related industry

viii) Activity and adventure holidays

h) Excellent mobile communications and high usage of home computers

Figure 18 The resources of the West Fjords, and industries that could be developed as the economy diversifies

---

Activity

20 a) Choose an appropriate graphical technique to represent the data in Figure 17.
   b) Describe the trend of your graph.

21 Suggest the point of view of each of the following to both whale hunting and whale-watching:
   a) A member of Greenpeace in the UK.
   b) The owner of a whaling boat in Isafjordur.
   c) The owner of a hotel in Isafjordur.

22 Explain why it is important for the rural economy of Iceland to diversify.

23 Study Figure 18.
   a) Match the West Fjords' resources a)–h) to potential industries that could be attracted to the region i)–viii).
   b) Use your list to describe how you think the West Fjords should diversify its economy. Suggest the possible advantages of your scheme compared with alternative types of diversification.

Chapter 9
Problem-solving exercise

Creating sustainable rural communities in South Africa

Many rural South Africans are currently leaving their homes and migrating to the city. In this chapter we examine in more detail the quality of life for rural families living in Limpopo in the northern part of South Africa. Are these rural communities sustainable? Do they have any future? Can you design a plan that will help to give communities like this a better quality of life and make rural life more sustainable?

Your enquiry ...

What is the quality of life for this South African family?

Why are they cooking on a wood stove?

Do they have electric light?

Do they know what they are missing in the city?

Can this rural community survive?

Your decision ...
How can this family have a better quality of life and a better future without moving to the city?

Figure 1 Cooking over an open wood fire in a traditional rural home in South Africa

Part A: what is it like to live in Limpopo, South Africa?

Limpopo is the most rural of South Africa's nine provinces and most people have farm occupations. The province also has stunning scenery and wildlife so some people are employed in tourism. Most tourists visit the Kruger National Park, although Africa's big five (elephant, lion, leopard, buffalo and rhinoceros) can be seen in several other parts of the province.

Limpopo's largest city is Polokwane (formerly Pietersburg). With a population of 90,000, this city is similar in size to some of England's smaller county towns, such as Shrewsbury in Shropshire.

Quality of life in Limpopo

Most farm workers in Limpopo are poorly paid; many earn less than US$1 a day. The average household income is below 1,000 Rand (US$140), so 60 per cent of families live below the poverty line. Many farm workers do not have security of tenure; in other words, they do not have full legal rights to live in their own home. Other kinds of work are scarce and unemployment is high. Recent surveys suggest that only 23 per cent of the population between the ages of 15 and 65 have formal employment.

Almost 20 per cent of the houses in Limpopo are traditional timber frame and thatch huts, and in some districts, such as Mutale in the north of the province, this percentage rises to almost 50 per cent. These homes can be very uncomfortable. The roofs leak in the rainy season and they are badly ventilated so smoke from cooking stoves is trapped inside the building. People prefer to live in 'formal' concrete block houses.

Key
Dwelling type
- Formal
- Informal
- Traditional
- Multiple
- Municipality
- Province

Figure 2 The distribution of traditional housing in Limpopo

Figure 3 Traditional housing in Limpopo. This household benefits from electricity provided by a photovoltaic cell

Activity

1 Use Figure 2 to complete the following description:
 Limpopo is located in the … of South Africa. To the … it shares borders with Botswana and …. It also shares a border with … in the ….

2 Use Figure 2 to describe the location of the district of Kruger.

3 Describe the distribution (see page 25) of traditional homes in Limpopo.

4 a) Explain what is meant by push and pull factors.
 b) Explain three push factors that cause migration from Limpopo.

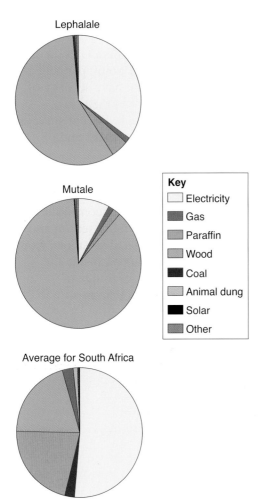

Lephalale

Mutale

Key
☐ Electricity
▨ Gas
▨ Paraffin
▨ Wood
■ Coal
▨ Animal dung
■ Solar
▨ Other

Average for South Africa

Figure 4 The percentage of homes using electricity or other energy sources for cooking

Part B: how can rural standards of living be improved?

There are a large number of strategies being used to improve the standard of living and quality of life in rural areas of Limpopo. This part of the chapter examines four such strategies.

Rural electrification

Since 1994 South Africa has been extending the supply of electricity to both urban and rural communities. By 2000 about 70 per cent of households had an electricity supply, but the network extended to more urban homes than rural ones. As you can see in Figure 4, large parts of Limpopo were still using wood stoves for cooking in 2001. The use of wood-burning stoves for cooking causes health problems such as eye and chest irritations. The inhalation of wood smoke is also linked to the development of some cancers.

The South African government aims to extend the electricity supply into rural areas so that 85 per cent of homes have a supply by 2010. In many places this is done by extending the national grid of power cables. However, in some more remote areas **off-grid electricity** is being supplied by using car batteries or photovoltaic cells.

This strategy has obvious benefits. Women's health benefits because they no longer have to cook on wood stoves. Rural schools can start to invest in televisions and computers. Lighting in rural areas means that children can do their homework in the evening. However, studies have shown that rural electrification does not always create the benefits that might be expected. The poorest households cannot afford to pay their electricity bills and continue to use wood stoves after electricity has been connected. In one study, 44 per cent of households had still not purchased an electric stove three years after electrification.

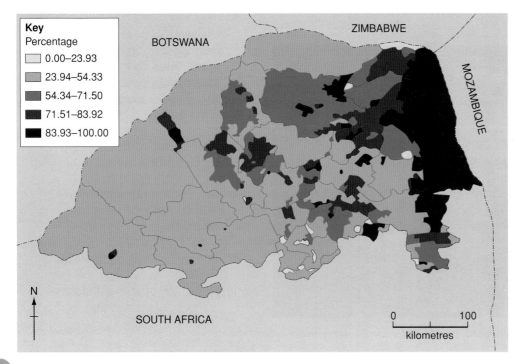

Key
Percentage
☐ 0.00–23.93
▨ 23.94–54.33
▨ 54.34–71.50
■ 71.51–83.92
■ 83.93–100.00

ZIMBABWE

BOTSWANA

MOZAMBIQUE

N

SOUTH AFRICA

0   100
kilometres

Figure 5 Percentage of households in Limpopo with access to piped water

Improving rural water supplies

Many isolated rural communities in Limpopo still collect water from rivers or pools where the water can be dirty and cause ill health. Rural houses can be adapted for **rainwater harvesting** by collecting rainwater from the roof in a large rainwater tank. However, at the moment, only 3,100 houses in Limpopo have this system.

Main water supply	Lephalale	Mutale	Limpopo	South Africa
Piped water to the dwelling	19.9	3.1	9.4	32.3
Piped water inside yard	39.2	18.4	29.0	29.0
Piped water to community stand <200 m	19.0	23.6	15.9	10.7
Piped water to community stand >200 m	17.3	32.9	23.7	12.4
Other (includes boreholes, rivers, pools)	4.6	22.0	22.0	15.6

Figure 6 The percentage of homes with a piped water supply compared with other sources of water

Activity

5 Use Figure 5 to describe the distribution (see page 82) of districts where more than 71.51 per cent of households are connected to a piped water supply.

6 Use Figure 4.
   a) Compare the use of energy sources for cooking in Lephalale with the average for South Africa.
   b) Which district, Lephalale or Mutale, needs the rural electrification project most? Justify your choice.

7 Explain why lack of electricity and piped water are a possible cause of rural to urban migration.

8 Explain the benefits of rural electrification for:
   a) women
   b) children.

9 Use Figure 6.
   a) Produce pie charts to represent the data.
   b) Which district, Lephalale or Mutale, most needs better water supplies? Justify your choice.

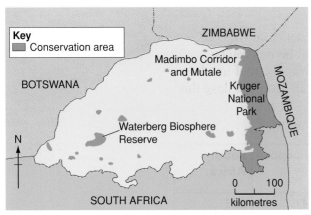

Figure 7 Conservation areas in Limpopo

Creating more jobs in ecotourism

There is an urgent need to diversify the rural economy by creating new jobs that are not connected to farming. Tourists already visit Limpopo. Most visit the Kruger National Park in the east of the province. Other areas of Limpopo could benefit, including:

- The Madimbo Corridor and Mutale in the north
- the Waterberg Biosphere Reserve in Laphalale in the west of the province.

The Waterberg Biosphere Reserve was created in 1999. 77,000 people live in the reserve. It is a large area where the dry climate makes farming difficult and incomes are low. Farmers are gradually switching to **ecotourism**. Tourists pay to stay with local families or in luxury lodges. Local people are employed to act as guides and wardens. The reserve contains 75 mammal species (including the big five) and 300 species of bird. A limited amount of hunting is allowed. Tourists pay large sums to shoot impala and other wild animals. This money is then used to pay for conservation projects such as breeding programmes, habitat conservation and anti-poaching patrols.

The Madimbo Corridor is a narrow strip of land between the district of Mutale and Zimbabwe. Many hippo and crocodile live in its rivers and pools. The area is on a migration route for elephants and buffalo between Zimbabwe and the Kruger National Park. The creation of a conservation project and jobs in ecotourism would benefit wildlife and create badly needed jobs.

Activity

10 Use Figure 7 to describe the distribution of conservation areas in Limpopo.

11 a) Explain what is meant by the phrase 'diversify the rural economy'.

   b) Explain what could happen to districts like Mutale if the economy is not diversified.

12 Explain how a new ecotourism project would:
   a) improve standards of living
   b) conserve wildlife.

Figure 8 Hunting for wild animals is strictly limited. This tourist will have paid a high price for the right to shoot game in Limpopo. Tourist fees are divided between local communities and conservation groups

Creating more jobs in mining

Limpopo is rich in mineral deposits. Some are already mined, but many new jobs would be created if new mining operations were permitted. The Madimbo Corridor, for example, has deposits of diamonds. These diamonds could be mined creating hundreds of jobs, but conservationists worry that this would prevent the development of tourism.

Meanwhile, in Lephalale district, to the immediate west of the Waterberg Biosphere Reserve, Kumba Coal (a multi-national mining company) would like to develop a new open-cast coal mine. The Waterberg area already produces 8 per cent of South Africa's coal, but the region contains huge reserves that are yet to be mined: approximately 44 per cent of the country's coal reserves are in Waterberg. A new mine is being proposed that would produce approximately 3 million tonnes of coal a year for the next 20 years.

Part C: how can rural communities have a sustainable future?

- Some of the strategies discussed in Part B are more appropriate to some groups of people than others. You should consider who benefits most from each of these schemes.
- You also need to create a plan that will be achievable: you can't do everything at once so you will need to think about your priorities.
- It would be sensible to focus your resources on just one rural community. So consider which schemes are most appropriate for Mutale, and which would work best in Lephalale.

Activity

13 Use what you have learned so far to complete each of the following tables:

Group of people	Strategies that create most benefits
Those who do the household chores, especially women and children	
School children	
Farmers	
Isolated rural communities	
The population of larger rural towns such as Polokwane and Lephalale	

Scheme	Main advantages	Main disadvantages
Rural electrification		Some households cannot afford electricity bills or electric stoves
Improving water supplies		Few if any
Ecotourism projects		Would prevent mining operations nearby
Mining		Would prevent tourism locally until the mining operation was complete

14 Look at the information on pages 82 to 85 and either:
  a) Produce a development plan for the sustainable development of a rural district of Limpopo. Justify your choice of strategies.
  or
  b) Choose the best one of the three strategies for the future development of a rural area of Limpopo. Explain your choice of strategy and why you rejected the other two options.

EXAMINER'S TIPS

Getting the best mark for part C of this problem-solving exercise I

In Section C of Paper 2 you will be asked to explain how you think a particular problem could best be solved. You will be marked on how well you solve this problem: this means you need to explain why you think your solution is a good one.

Take a look at a typical problem-solving exercise (see question 14 on page 85.)

Step 1

The first thing to do is to decide which of the schemes has most advantages and fewest disadvantages. Are you going to recommend:

- improving rural service provision?
- encouraging the development of ecotourism?
- creating more mining jobs?

You could suggest a combination of these approaches or ideas of your own, such as improved school facilities.

Step 2

In order to get a high mark, you will need to justify your plan. This means explaining why you think your plan will be successful.

Stages in writing your report		
	If you chose option A:	**If you chose option B:**
1	Decide which strategy or combination of strategies you will use	Decide which one of the three strategies you will use
2	Outline the main advantages of your plan	Describe and explain the advantages this strategy will bring to the rural area
3	Briefly explore any disadvantages your plan may have	Briefly describe and explain any disadvantages of your chosen strategy
4	Briefly state advantages of strategies you have not chosen to incorporate in your plan	Briefly describe the advantages of the strategies you have not chosen
5	Explain why you did not select those strategies that are not in your plan	Use the disadvantages of these two strategies to explain why you did not choose them
6	Conclude by restating briefly the positive effects of your plan on the people	Conclude by restating briefly the positive effects of your choice of strategy on the people

(Tip)

Think about the short- and long-term benefits of your plan

The aim of this problem-solving exercise is to put in place rural development strategies that will be sustainable. In other words, you need to prove that your plan will have lasting benefits. You could structure your answer around two headings:

1 The benefits that might be created in the first few months of your plan. These are the **short-term benefits** or advantages.

Example:
Short-term benefits:
If the rural electrification project was speeded up in the Mutale region the immediate or short-term benefits would be … (consider health benefits for women, and educational benefits for children).

2 The benefits that might be created for future generations. These are the **long-term benefits**.

Example:
Long-term benefits:
If this region had better water and electricity supplies it would be more appealing to foreign tourists. Such people expect to be able to have hot showers and air-conditioning. So, in the longer term the benefits of rural electrification would be …

The Big Picture

Human actions change ecosystems, e.g. rainforest destruction

Human actions have unintended consequences on the environment

Soil erosion

Disrupt water cycle

Carbon emissions

Climate

Enhanced greenhouse effect

How are plants and animals adapting?

Ecosystems

How do ecosystems help keep nature in balance?

How is climate changing?

How does the loss of habitat affect the living environment?

How will plants and animals be affected by climate change?

More extreme?

Is climate change responsible for the melting of Antarctic ice shelves?

Less predictable?

Are climatic hazards such as hurricanes becoming more frequent?

Are some groups of people more vulnerable than others?

How will these changes affect people?

What can we do to reduce the risk?

Are some places more at risk than others?

Chapter 1
Investigating climate patterns

KEY QUESTIONS

- ✪ What causes contrasting types of pressure systems in different parts of the world?

- ✪ How does contrasting pressure in the atmosphere lead to variations in weather and climate?

- ✪ To what extent are people's activities and quality of life influenced by weather and climate?

Figure 1 Solar heating of the Earth varies with latitude

What are pressure systems and how are they formed?

Our atmosphere is made of tiny molecules of nitrogen, oxygen, carbon dioxide and other rarer gases. Despite their tiny size, these molecules have mass and actually press down on us. This is what we call **air pressure**.

Variations in air pressure are usually caused by heating and cooling. In warm air the molecules are further apart than in cold air. Warm air rises, the molecules get further apart and there is less mass pressing down. This causes low air pressure. The opposite is true where air is cool.

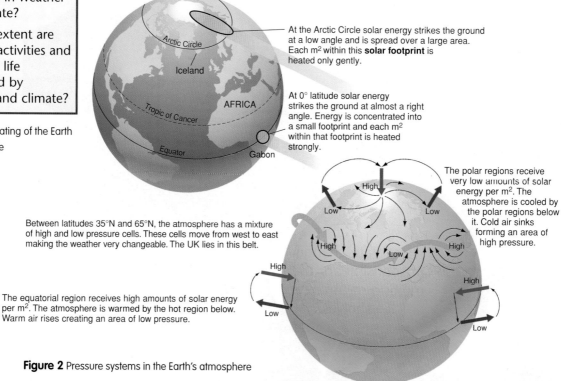

At the Arctic Circle solar energy strikes the ground at a low angle and is spread over a large area. Each m² within this **solar footprint** is heated only gently.

At 0° latitude solar energy strikes the ground at almost a right angle. Energy is concentrated into a small footprint and each m² within that footprint is heated strongly.

The polar regions receive very low amounts of solar energy per m². The atmosphere is cooled by the polar regions below it. Cold air sinks forming an area of high pressure.

Between latitudes 35°N and 65°N, the atmosphere has a mixture of high and low pressure cells. These cells move from west to east making the weather very changeable. The UK lies in this belt.

The equatorial region receives high amounts of solar energy per m². The atmosphere is warmed by the hot region below. Warm air rises creating an area of low pressure.

Figure 2 Pressure systems in the Earth's atmosphere

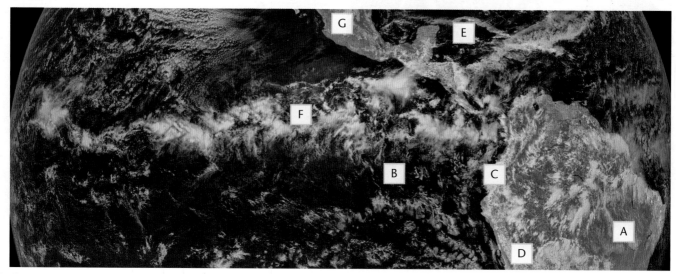

Figure 3 A satellite image of the Pacific Ocean

Air pressure is measured in units called millibars. The name comes from the Greek word *baros*, or bar, meaning pressure. A millibar (mb) is one thousandth of a bar. Air pressure varies with altitude, as you can see in Figure 4. Average air pressure at sea level is 1,013.2 mb. Air pressure at sea level varies approximately 80 mb either side of this value. So 970 to 990 mb is **low pressure** while 1,020 to 1,040 millibars is **high pressure**.

www.noaa.gov
The National Oceanic and Atmospheric Administration website: a fantastic resource of recent and archive satellite images of the Earth and its atmosphere.

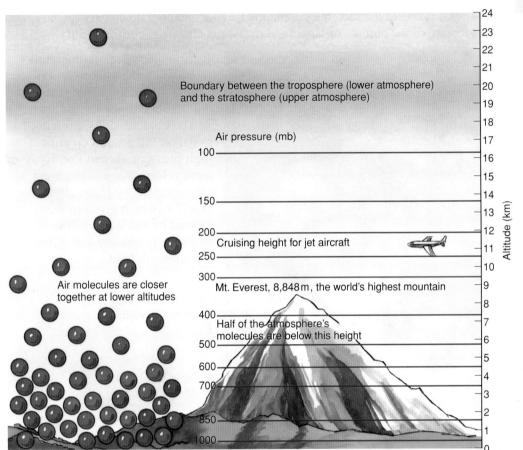

Figure 4 The change in air pressure (in mb) in relation to altitude (in km)

Activity

1 Study Figures 2 and 3 and an atlas:
   a) Name the countries A, B, C, D and E.
   b) Working in pairs, match the following labels to letters F and G:
      • The atmosphere is warmed by the hot region below. Warm air rises, creating clouds and an area of low pressure.
      • Sinking air creates high pressure and cloudless skies.
   c) Explain why the clouds on Figure 3 indicate areas of low pressure.

2 Use Figure 2 and your understanding of solar heating of the Earth (Figure 1) to explain why:
   a) the polar regions generally have high pressure
   b) the equatorial region generally has low pressure.

3 Explain why the weather between latitudes 35 °N and 65 °N is so changeable.

Arctic

High pressure systems and the continental climate

Around the edge of the Arctic region, between 60 °N and 70 °N, are large parts of the North American, European and Asian land masses. The climate here is characterised by severe winters and relatively short, cool summers. The most extreme temperatures are experienced in places far from the sea such as Norilsk in Russia. Here, the average winter temperature is -32 °C whereas summer temperatures reach a comparatively high 15 °C. This enormous **temperature range** (of 47 °C) is due to the fact that continents heat up and cool down very quickly. This feature of the climate of large land masses is known as **continentality**.

Figure 5 A satellite image of the Arctic

During the winter, temperatures in Russia and Canada can fall to -20 °C and below. The extremely cold ground chills the air above it. The cold air sinks, pressing down on the ground creating a high pressure system known as an **anticyclone**. Anticyclones are characterised by clear, cloudless skies. Any heat given to the ground by the weak winter sunshine is quickly lost in the cloudless night sky.

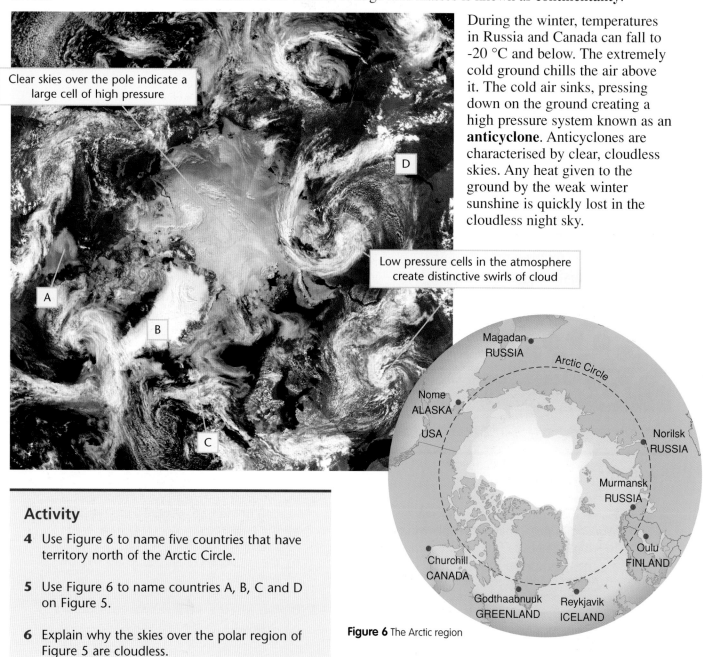

Clear skies over the pole indicate a large cell of high pressure

Low pressure cells in the atmosphere create distinctive swirls of cloud

Figure 6 The Arctic region

Activity

4 Use Figure 6 to name five countries that have territory north of the Arctic Circle.

5 Use Figure 6 to name countries A, B, C and D on Figure 5.

6 Explain why the skies over the polar region of Figure 5 are cloudless.

Station	Latitude/ Longitude	Min temp (°C)	Max temp (°C)	Temp range
Reykjavik, Iceland	64 °13'N 21 °90'W	−1	11	12
Oulu, Finland	64 °93'N 25 °36'E		16	26
Murmansk, Russia	68 °96'N 33 °5'E	−12		24
Norilsk, Russia	69 °33'N 88 °10'E	−32	15	
Magadan, Russia	59 °58'N 150 °78'E	−18	12	
Nome, Alaska	64 °30'N 165 °25'W	−16	11	
Churchill, Canada	58 °75'N 94 °6'W		12	38
Godthaabnuuk, Greenland	64 °16'N 51 °75'W	−10		16

Figure 7 Climate data for selected climate stations between 58 °N and 70 °N

Activity

7 Make a copy of Figure 7:
  a) Calculate the missing value for each climate station.
  b) Which station has the:
    i) lowest minimum temperature
    ii) largest temperature range?
  c) Suggest reasons for the wide variation in temperature ranges at these climate stations.

8 a) Suggest a hypothesis you could investigate using climate data that links the following variables:

  minimum temperature
  latitude
  distance from the sea.

  b) Predict the likely outcome of your enquiry and explain why you expect this outcome.
  c) Compare the minimum temperatures in Iceland and Greenland. Do these temperatures follow your expected outcome?

EXAMINER'S TIPS

Describing a climate graph

Tip 1

Each climate graph has four features you may be asked about in the exam.

1 What is the **total annual rainfall**? This may be given to you as a written statement or you may have to calculate it by adding together the totals for each of the twelve months. Make sure you accurately read each individual month's total.
2 Are there any distinctive **wet and dry seasons**? In which months or seasons are they found and how wet are they? Remember that seasons in the southern hemisphere are the reverse of ours in the United Kingdom.
3 What is the **annual temperature range**? Work out the difference between the hottest and coldest two months of the year and state it in °C.
4 Is there a distinctive **seasonal temperature pattern**? If so, when are the hotter and colder seasons?

Tip 2

When asked to describe patterns on the graph, make sure that you quote figures in your answer. For example, give the temperatures of the hottest and coldest months or the rainfall totals for the wettest and driest months.

Tip 3

When asked to **describe** a climate graph, do not be tempted to explain why the patterns exist. Avoid terms used for explaining, like 'because' and 'as a result of', in your answer.

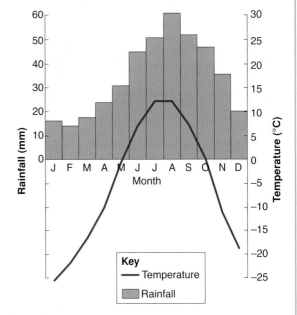

Figure 8 Climate graph for Churchill, Canada

 Iceland

Investigating the effect of the sea: a case study of Iceland's climate

Figure 9 Despite the Gulf Stream, Iceland has a cold and challenging winter climate. Europe's largest ice cap, Vatnajökull, and a number of smaller ice caps (like the one shown here) and glaciers cover around 11 per cent of the island

 www.vedur.is/english/
The English homepage of the official website of the Icelandic Met Office. Use the link to find climate data or whether Iceland's roads are blocked with snow.

We have seen how the land masses of Canada and Russia quickly lose their heat in the Arctic winter. By comparison, oceans cool down very slowly. So ocean currents are able to transfer heat from warm latitudes to cooler ones. Iceland's coastline is kept warm by one such current of warm water, the Gulf Stream. This brings warm water across the Atlantic from the tropics. This warm water heats the air above it and gives Iceland's coastal regions a **maritime climate** which is warmer and wetter than other places at similar latitudes.

How does Iceland's climate affect its people?

Iceland's climate has always been a challenge to the Icelandic people. Snow in the winter closes many roads and some are not passable until May. However, the Gulf Stream prevents ice forming in coastal waters so fishing boats can leave port throughout the year. Figure 13 summarises some of the impacts of Iceland's climate on the country's economy and its people.

Month	Vestmannaeyjar Islands °C	Precipitation (mm)	Akureyri °C	Precipitation (mm)
Jan	1.3	158	−2.2	52
Feb	2.0	139	−1.5	43
Mar	1.7	141	−1.3	43
Apr	3.4	117	1.6	29
May	5.8	105	5.5	19
Jun	8.0	102	9.1	28
Jul	9.6	95	10.5	33
Aug	9.6	140	10.0	34
Sep	7.4	131	6.3	39
Oct	5.0	161	3.0	58
Nov	2.4	154	−0.4	54
Dec	1.4	193	−1.9	53
	4.8 av.	1588.6 total	3.2 av.	489.5 total

Figure 10 Climate data for selected climate stations in Iceland

Activity

9 Use Figure 10 to draw climate graphs for each weather station.

10 Using the exam technique box 'Describing a climate graph' on page 91 to help you, describe the features of each of the climate graphs.

11 Draw an outline map of Iceland and a cross-section diagram like Figure 12. Use the additional labels to add extra annotations to your map and cross-section.

12 Use Figures 11 and 12 to explain why:
   a) winters in Akureyri are colder than in Reykjavik
   b) rainfall totals are relatively low in Akureyri but high in southern Iceland.

13 Look at Figure 13. Write a paragraph explaining how Iceland's climate affects its people.

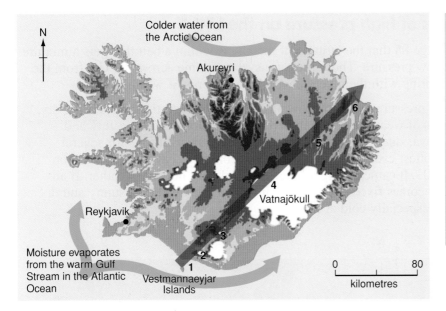

Additional labels for Figures 11 and 12

Air rises over the highlands of south Iceland.

An area of rain shadow where it seldom rains.

The wind often blows in from the south-west. This is the **prevailing wind** direction.

Some precipitation falls as snow on Vatnajökull, adding to the ice cap.

After crossing the highlands and ice cap, the air sinks and warms.

As the air rises it cools and water vapour condenses forming cloud and precipitation.

Figure 11 The factors that influence Iceland's regional patterns of climate

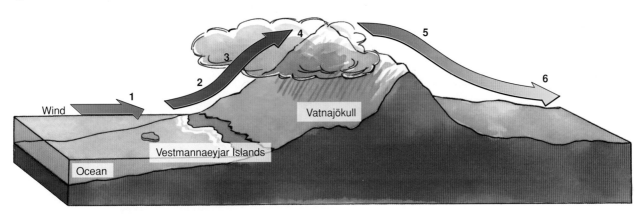

Figure 12 Relief rainfall: the reason for Iceland's regional pattern of rain

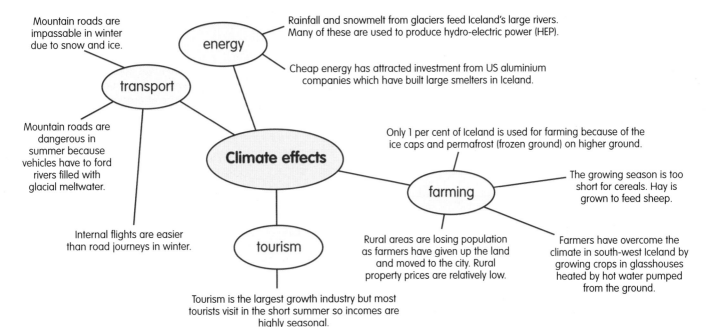

Figure 13 How Iceland's climate affects people

The effects of high pressure on the UK

We saw on page 88 that the latitude of the UK is within a belt that gets a mixture of high and low pressure. These pressure systems come across the UK from the Atlantic and bring with them very changeable patterns of weather.

Areas of high pressure are also known as anticyclones. Anticyclones bring dry, settled periods of weather. The long period of hot, dry weather in July and August 2003 was due to an anticyclone that stayed over Europe for several weeks. The hottest-ever day in the UK was recorded in Faversham, Kent, on 10 August 2003. It came during a long period of very hot, dry weather. If an anticyclone becomes fixed over the UK in winter the weather is sunny and dry but cold, and especially cold at night.

Figure 14 A weather map showing an anticyclone, 10 August 2003

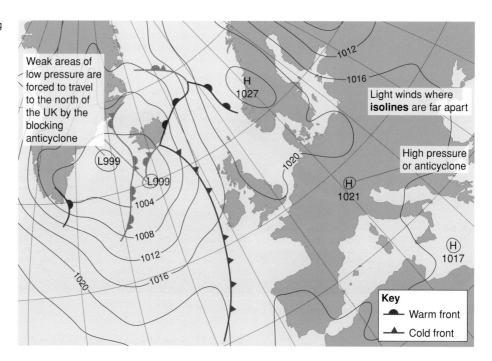

Figure 15 Rainfall in England in 2003 and 2004. Each month is shown as a percentage of the amount normally expected for that month (based on averages for 1961 to 1990)

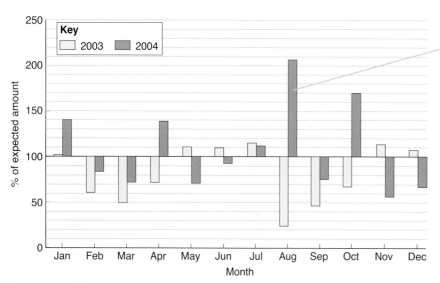

August 2004 was cooler and much wetter than August 2003. On the afternoon of 16 August, Boscastle, in Cornwall, was hit by a freak rainstorm that caused disastrous floods. In just four hours 200 mm of rain fell, causing the local river to burst its banks.

	2003 mean temp. anomaly (°C)	2004 mean temp. anomaly (°C)
Jan	0.8	1.5
Feb	0.3	1.7
Mar	2.0	1.0
Apr	1.9	1.8
May	1.2	1.2
Jun	2.0	1.5
Jul	1.7	0.0
Aug	2.5	1.9
Sep	0.9	1.3
Oct	−1.3	0.2
Nov	1.8	1.3
Dec	0.5	0.9

Figure 16 Temperature anomalies in England for 2003 and 2004. Figures are the temperature (°C) above or below the monthly average (1961 to 1990)

When extreme weather is a hazard

The extreme heat of August 2003 caused suffering and discomfort for millions of people across Europe. The heat caused heatstroke and dehydration, especially among elderly people. It is estimated that 30,000 people died in the extreme heat. France was worst hit. French doctors estimate that the heatwave caused 14,000 deaths. On a normal August day in France about 50 people are admitted to hospital suffering from heat exhaustion. In August 2003 that number rose to 500. The hospitals struggled to cope. In addition, the heatwave also caused several forest fires in southern Europe. All in all, the extreme heat is estimated to have caused €1 billion of damage.

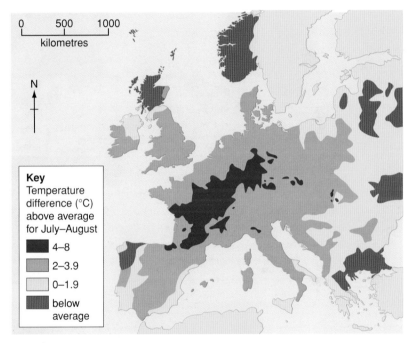

Figure 17 Temperature anomalies in Europe in August 2003

Activity

14 Use Figure 14 to describe the location of the regions of high and low pressure.

15 Use Figure 15 to describe the pattern of rainfall in 2003. In which months was the rainfall:
a) above average
b) average
c) below average?

16 a) Use the data in Figure 16 to draw a graph similar to Figure 15.
b) Pick out one similarity and one difference between the temperatures of 2003 and 2004.

17 Use Figure 17 and an atlas to list five countries where temperatures were at least 4 °C above average in 2003.

18 Use Figures 15, 16 and 17. Describe how these two summers might have affected the following businesses:
a) supermarket sales at Tesco and Sainsbury
b) bed and breakfasts in Cornwall
c) accident and emergency departments in France.

19 Describe and explain how the extreme weather in one of these summers caused a hazard.

The effects of low pressure (or depressions)

Regions of low pressure in the atmosphere are formed when air lifts off the Earth's surface. It is common for several cells of low pressure, also known as **depressions**, to form in the North Atlantic at any one time. They then track eastwards towards Europe bringing changeable weather characterised by wind, cloud and rain. Depressions are more likely to be deeper (have lower pressure) in the winter months. These weather systems can bring damaging gusts of wind and large waves onto the coast as well as heavy rain. However, low pressure in the summer months is quite common: the floods of June and July 2007 were caused by depressions.

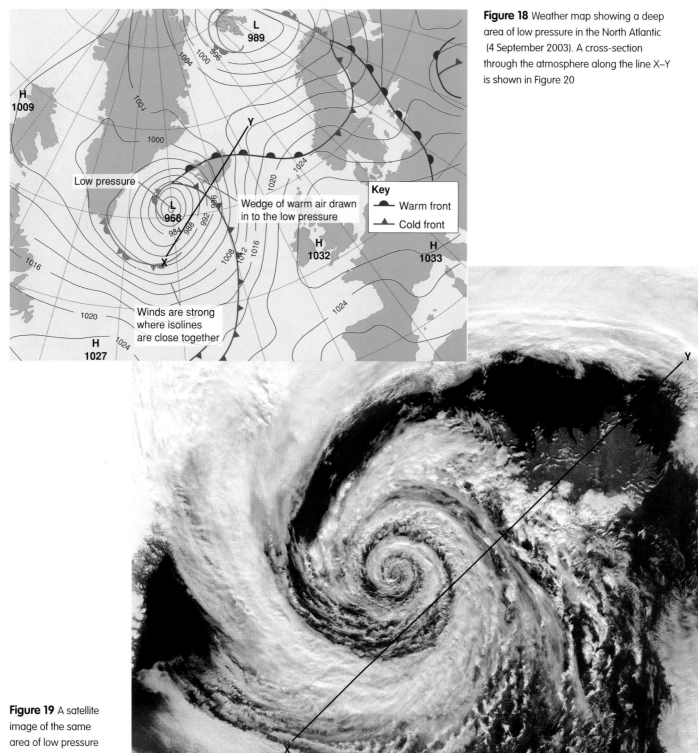

Figure 18 Weather map showing a deep area of low pressure in the North Atlantic (4 September 2003). A cross-section through the atmosphere along the line X–Y is shown in Figure 20

Figure 19 A satellite image of the same area of low pressure off Iceland (4 September 2003)

Inside the depression there is a battle between huge masses of warmer and colder air. These air masses revolve slowly around each other in an anti-clockwise direction (in the northern hemisphere) as the whole system tracks eastward. As the warmer air rises and rotates its moisture condenses, forming huge banks of cloud. Seen from above, these curving banks of cloud give the depression a characteristic shape.

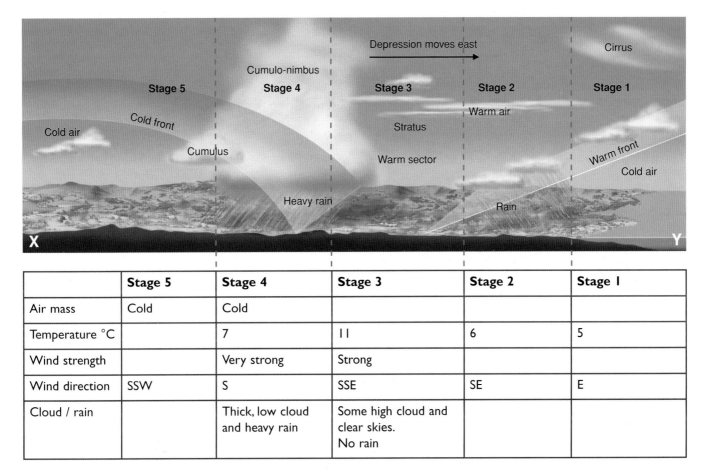

	Stage 5	Stage 4	Stage 3	Stage 2	Stage 1
Air mass	Cold	Cold			
Temperature °C		7	11	6	5
Wind strength		Very strong	Strong		
Wind direction	SSW	S	SSE	SE	E
Cloud / rain		Thick, low cloud and heavy rain	Some high cloud and clear skies. No rain		

Figure 20 Weather that would have been associated with the easterly progress of the depression shown in Figures 18 and 19

Feature	Cyclones or depressions	Anticyclones
Air pressure		High, usually above 1020 mb (millibars)
Air movement	Rising	
Wind strength	Strong	
Wind circulation		Clockwise
Typical winter weather		Cold and dry. Clear skies in the daytime. Frost at night.
Typical summer weather	Mild and wet. Cloudy with periods of heavy rain separated by showers.	

Figure 21 Comparing cyclones and anticyclones

Activity

20 Use an atlas and Figures 18 and 19. Describe the location of the areas of high and low pressure.

21 a) Make a copy of Figure 20. Use the evidence in Figures 18 and 19 to complete the missing sections.

b) Imagine you are a weather forecaster working in north-east Iceland. Prepare a local weather forecast for the next few hours.

22 Make a large copy of Figure 21 and use the information on pages 94–7 to complete the blank spaces.

Burma

Cyclone Nargis

Cyclones are severe storms that occur in tropical regions. They are extreme weather events caused by very low air pressure. Cyclones get their energy from the warm tropical waters beneath them. The sea has to be at a temperature of at least 26 °C for a few weeks to generate such a storm. The warm water acts like fuel. It heats the air above it, which rises, creating storm clouds and heavy rainfall. The storm loses strength when it moves over land and loses its fuel supply.

In early May 2008 Cyclone Nargis crossed the Bay of Bengal and hit the coast of Burma (also known as Myanmar) killing an estimated 130,000 people. The winds peaked at 215 km/hr as the storm approached the coastline and these winds certainly caused damage as they would have flattened trees and torn the roofs off buildings. However, most deaths were caused by drowning. The very low air pressure during a cyclone means that there is less pressure on the surface of the ocean from above. Consequently the ocean bulges upwards beneath the storm creating what is known as a **storm surge** (or tidal surge). In the case of Cyclone Nargis the air pressure fell to 960 millibars and it is estimated that the sea level rose by 3.6 m during this storm surge. Unfortunately the storm hit the coast at high tide, meaning that the storm surge was higher than the level of the flat coastal plain. As the storm tracked along the densely populated southern coastline of Burma, the storm surge caused flooding for long distances inland. In addition to this the strong storm winds blowing over the ocean create huge waves. In the case of Nargis it is thought these waves reached a maximum height of 7.6 m on top of the storm surge.

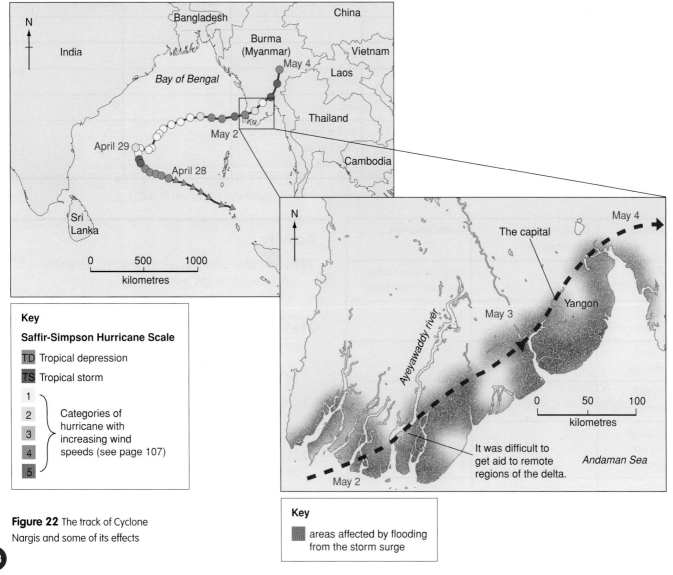

Key

Saffir-Simpson Hurricane Scale

TD Tropical depression

TS Tropical storm

1
2
3
4
5
} Categories of hurricane with increasing wind speeds (see page 107)

Figure 22 The track of Cyclone Nargis and some of its effects

Key

▨ areas affected by flooding from the storm surge

How were people affected by Nargis?

Nargis and its terrible floodwaters affected people in both the short term and long term. About 800,000 homes were damaged and many survivors were **displaced**. Most of these moved in with family members and 260,000 moved into refugee camps. Surprisingly, 80 per cent of the damaged homes were rebuilt by the end of June 2008. Land was flooded and rice crops destroyed. Over half of the survivors in the worst hit areas were short of food. Around 65 per cent of the population reported health problems in early June. These included 37 per cent of the population suffering from fever and 34 per cent from diarrhoea.

Only 8 per cent reported injuries but 23 per cent were suffering from mental health problems. Diseases such as diarrhoea are common after such events, because drinking water becomes polluted with sewage. After Nargis the number of people using pit latrines fell from 77 per cent to 60 per cent (because the latrines were damaged) which means that 40 per cent of people were not getting rid of sewage safely. Three-quarters of health centres in the region were damaged by the storm, so families had less access to immunisation and other types of care just when they needed it most. In the long term these facilities had to be rebuilt.

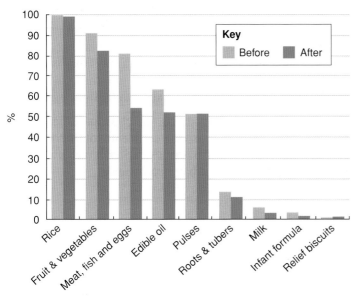

Figure 23 Diet in the delta before and after the cyclone

Figure 24 Percentage of deaths by age and gender

	Male	Female
Under 5	10	12
5–11	11	15
12–17	3	3
18–60	12	26
Over 60	3	5
Total	39	61

Activity

23 a) Describe the track of Cyclone Nargis.
   b) Describe the distribution of land affected by flooding.

24 Study Figure 23.
   a) Compare the quality of the diet before and after the cyclone.
   b) Suggest how this may have affected people.

25 a) Use the data in Figure 24 to draw a simple age–sex pyramid.
   b) Describe the shape of your pyramid. What does it tell you about the type of people who were worst affected?

26 Suggest how the activities of the following people might have been affected by the cyclone in both the short term (the first month) and longer term.
   a) A rice farmer who owned land that was flooded in one of the remote regions of the delta
   b) A family living in a shanty town in one of the affected cities.

Chapter 2
Climate change

- How does human activity affect climate?
- To what extent does human activity influence climate change and global warming?
- What are the social, economic and environmental consequences of climate change?

Figure 1 London's urban heat island, night-time temperatures in mid-May

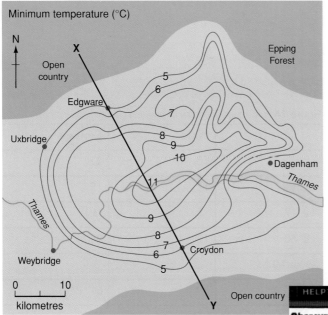

The urban heat island

The buildings and traffic in a large city influence the local climate, an effect known as the **urban microclimate**. One of the main impacts of a city on the local climate is to create temperatures that are higher than in the surrounding rural area. This is known as the **urban heat island**. The city acts like a huge storage heater, transferring heat from buildings and cars to the dome of air that covers the city:

- Concrete, brick and tarmac absorb heat from the sun during the day. This heat is then radiated into the atmosphere during the evening and at night.
- Buildings that are badly insulated lose heat, especially through roofs and windows. Heat is also created in cars and factories and this heat is also lost to the air from exhausts and chimneys.

Figure 2 shows that frogspawn, which is an indicator of the arrival of spring, arrives earlier in southern regions of the UK. It also arrives earlier in urban areas as a result of the urban heat island.

Figure 2 Map of the first sightings of frogspawn up until 12 February 2005 from the BBC Springwatch website. The graph shows the total number of sightings each day between 24 November 2004 and 16 April 2005

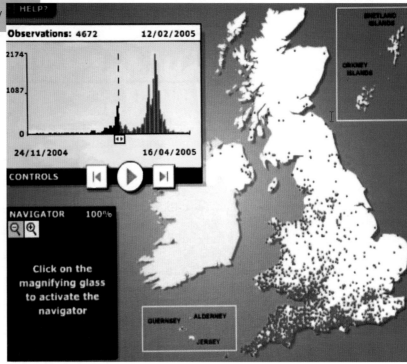

Activity

1 Use Figure 1.
   a) Describe the location of the area of highest temperature in London.
   b) Describe the distribution of places with lower temperatures.
   c) Suggest reasons for the pattern shown on the map.

2 Use Figure 1 to draw a cross section of London's urban heat island along the line X–Y.

How do cities affect patterns of wind and rain?

Tall buildings in a city are able to affect local wind patterns. The shelter they provide means that average wind speeds in cities are lower than in the surrounding countryside. However, rows of tall buildings can also funnel the wind into the canyon-like streets between them. Where wind is forced to flow around or over tall buildings the wind can suddenly gust at speeds that are two to three times the average wind speed. This may cause hazards for pedestrians and in some extreme weather conditions has led to the collapse of scaffolding.

Urban air has ten times more dust particles in it than rural air. The dust comes from car exhausts, heating systems, industry and building sites. When water vapour condenses it forms water droplets by attaching itself to these dust particles. So more dust means that cities can have more clouds. During the summer months the urban heat island can cause more frequent convectional rainstorms over the city. In this way the atmosphere is self-cleaning: rainfall helps to remove pollution from the urban atmosphere.

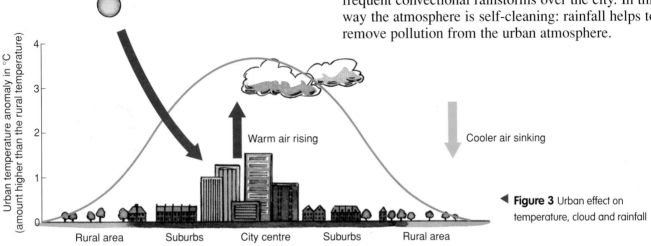

Warm air rising

Cooler air sinking

◀ **Figure 3** Urban effect on temperature, cloud and rainfall

Urban temperature anomaly in °C (amount higher than the rural temperature)

Rural area Suburbs City centre Suburbs Rural area

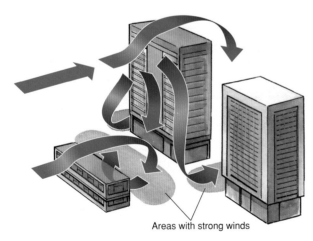

Areas with strong winds

Figure 4 Urban wind patterns

Additional labels for Figures 3 and 4

Wind is funnelled by tall buildings

Prevailing wind

Decreased air pressure

Increased air pressure

Sun's energy is absorbed by building materials

Gusty winds may be two to three times stronger than average

Cumulus clouds form where rising warm air meets colder air

Activity

3 Predict how the urban heat islands would affect people in each of the following pairs of cities:
   a) two cities in the UK, one larger, the other with a much smaller population
   b) two cities of similar size, one in the tropics, the other in higher latitudes (e.g. Moscow).

4 Use Figure 2.
   a) Describe the distribution of sightings of frogspawn on the map.
   b) Explain why there may have been more sightings in some parts of the UK than others.
   c) Describe the pattern shown on the graph.
   d) Suggest why the graph has this distinctive shape.
   e) Explain how you could investigate the actual reason for the shape of this graph.

5 Make copies of Figures 3 and 4. Sort the 'additional' labels and add them to appropriate places on your diagrams.

How does the urban heat island affect people?

What are the effects of urban microclimate?

The urban heat island has both positive and negative effects. Cities such as London have fewer frosts and less ice on the roads in the winter. Summers are hotter and there are more days when people can suffer the effects of heat stress. Discomfort and heat-related deaths increase when night-time temperatures stay above 25 °C. In July 2001 a tube train broke down in London, trapping 4,000 people underground. The temperature rose to 40 °C and 600 people had to be treated for heat exhaustion. During the heatwave of August 2003 the temperature in central London was 9 °C higher than the surrounding countryside. Paris too was exceptionally hot and the extreme conditions caused at least 14,000 deaths in France.

A combination of rising summer temperatures due to **global warming** and the urban heat island effect could mean that large urban areas such as London, New York, Paris and Tokyo suffer more from climate change than smaller towns.

What can be done about the urban heat island?

As temperatures rise, more people install air-conditioning in their homes, but air-conditioning uses a lot of electrical energy and the production of much electricity creates the greenhouse gases that are causing climate change. It is estimated that the use of an air-conditioner for just one year in a hot climate such as Florida produces more carbon dioxide than a person in Cambodia produces in a lifetime.

Sunshine duration	5–15% less
Annual mean temperature	1–2 °C warmer
Temperatures on sunny days	2–6 °C warmer
Occurrence of frosts	2–3 weeks fewer
Total precipitation	5–30% more
Number of rain days	10% more
Number of days with snow	14% fewer
Cloud cover	5–10% more
Occurrence of fog in winter	100% more
Amount of dust	10 times more

Figure 5 The effects of the urban climate in the UK

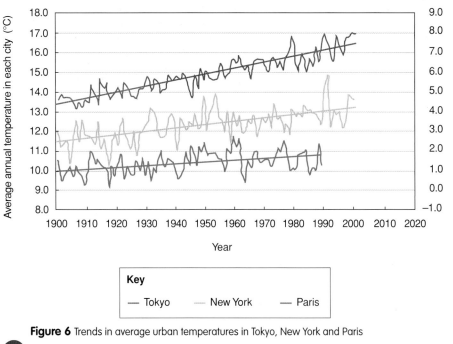

Figure 6 Trends in average urban temperatures in Tokyo, New York and Paris

Key
— Tokyo   — New York   — Paris

Activity

6 Study Figure 5. Outline the advantages and disadvantages of the urban microclimate for the people who live in cities.

7 Use Figure 6.
   a) Compare the urban heat island in each of the cities.
   b) Use the trend to predict the urban heat island in each city by 2020.

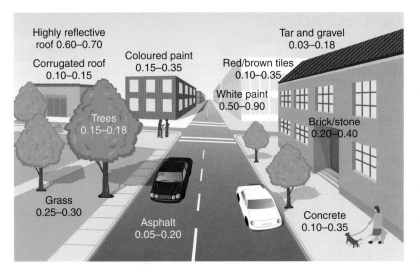

Highly reflective
roof 0.60–0.70

Corrugated roof
0.10–0.15

Coloured paint
0.15–0.35

Tar and gravel
0.03–0.18

Red/brown tiles
0.10–0.35

White paint
0.50–0.90

Trees
0.15–0.18

Brick/stone
0.20–0.40

Grass
0.25–0.30

Asphalt
0.05–0.20

Concrete
0.10–0.35

Figure 7 How the urban environment reflects the sun's energy. The closer the number to 1.0 the more energy is reflected. Surfaces with very low numbers are absorbing more of the sun's energy. They then emit this heat at night

Activity

8 Use Figures 7 and 8 to explain how the creation of more parks, woodlands and lakes in our cities might:
   a) affect the urban microclimate
   b) make urban areas more sustainable in the future.

We need to reduce energy use. All new buildings must be well insulated to reduce heat loss. We need to design cars and air-conditioning that use less energy and have low emissions of greenhouse gases.

We need more green spaces. Parks reflect more of the sun's energy. More trees must be planted. The shade from trees reduces air temperatures. Trees soak up carbon dioxide and pollution from traffic.

Figure 8 Possible ways of reducing the urban heat island

Scientist

Engineer

Urban planner

Politician

We should create a network of parks so that the wind can blow through our cities and remove some of the heat. Cold groundwater can be pumped through pipes in our underground train stations. That would cool the air. The roofs of buildings can be coated in light-coloured materials to reflect sunshine.

People need to change their lifestyles. People should take long holidays away from the city in the summer. We need to cut traffic by encouraging car users to switch to public transport. We can do this by congestion charging, as in Central London.

Activity

9 Use Figure 8 to outline the arguments for and against each of the following:

Strategy to reduce the urban heat island	Arguments for	Arguments against	Who might oppose this plan?
Create more green spaces			
Reduce number of cars			
Design better homes			

Is global warming natural or is it due to our actions?

It is known that the global climate changes naturally. Ice ages have come and gone. Changes to currents in the Pacific Ocean every few years are known to cause extreme weather events. Big volcanic eruptions can also affect the global climate. The eruption of Mount Pinatubo in June 1991 pumped huge quantities of ash and sulphur dioxide into the atmosphere. This blocked incoming solar energy and average temperatures in the northern hemisphere fell by between 0.5 °C and 0.7 °C. This sounds like a small change but it was enough to influence climate at a global scale. During 1992 the USA had its third-coldest and third-wettest summer for 77 years. Some believe the cooling climate may have also contributed to the floods along the River Mississippi in 1993. Certainly the town of Churchill in Canada had a long hard winter in 1992.

Most scientists believe that human actions are also causing climate change. Certain gases, including carbon dioxide and methane, are known to trap heat in the atmosphere. These are the so-called **greenhouse gases**. Many human activities release these gases, including the burning of fossil fuels for energy, and their concentration in the atmosphere is gradually increasing.

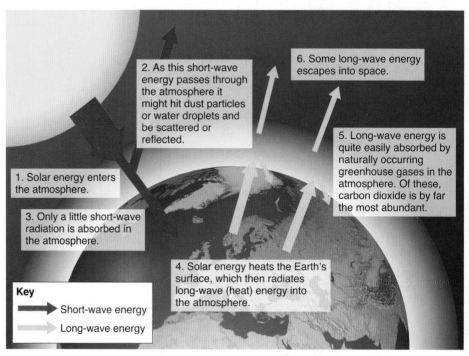

2. As this short-wave energy passes through the atmosphere it might hit dust particles or water droplets and be scattered or reflected.

6. Some long-wave energy escapes into space.

5. Long-wave energy is quite easily absorbed by naturally occurring greenhouse gases in the atmosphere. Of these, carbon dioxide is by far the most abundant.

1. Solar energy enters the atmosphere.

3. Only a little short-wave radiation is absorbed in the atmosphere.

4. Solar energy heats the Earth's surface, which then radiates long-wave (heat) energy into the atmosphere.

Key

→ Short-wave energy

⇒ Long-wave energy

Figure 9 The greenhouse effect

Evidence for man-made climate change

There are many separate pieces of evidence for climate change caused by humans. They are rather like the pieces of a jigsaw. One piece of evidence comes from scientists studying polar bears in Canada. Studies by the Canadian Wildlife Service show that the ice in Hudson Bay now melts three weeks earlier than it did when studies began in the early 1970s. Polar bears feed on young seals during March and April and put on a lot of weight to survive the summer, when they hardly eat at all. For each week that the thaw comes early, the bears have less chance to feed, and come on shore 10 kg lighter. The consequences of further climate change are worrying:

- More young bears and pups will starve over the longer summer.
- Females will be less fertile.
- Hungry bears are more likely to forage for food in towns where they come into conflict with people.

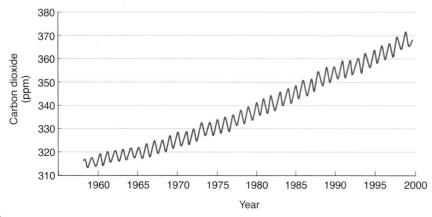

Figure 10 The rise of carbon dioxide in the atmosphere since monitoring the atmosphere began in the 1950s (ppm = parts per million)

Figure 11 Polar bears in Hudson Bay are the most studied group of polar bears in the world

| Year | °C | |
	April	May
1974	−11.4	−2.1
1977	−6.9	2.3
1981	−14.1	−0.6
1988	−9.1	−3.4
1990	−10.8	−1.2
1991	−8.5	0.1
1992	−13.5	−2.3
1999	−2.6	3.8
2000	−11.9	−1.4

Figure 13 Mean (average) temperature in Churchill, Canada in April and May in selected years

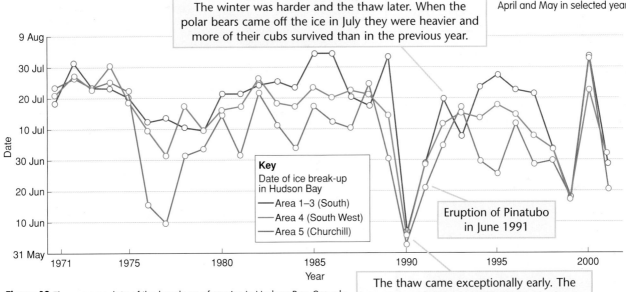

Figure 12 The average date of the break-up of sea ice in Hudson Bay, Canada

Activity

10 a) Use Figure 9 to describe the source of the energy that is trapped by greenhouse gases.
b) Explain why the greenhouse effect is a good thing for human life.

11 a) Describe the trend of the line on Figure 10.
b) Explain how this trend might affect the natural greenhouse effect shown in Figure 9.

12 Study Figure 12.
a) i) What was the average date of the thaw in area 5 in 1971–1975 compared with 1995–1999?
ii) What does this suggest was happening to the climate?

b) i) Describe the thaw in the years 1990–1993.
ii) Explain why this happened and the effect it had on the bears.

13 a) Use the evidence in Figures 12 and 13 to investigate the link between temperatures in April/May and the date of the thaw of the sea ice.
b) Outline how the evidence from Churchill in Canada supports the view that climate change can be caused by both natural and human factors.

How could climate change affect us in the next 100 years?

Global changes in the climate due to greenhouse gas emissions are likely to have a wide variety of impacts, and some places could be worse hit than others.

In 2005, New Orleans was flooded by a storm surge of water created by Hurricane Katrina. A total of 1,836 people were killed by Katrina. Much of the city is built below sea level. The city is built on the soft sands of a river delta and as these dry out the city gradually sinks. This subsidence, combined with rising sea levels, means that New Orleans is at increasing risk of more floods.

About 3.6 billion people (or 60 per cent of the world's population) live within 60 km of the coast. This is likely to rise to 6.4 billion (75 per cent of the world's population) by 2030.

Between 1900 and 2000 the world's sea levels rose on average by 2 mm per year. This is mainly due to the expansion of sea water as global temperatures increase.

Of the world's 23 mega-cities, 16 are in coastal regions and are at risk from further sea-level rise. Many of these cities are in Less Economically Developed Countries (LEDCs) and are continuing to grow rapidly. This photograph was taken in Mumbai, one of the world's largest cities, during the floods in August 2005.

If greenhouse emissions continue at their present rate it is likely that sea levels will continue to rise by, on average, 4 mm a year over the next 100 years.

The Thames flood barrier was completed in 1982 to protect London from tidal surges of water coming up the river from the North Sea. Sea levels are rising in the Thames estuary by about 6 mm per year (60 cm in 100 years). A major flood would perhaps cause damage to the value of £30,000 million and would certainly cause many deaths.

What will be the impact on the billions of people living in coastal regions?

Figure 14 The impact of climate change on coastal populations

Category 5: Over 250 kph. Complete failure of some smaller buildings. Failure of the roofs of large industrial buildings. Extensive coastal flooding damages the ground floor of many buildings.

Category 4: 211–250 kph. Complete destruction of the roofs of smaller buildings and more extensive damage to the walls. All signs and trees are blown down. Flooding of coastal areas 3 to 5 hours before the arrival of the storm may cut off escape routes.

Category 3: 178–210 kph. Severe damage to the roofs of small buildings. Some structural damage to walls. Mobile homes destroyed. Poorly constructed road signs destroyed. Large trees blown down.

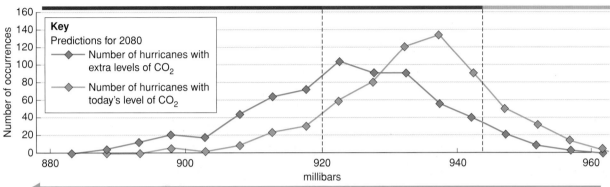

Key
Predictions for 2080
◆— Number of hurricanes with extra levels of CO_2
◆— Number of hurricanes with today's level of CO_2

Lower air pressure and stronger winds

The strongest hurricanes in the present climate may be upstaged by even more intense hurricanes over the next century as the Earth's climate is warmed by increasing levels of greenhouse gases in the atmosphere. Although we cannot say at present whether more or fewer hurricanes will occur in the future with global warming, the hurricanes that do occur near the end of the 21st century are expected to be stronger and have significantly more intense rainfall than under present-day climate conditions.

Figure 15 The National Oceanic and Atmospheric Administration (NOAA) has used computer models to predict frequency and intensity of hurricanes in 2080

Activity

14 Study Figure 15. Describe how the frequency and violence of hurricanes are expected to change.

15 a) Use the data in Figure 17 to produce a graph of closures.
   b) Describe the trend of your graph.
   c) Explain how this graph could be seen to be more evidence for climate change.

16 Use evidence from pages 104–107 to explain why global warming is an 'issue of international concern'.

17 Outline how climate change could affect:
   a) people living in coastal areas
   b) wildlife in the Arctic.

18 Suggest why people living in MEDC cities may be able to cope with climate change and extreme weather better than people living in LEDC cities.

The potential for fairly significant rises in temperature in Arctic regions seems to be quite high. And should that happen, especially over a time scale of decades, the possibility of marine mammals being able to adapt rapidly enough is very low.

Figure 16 The opinion of Dr Malcolm Ramsay, Professor of Biology at the University of Saskatchewan, Canada

Figure 17 Closures of the Thames Barrier to protect against storm (tidal) surges, 1983–2007. Source: Environment Agency

Year	Number of closures
1983	1
1984	0
1985	0
1986	0
1987	1
1988	1
1989	0
1990	3
1991	0
1992	1
1993	5
1994	1
1995	3
1996	4
1997	0
1998	3
1999	3
2000	6
2001	11
2002	2
2003	8
2004	2
2005	5
2006	1
2007	11

How will climate change affect Iceland?

The Arctic is one region where climate change is predicted to have huge impacts. Iceland's landscape will certainly change as its ice caps and glaciers melt. However, in the short term the economy could benefit as melting glaciers feed Iceland's rivers and these provide hydro-electric power (HEP) for Iceland's industry. Run-off from glaciers will peak sometime in the next 100 years and, according to computer models, Iceland's glaciers will have disappeared by 2200.

Figure 18 Fording the rivers of central Iceland can only be attempted during July and August

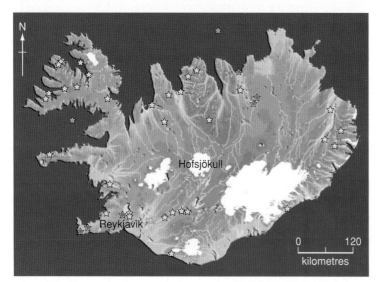

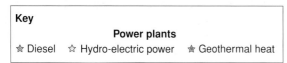

Key

Power plants
☆ Diesel   ☆ Hydro-electric power   ☆ Geothermal heat

Figure 19 Iceland's power stations

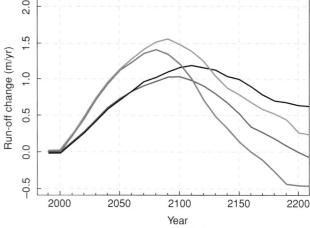

The four lines show predicted run-off using four different computer models

Figure 20 Predicted changes in run-off (river discharge) from Hofsjökull ice cap in central Iceland. The lines show predicted run-off compared with averages in the year 2000

Between 1570 and 1890 Iceland's climate was at least 1 °C cooler than today. Sea ice came down from the Arctic and surrounded Iceland, making it difficult to bring fishing boats onshore. Glaciers expanded and covered some farms. Grain and hay crops failed and there was famine. If the temperature rises 1 °C above today's temperature then farmers will be able to start growing wheat. They will also greatly increase the number of cattle and sheep they keep because they will be able to grow 20 per cent more hay.

We are obviously concerned about the negative impacts of climate change. Most of the 300,000 people in Iceland live close to the coast. Sea-level rise will threaten Reykjavik and many other smaller towns. Extreme weather events caused by low pressure will become more common. Storm surges will cause coastal erosion and flooding. Of greatest concern is the future of the fishing industry which is so important to our economy. Even small changes in the ocean currents could affect fish stocks in the seas around Iceland but the scientific predictions on this are still unclear.

A climate expert

Spokesperson for a power company

A government spokesperson

A tour rep

Around 87 per cent of Iceland's electricity is generated by HEP stations (and most of the rest comes from other renewables, particularly geothermal power). The construction of a new dam at Kárahnjúkar in East Iceland recently has been criticised by environmentalists. They don't like the loss of wilderness, but I say that Iceland is creating clean energy because we do not rely on fossil fuels. Climate change will gradually cause the glaciers and ice caps to melt. This means that rivers will have even greater discharges during the spring and summer months. We will be able to create even more electricity. That will make Iceland an even bigger attraction to energy-hungry industries such as aluminium smelting and web servers.

Iceland's tourist industry has grown rapidly in the last 20 years. Most tourists arrive by air but environmental campaigners criticise air travel, saying that it causes carbon dioxide emissions. They say flying should cost more. Will people still come here if the cost of flying becomes more expensive? Something else worries me: most tourists come here to see our beautiful landscape and wilderness areas. Will people still visit Iceland if there is no ice?

Figure 21 Differing viewpoints on climate change in Iceland

Activity

19 Discuss Figure 18. List the changes you might expect to see in this landscape in 30 years' time and in 200 years' time.

20 a) Describe the location of the Hofsjökull ice cap.
b) Describe the distribution of:
  i) geothermal power stations
  ii) HEP stations.

21 Use Figure 20 to predict what might happen to Iceland's production of HEP by 2050, 2100 and 2200. Explain why Iceland's energy companies need to find alternative sources of power.

22 a) Use the views in Figure 21 to complete a copy of the following table:

	Short-term changes	Longer-term changes
Views that are generally positive		
Views that are generally negative		

b) Use your completed table to explain what you would do if you were in government in Iceland to try to create a sustainable future for your country.

Chapter 3
Ecosystems

KEY QUESTIONS

☼ How do natural and human processes change ecosystems?

☼ How do changes affect their structure, process and stability?

☼ What are the consequences of changes in the ecosystem:
- for people within the ecosystem
- for people and environments beyond the ecosystem?

☼ How might ecosystems be both exploited and conserved in a sustainable way?

What are ecosystems?

An **ecosystem** is a community of plants and animals and the environment in which they live. Ecosystems contain both living and non-living parts. The living part includes such things as plants, insects and birds, which depend on each other for food. Plants may also depend on insects and birds for pollination and seed dispersal. The non-living part of an ecosystem includes such things as the climate, soils and rocks. This non-living environment provides nutrients, warmth, water and shelter for the living parts of the ecosystem.

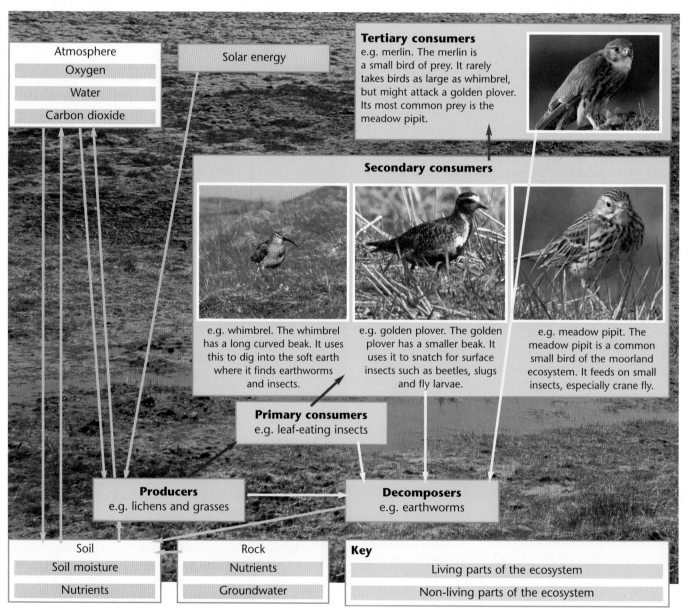

Atmosphere
Oxygen
Water
Carbon dioxide

Solar energy

Tertiary consumers
e.g. merlin. The merlin is a small bird of prey. It rarely takes birds as large as whimbrel, but might attack a golden plover. Its most common prey is the meadow pipit.

Secondary consumers

e.g. whimbrel. The whimbrel has a long curved beak. It uses this to dig into the soft earth where it finds earthworms and insects.

e.g. golden plover. The golden plover has a smaller beak. It uses it to snatch for surface insects such as beetles, slugs and fly larvae.

e.g. meadow pipit. The meadow pipit is a common small bird of the moorland ecosystem. It feeds on small insects, especially crane fly.

Primary consumers
e.g. leaf-eating insects

Producers
e.g. lichens and grasses

Decomposers
e.g. earthworms

Soil
Soil moisture
Nutrients

Rock
Nutrients
Groundwater

Key
Living parts of the ecosystem
Non-living parts of the ecosystem

Figure 1 The living and non-living parts (or components) of the treeless moorland ecosystem in Iceland: an example of **tundra**

Figure 2 The emperor dragonfly is commonly seen at ponds in the UK

Ecosystems exist at different scales

Ecosystems exist at a variety of scales. The largest, such as tropical rainforests or desert ecosystems, cover large parts of the Earth and are known as **biomes**. But ecosystems also exist at much smaller scales, for example salt marshes and sand dunes may cover only a few hectares while a garden pond is an ecosystem that is only a few metres across.

Sadly logging, oil exploration, intensive farming and over-fishing are all damaging natural ecosystems. However, people can also conserve ecosystems. We can even create new ones. Creating a small garden pond can increase the variety of plants, insects and other wildlife in your garden, as is shown in Figure 3.

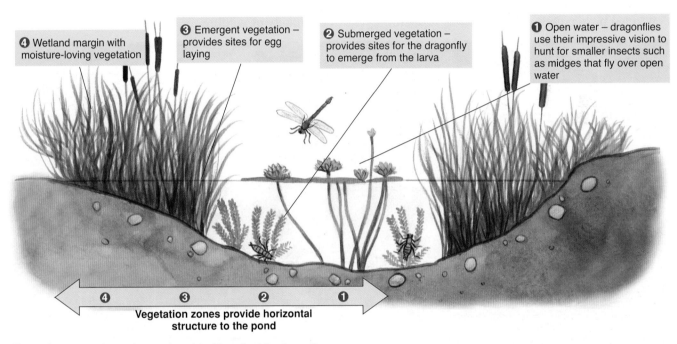

❹ Wetland margin with moisture-loving vegetation

❸ Emergent vegetation – provides sites for egg laying

❷ Submerged vegetation – provides sites for the dragonfly to emerge from the larva

❶ Open water – dragonflies use their impressive vision to hunt for smaller insects such as midges that fly over open water

Vegetation zones provide horizontal structure to the pond

Figure 3 Structure of a garden pond, and the life cycle of the dragonfly

---

Activity

1 a) Use Figure 1 to draw a food chain that includes the meadow pipit.

b) What would happen to the merlin if the population of meadow pipit fell for some reason (perhaps because a new predator was introduced to Iceland)?

2 Work in pairs. Using the text and diagrams on these pages, discuss as many links as you can think of between:
a) animals and plants
b) wildlife and climate
c) people and wildlife.

3 Still working in your pairs, use your discussion to draw a spider diagram or concept map to show how people fit into an ecosystem as shown in Figure 1.

4 a) Make a copy of Figure 3.
b) Describe the structure of this ecosystem.

5 Explain how the structure of this ecosystem provides a variety of habitats for insects such as dragonflies.

Investigating urban ecosystems

We tend to think that ecosystems and their wildlife are all in distant places and that there is little we can do to save or conserve them. However, there is an important ecosystem that is literally on your doorstep. Recent scientific studies have highlighted the importance of the UK's gardens as a wildlife habitat.

From above, like the aerial photo in Figure 4, the average town or city in the UK can be seen to be a patchwork of gardens, parks, golf courses and small woodlands. A detailed study of the wildlife in Sheffield discovered that 33 km², almost one-quarter of the city, was covered in gardens. These green areas are connected by hundreds of kilometres of hedgerows

planted along many garden boundaries. The hedgerows are important wildlife corridors; they allow birds and mammals such as hedgehogs and foxes to move safely from one garden to another without being spotted by predators such as cats or birds of prey. So, the urban ecosystem is woodland with a discontinuous canopy: scattered trees and shrubs linked by dense hedgerows. Within this ecosystem are a number of much smaller ecosystems: garden ponds, compost heaps and log piles are just three examples of miniature ecosystems found within many gardens. Each of these small-scale ecosystems has its own distinctive set of interactions between the non-living environment and a specialised community of wildlife.

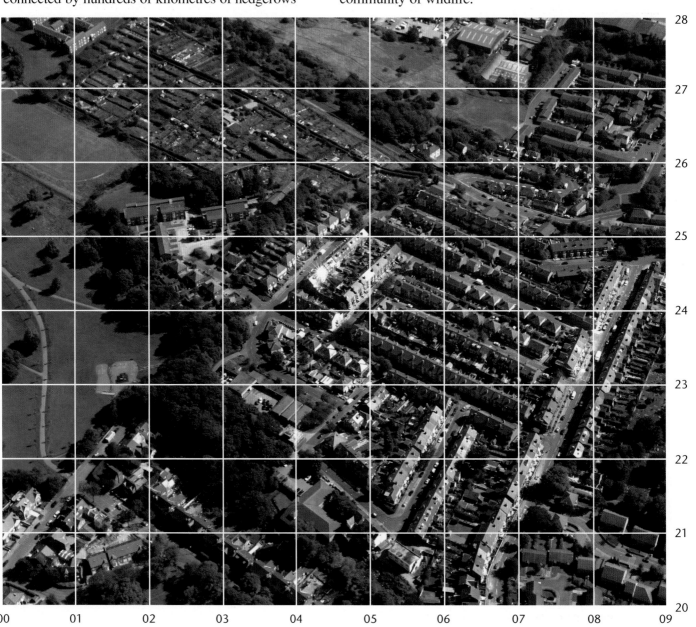

Figure 4 An aerial view of the ecosystems of Sheffield

Figure 5 The larvae of the stag beetle spend four years feeding on decaying wood. The adult male beetle is the UK's largest beetle at 5 cm long

How can people help the wildlife in the UK's cities?

Gardeners can encourage wildlife by being a little less tidy around their garden. By mowing the grass less frequently and allowing some areas of grass to grow long you will encourage more insects as well as voles. Rather than burning or shredding branches that have been pruned from the tree, why not make a log pile? A small pile of decaying wood is a miniature ecosystem. The rotting wood provides a habitat for fungi. Wood-boring insects such as stag beetle grubs (Figure 5) and woodlice burrow through the decaying wood. The crevices between the sticks provide a place for insects such as bumblebees to overwinter.

Planners and developers can help by designing new estates that have plenty of space for gardens that are big enough for people to plant trees and create ponds and compost heaps. If the government tries to tackle the shortage of affordable homes (discussed on pages 36–37) by building high-density housing developments then there may not be enough room for wildlife.

Activity

6 Outline the different land uses in Figure 4.

7 Give at least three examples of urban ecosystems that are at different scales.

8 You are going to sample the land use in Figure 4.
   a) Choose five grid lines (vertical or horizontal) across Figure 4.
   b) Measure the total length of the five lines in millimetres.
   c) Measure the length of each of the following land uses along each line:
   - gardens
   - housing
   - roads
   - parks
   - other.
   d) Calculate the total length of each land use, and then calculate these as percentages of the whole.

9 Explain how you could improve the accuracy of your estimate of the percentage land use in Sheffield.

10 Design a garden, no more than 10 m by 10 m, that would be attractive to wildlife. Include at least three different miniature ecosystems in your design.

11 Discuss how the environment of your school grounds could be improved for wildlife. If you have a college council, make a poster that shows your plans and present it to them.

Figure 6 Insects are an essential living part of the urban ecosystem. They pollinate plants and provide food for birds. Red mason bees are particularly useful because they pollinate fruit trees. They lay their eggs in tubes. You can encourage them to use your garden as a nest site by providing a bee box like this one. It should be sited high on a post or in a tree in direct sunlight

Investigating the rainforests of Central America

Emergent trees such as brazil nut and caypock grow through the canopy.

The continuous canopy is formed by the crowns of individual trees growing next to each other.

Figure 7 Structure of the tropical rainforest

The tropical rainforest biome contains a number of distinctive types of forest: ecosystems that exist at the regional scale. For example, within South and Central America, the rainforest biome can be divided into several ecosystems which include:

- lowland rainforest such as most of the Amazonian rainforest
- **cloud forests** that grow in more mountainous areas
- **mangrove forests** that grow in coastal areas.

Cloud forests are cooler than lowland rainforests and, because they are in mountain regions, they are often blanketed in cloud or mist. They are home to many species of frog and toad that rely on the moisture in the atmosphere.

Viewed from above, a tropical rainforest is an unbroken **canopy** of green vegetation. This continuous canopy is a characteristic part of the structure of the rainforest ecosystem. It plays an essential role in regulating the regional **water cycle**, preventing soil erosion and preventing river floods.

The rainforest is said to provide **key services** in protecting the water supply and safety of people who live in the forest and in the wider region. Figure 8 shows how rainforests play an essential role in the regional water cycle of tropical areas. The forest acts as a **store** for water in between rainfall events. After a rainstorm it is thought that about 80 per cent of the rainfall is transferred back to the atmosphere by **evaporation** and **transpiration**. So, rainforests are a source of moisture for future rainfall events.

At least 200 million people live in the world's tropical rainforests. This includes the tribal groups, or **indigenous peoples**, of the rainforest. Many more people live downstream of the rivers that leave these forests. The forest maintains a constant and even supply of water to these rivers. If the rainforest water cycle were to be broken, the water supply of many millions of people could be put at risk. The total amount of water flowing in the rivers would be reduced and the supply would become more uneven with periods of low water supply punctuated by sudden flooding.

Activity

12 Using Figure 8:
  a) List the places where water is stored in the rainforest.
  b) Explain how water flows from the atmosphere to the forest and back again.

13 Explain how the canopy of the rainforest reduces the risk of soil erosion.

14 Describe and explain why:
  a) areas of rainforest maintain a steady supply of water for local communities

  b) damaging the structure of the rainforest could affect local people, as well as people in the wider region.

15 Make a copy of Figure 9. Add the following labels to appropriate places on your diagram:
  evaporation   **warm air rising**
  condensation   **precipitation**

16 Explain why the cloud forest climate is cooler and wetter than the lowland forest.

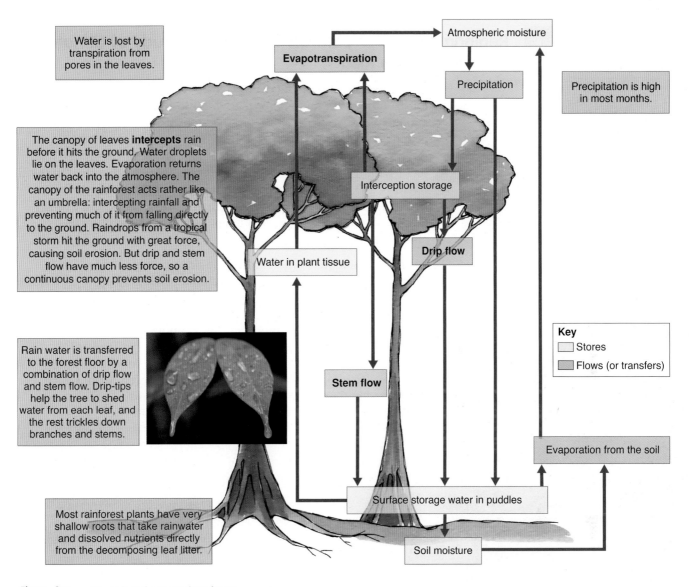

Water is lost by transpiration from pores in the leaves.

Atmospheric moisture

Evapotranspiration

Precipitation

Precipitation is high in most months.

The canopy of leaves **intercepts** rain before it hits the ground. Water droplets lie on the leaves. Evaporation returns water back into the atmosphere. The canopy of the rainforest acts rather like an umbrella: intercepting rainfall and preventing much of it from falling directly to the ground. Raindrops from a tropical storm hit the ground with great force, causing soil erosion. But drip and stem flow have much less force, so a continuous canopy prevents soil erosion.

Interception storage

Drip flow

Water in plant tissue

Rain water is transferred to the forest floor by a combination of drip flow and stem flow. Drip-tips help the tree to shed water from each leaf, and the rest trickles down branches and stems.

Stem flow

Key
☐ Stores
▨ Flows (or transfers)

Evaporation from the soil

Surface storage water in puddles

Most rainforest plants have very shallow roots that take rainwater and dissolved nutrients directly from the decomposing leaf litter.

Soil moisture

Figure 8 The water cycle in the tropical rainforest

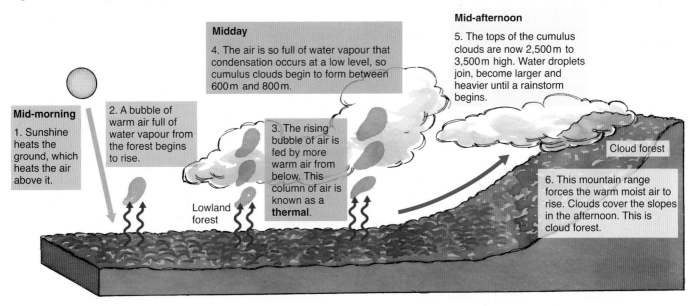

Mid-afternoon

5. The tops of the cumulus clouds are now 2,500 m to 3,500 m high. Water droplets join, become larger and heavier until a rainstorm begins.

Midday

4. The air is so full of water vapour that condensation occurs at a low level, so cumulus clouds begin to form between 600 m and 800 m.

Mid-morning

1. Sunshine heats the ground, which heats the air above it.

2. A bubble of warm air full of water vapour from the forest begins to rise.

3. The rising bubble of air is fed by more warm air from below. This column of air is known as a **thermal**.

Lowland forest

Cloud forest

6. This mountain range forces the warm moist air to rise. Clouds cover the slopes in the afternoon. This is cloud forest.

Figure 9 Convectional rainfall over lowland rainforest and cloud forest

 Costa Rica

Regional effects of deforestation: a case study of climate change in Costa Rica

Figure 10 The location of the cloud forest in Costa Rica

Figure 11 The golden toad of Costa Rica

The cloud forest of Monteverde, Costa Rica, is an international tourist attraction, famous for the wide **biodiversity** of plants and animals that live here. However, this delicate ecosystem is being damaged. Since the 1970s, 20 species of frog and toad have disappeared from Monteverde, including the beautiful golden toad pictured in Figure 11. Meteorologists have noticed that mist in the forest is a less frequent event than it used to be and that the base height of the clouds is now higher than it was. This could explain the extinction of the frogs and toads. But why is the climate changing?

At first the scientists thought that the drier climate in the cloud forest might be evidence of global climate change. However, it now seems that these changes are due to **deforestation** in the region. As we have seen, rainforests recycle approximately 80 per cent of their moisture back into the atmosphere by **evapotranspiration**. The lowlands around Monteverde used to be covered in lowland rainforest. These forests would have provided a lot of moisture which, on rising over the mountains of Monteverde, would have condensed and produced low-level cloud and mist.

Figure 12 Deforestation of the lowland areas to the west of Monteverde has left a grassland environment

However, over the last few decades, deforestation has reduced the lowland forest to just a few isolated patches. The deforested land, which can be seen in Figure 12, is now largely used for cattle grazing. This vegetation produces much less water by evaporation and transpiration than forested areas, so the clouds that should be forming over Monteverde no longer have a source.

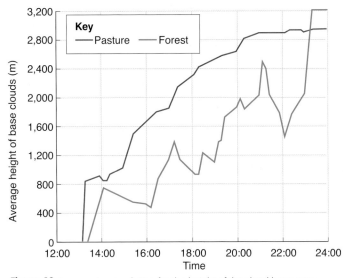

Figure 13 A computer simulation for the height of the cloud base over pasture and forest

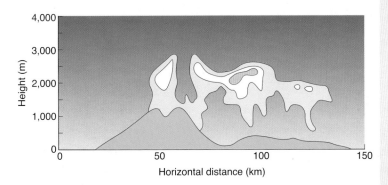

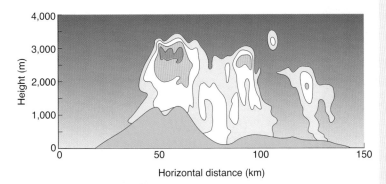

Figure 14 A computer simulation showing the expected cloud cover at midday for a) a deforested area, and b) a forested area

From our point of view, there are a number of reasons to worry about the cloudiness of mountain forests. One involves just the conservation implications. These cloud forests are communities of organisms adapted to cloud forest conditions. Take away the cloudy conditions, and we might expect to see all sorts of changes. How many cloud forest organisms could go the way of the golden toad?

The other interesting problem is that cloud forests are such important components of many mountain watersheds that provide either drinking water supplies or the water for hydro-electric facilities. Monteverde's forests feed the Lake Arenal hydro-electric project. So one of the serious questions is to what extent cloud input is important to the water budgets of watersheds like Arenal. If it is really important, then there are big economic reasons – in addition to conservation reasons – to care about cloud forests.

Robert Lawton, Department of Biological Sciences, University of Alabama

Figure 15 The view of Robert Lawton, a scientist studying the effects of climate change in Monteverde

Activity

17 Describe the location of the Monteverde cloud forest.

18 a) Use Figure 13 to describe the height of the cloud base at 2 pm, 4 pm and 6 pm over the forest and pasture.
 b) Use Figure 14 to explain how cloud height affects the frequency of mists in the cloud forests of Monteverde.

19 a) Draw a diagram to show how the lowland forest used to supply moisture to the cloud forest. Show stores (such as the lowland forest) and transfers (such as evaporation) on your diagram.
 b) Draw a second diagram to show how deforestation has affected the water cycle at a regional scale.

20 a) Read Figure 15. Use it to identify three regional consequences of deforestation in Costa Rica.
 b) Explain how this research might make conservation of the remaining forest easier to achieve.

Costa Rica

What is being done to protect Costa Rica's environment?

Despite the problems in Monteverde, Costa Rica has a relatively good record for conservation work. The government has established a large number of National Parks and Forest Reserves. It is also co-operating with neighbouring countries in an ambitious project to create a continuous **wildlife corridor** through the length of Central America. Deforestation creates a major problem for wildlife: the forest becomes fragmented. As clearings get bigger the wildlife is restricted to isolated fragments of forest that are separated by farmland. By planting strips of forest to connect the remaining fragments together, conservationists create wildlife corridors. The seven governments of Central America, and Mexico, are working jointly on a project called the Mesoamerican Biological Corridor (known by its Spanish initials, CBM). This project aims to connect and conserve all the protected lands that stretch through Central America (Mesoamerica). This region is a **biodiversity hotspot**. It amounts to only 1 per cent of the world's land surface, but it is estimated to contain 7 per cent of the world's terrestrial (land-based) species.

Figure 16 Satellite image of the Mesoamerican Biological Corridor (CBM). The red dots indicate where forest fires are burning

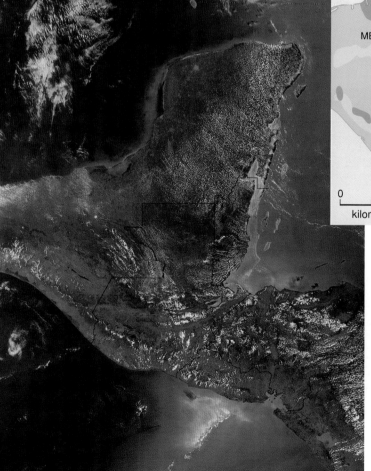

Key
- Existing conservation areas and National Parks
- New conservation zones will make wildlife corridors to link the National Parks together

Gulf of Mexico

MEXICO

Tikal National Park

BELIZE

Caribbean Sea

GUATEMALA

HONDURAS

EL SALVADOR

NICARAGUA

0   200
kilometres

Figure 17 The structure of the CBM project

The government and businesses in Costa Rica have also encouraged the growth of ecotourism: small-scale tourist projects that create money for conservation as well as creating local jobs. It is estimated that 70 per cent of Costa Rica's tourists visit the protected environments. In 2000 Costa Rica earned $1.25 billion from ecotourism. One successful example is the creation of a canopy walkway through a small, privately owned part of the Monteverde reserve (see Figure 19). Tourists are charged $45 to climb up into the canopy and walk along rope bridges, the longest of which is 300 m long.

Country	Protected land as % of total area
Belize	47.5
Costa Rica	23.4
El Salvador	2.0
Guatemala	25.3
Honduras	20.8
Mexico	5.0
Nicaragua	21.8
Panama	19.5

Figure 18 Protected areas (including forest reserves) in Central America and Mexico. Source: Earthlands

Figure 19 The canopy walkway allows visitors to see the birds and other wildlife that live in the canopy of the cloud forest

Activity

21 Study the satellite image and map in Figures 16 and 17.
  a) Estimate the percentage of Guatemala that is conserved as National Park.
  b) Suggest how the new conservation zones will help wildlife.

22 Study Figure 18.
  a) Calculate the average amount of land that is protected in Central America and Mexico.
  b) Graph the data, and include a bar for the average.
  c) How good is Costa Rica's record on conservation compared with its neighbours?

23 Draw a spider diagram that shows how fragmentation of the rainforest affects wildlife. Consider the likely impacts of fragmentation on:

- food chains
- success of mating
- predator/prey relationships
- pollination and seed dispersal.

24 For an ecosystem you have studied:
  a) name and locate the case study
  b) describe the main features of the ecosystem
  c) describe and explain how it is being managed by people.

Chapter 4
Water supply

KEY QUESTIONS

- ○ How does the hydrological cycle link components operating within the hydrosphere?

- ○ What are the main sources of fresh water?

- ○ How does the provision of a sustainable supply of water vary in different areas of the world?

What are the main sources of fresh water?

More than 69 per cent of the surface of planet Earth is covered in water. But only about 4 per cent is fresh water. There are five main types of freshwater store, as you can see in Figure 1.

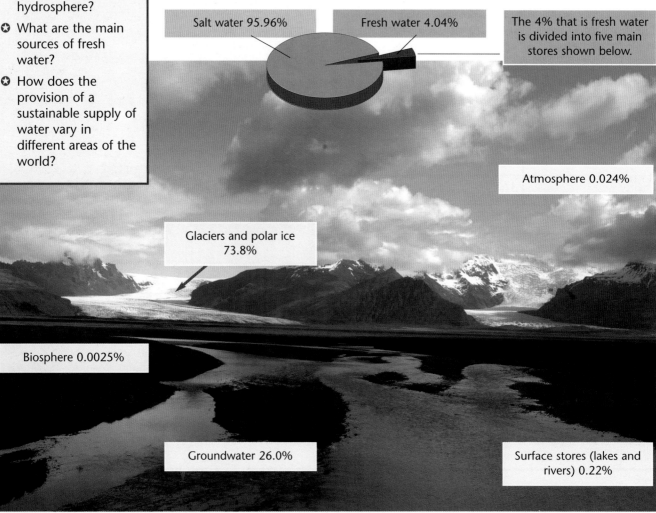

Salt water 95.96%

Fresh water 4.04%

The 4% that is fresh water is divided into five main stores shown below.

Atmosphere 0.024%

Glaciers and polar ice 73.8%

Biosphere 0.0025%

Groundwater 26.0%

Surface stores (lakes and rivers) 0.22%

Figure 1 The sources of fresh water

Activity

1 Using Figure 1, make a list of the five freshwater stores. Do this in rank order, starting with the largest.

2 Describe the water cycle in your own words using the terms **stores** and **flows**. This is a common exam question. When you have finished, check your descriptions with a partner.

3 This chapter contains many new terms. Make a list of 20 unfamiliar words and write your own definitions for each one. You may like to classify them into different categories.

4 How would the different flows through the water cycle change due to climate and vegetation in Antarctica compared with the Amazon rainforest?

The water cycle

The water cycle is driven by the sun's heat, which evaporates water into the **atmosphere**, and by gravity, which continually makes it flow downwards. As with all systems, the water cycle has a set of stores with flows connecting them. A store is a place where water is found and will collect. A **flow** is the way in which water moves from one store to another.

On hitting the ground water flows as **infiltration** into the soil and as **overland flow** across the surface. Once in the **soil store** it flows more slowly downhill as **throughflow**. **Percolation** eventually lets water flow through the bedrock where it continues to travel as **groundwater flow**.

Rates of infiltration, throughflow and groundwater flow will depend on the type of soil and rock:

- Clay soils or soils with the smallest particles do not let water pass through easily and become waterlogged. Such soils are said to be **impermeable**. Rocks such as granite that do not allow water to pass through them are also considered to be impermeable.
- Sandy soils are more free draining because soil particles are larger. Such soils will have faster throughflow rates. Chalk and sandstone are sedimentary rocks that contain many pore spaces; water moves easily through these **porous** rocks.
- Limestone, another sedimentary rock, has many **joints** and **bedding planes** through which water can flow. Limestone also dissolves in rainwater forming underground rivers and caverns. Water can flow along these joints and bedding planes, making limestone **permeable** but not porous.

Figure 2 How the water cycle works

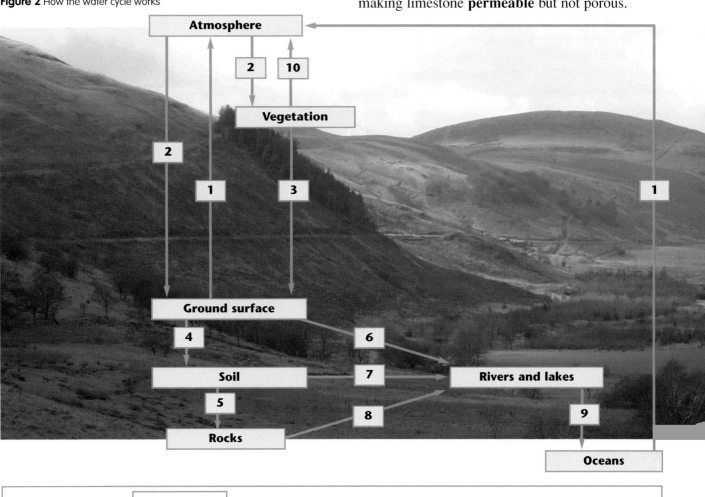

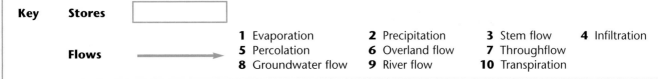

Key	Stores				
	Flows	**1** Evaporation	**2** Precipitation	**3** Stem flow	**4** Infiltration
		5 Percolation	**6** Overland flow	**7** Throughflow	
		8 Groundwater flow	**9** River flow	**10** Transpiration	

Surface and groundwater stores

Surface stores include lakes and rivers. Rivers can be dammed to control flooding and create reservoirs for water supply. There are more than 47,000 large dams in the world and nearly half of these are in China. However, surface stores can also be very small. Take rainwater harvesting, for example. If you have a water-butt in your garden that collects rainwater from the gutters, you are creating a small surface store of fresh water.

Groundwater stores occur when water infiltrates into the ground and gets trapped in the fractures and the pore spaces of rocks and sediments. A large store of underground water is called an **aquifer**. Water that enters an aquifer is called **recharge**; water that leaves an aquifer is **discharge**. When water is taken from either a surface or groundwater store by human action we say the water is **abstracted**. If water is taken from a store faster than it can be recharged we say that **over-abstraction** is taking place.

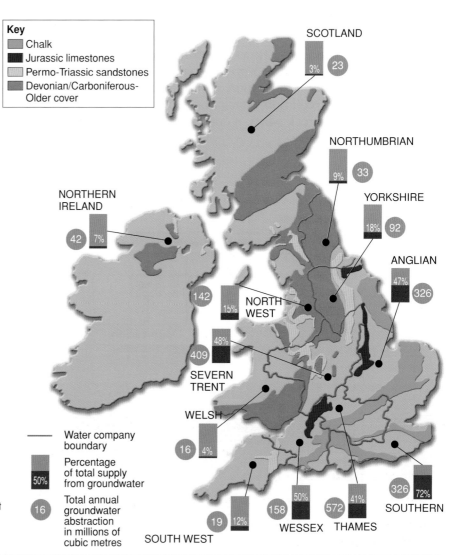

Figure 3 Major aquifers in the UK. Located bar graphs indicate the percentage of water supply that comes from groundwater supply. The remainder will come from surface stores (rivers and reservoirs)

Activity

5 Define the following terms when applied to an aquifer:
   discharge   abstraction   over-abstraction

6 Use Figure 3.
   a) Make a table of the 12 water companies and put them in rank order by the percentage of their water supply that comes from groundwater.
   b) For each company calculate the percentage of its supply that comes from surface stores.

7 Use Figure 3 and an atlas.
   a) Describe the distribution of water companies that abstract more than 300 million cubic metres of water a year from groundwater.
   b) Describe the distribution of water companies that take less than 10 per cent of their supply from groundwater.
   c) Find a population density map for the UK in your atlas. Predict what will happen to groundwater supplies in London and the South East if population continues to grow.

Drainage basin comparisons

A **hydrograph** is a graph that plots river flow (or discharge) over a period of time. An annual hydrograph shows discharge patterns over a full year. Figures 4 and 5 are hydrographs for two rivers that have similar-sized catchment areas. The geology of the two drainage basins is quite different and this affects the flows of water through each basin.

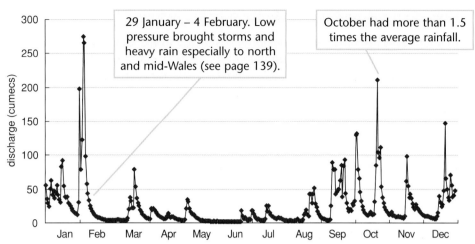

29 January – 4 February. Low pressure brought storms and heavy rain especially to north and mid-Wales (see page 139).

October had more than 1.5 times the average rainfall.

Figure 4 Hydrograph for the River Dyfi, Wales (2004)

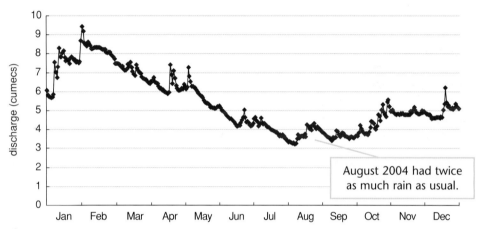

August 2004 had twice as much rain as usual.

Figure 5 Hydrograph for the River Itchen, England (2004)

River	River Dyfi	River Itchen
Location	West Wales	South-east England
Total average rainfall	1834 mm	838 mm
Geology	100% impermeable rocks	90% chalk
Size of catchment area (above the gauging station)	471 km²	360 km²
Landscape	Steeply sloping hills and mountains reaching a maximum of 907 m above sea level	Rolling hills. Maximum height 208 m above sea level
Land use	60% grassland (sheep pasture); 30% forest; 10% moorland	Mainly arable (cereal) farmland with some grassland
Human factors affecting run-off	There are virtually no human influences on run-off	Run-off is reduced by some abstraction for water supply Some water is used to recharge groundwater in the chalk aquifer

Figure 6 Fact file on the River Dyfi and River Itchen

Activity

8 Compare Figures 4 and 5. Describe:
   a) one similarity
   b) three differences.

9 Use Figure 6 to suggest how each of the following factors may have affected the flow:
   rainfall total   geology
   landscape   land use

10 Imagine you work for a water company. Suggest how each river could be used for water supply.

How do rivers and groundwater supplies respond to drought?

In south-east England a lot of water is abstracted in the summer months when there is little rainfall. Winter rainfall, however, is normally enough to recharge the aquifers. As long as the total annual recharge is equal to the total discharge then the aquifer stays the same size from year to year. However, if winter recharge is low, or demand for water increases, then the level of groundwater falls. This is over-abstraction. Low winter rainfall in 2005 and 2006 caused the drought in the South East in 2006. As the population of the region rises, and demand for water increases, experts warn that water shortages will become a more common problem.

The drought did not affect all areas of the UK. Rainfall in Scotland, Wales and western and northern regions of England over the same period was close to average. Birmingham, which gets its water from the Elan Valley in Wales, was not affected by the drought.

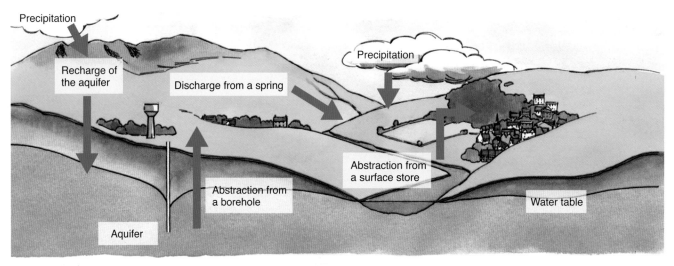

Figure 7 A cross-section showing how water enters both surface and groundwater stores

Figure 8 The relationship between rainfall and discharge for two contrasting winters (2002–2003) and (2004–2005) in the East of England. Discharge data for the Bedford Ouse at Bedford in cubic metres per second (cumecs) and rainfall (mm). The catchment area of the River Ouse is mainly clay

	Jun 2002	Jul	Aug	Sep	Oct	Nov	Dec	Jan 2003	Feb	Mar	Apr	May 2003
Rainfall (mm)	34	82	41	21	110	113	97	75	20	23	29	47
Discharge (cumecs)	5.2	4.6	4.5	2.9	10.2	36.9	36.4	51.1	16.7	12.6	5.7	5.8
	Jun 2004	Jul	Aug	Sep	Oct	Nov	Dec	Jan 2005	Feb	Mar	Apr	May 2005
Rainfall (mm)	26	50	118	30	112	54	26	20	36	37	37	34
Discharge (cumecs)	4.1	3.7	5.5	2.5	10.7	13.3	9.6	7.1	10.1	8.6	8.3	5.1

Activity

11 Explain how rainfall recharges an aquifer.

12 Use Figure 8 to investigate the effect of winter rainfall on river discharge. This catchment is mainly clay.

    a) Draw a pair of graphs: one for the winter 2002–2003 and one for the winter 2004–2005. Each graph needs bars to display the rainfall and a line to display discharge.

    b) Describe how the river discharge is affected by rainfall in 2002–2003.

    c) Compare the discharge pattern in the two graphs.

    d) Suggest how the lack of winter rainfall could affect:

        water companies   farmers   home owners.

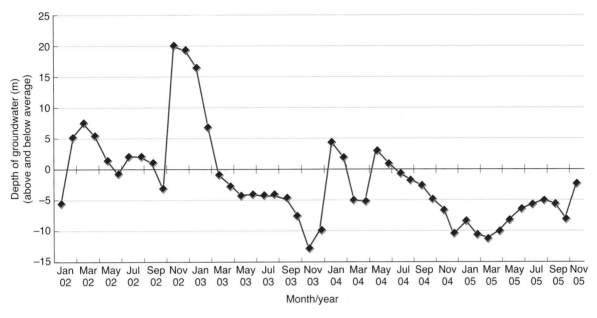

Figure 9 Depth of groundwater in the chalk rocks of southern England compared with average levels (m)

Activity

13 Use Figure 9.
   a) Describe the groundwater level in January 2002, 2003, 2004 and 2005.
   b) Explain why the lack of winter rainfall can cause water shortages in summer months.

14 Study Figure 10. Describe the distribution of aquifers that had:
   a) significantly lower levels (below −5 m)
   b) slightly lower levels (0 to −5 m).
   c) Suggest how these low groundwater levels might have affected people.

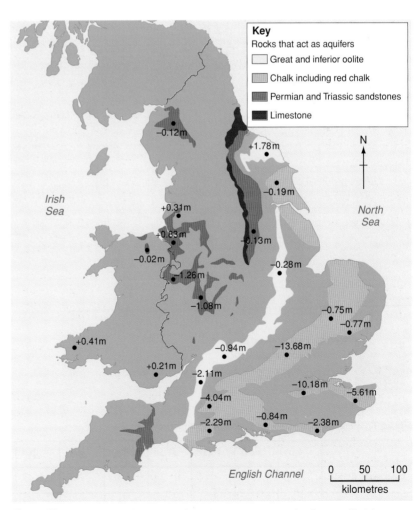

Figure 10 Water table levels in UK aquifers, May 2006, compared with normal height

South Africa

Investigating patterns of water supply in South Africa

On average, South Africa has about half as much rainfall as the UK. But rainfall is not distributed evenly over South Africa. The east coast receives a lot more rain than the west (see Figure 11). This is because moist air comes in from the Indian Ocean forming rain clouds over the highlands of eastern South Africa.

Geographical patterns of rainfall in this region don't match the distribution of population. For example, parts of Lesotho receive 1,200 mm of rain a year (similar to mid-Wales) but Lesotho has only a low population. This is good for Lesotho because it can sell its excess water to parts of South Africa where the population is higher but rainfall is lower.

The amount of precipitation also varies through the year. For some regions in South Africa this difference can be quite extreme, resulting in a dry season and a wet season. This seasonal variation in rainfall has an impact on the amount of water flowing in South Africa's rivers. Without careful management some parts of South Africa would suffer seasonal water shortages.

Activity

15 Use Figure 11 to describe the distribution (see page 25) of rainfall in South Africa.

16 Explain why Lesotho is able to sell water to South Africa and why South Africa wants to buy it.

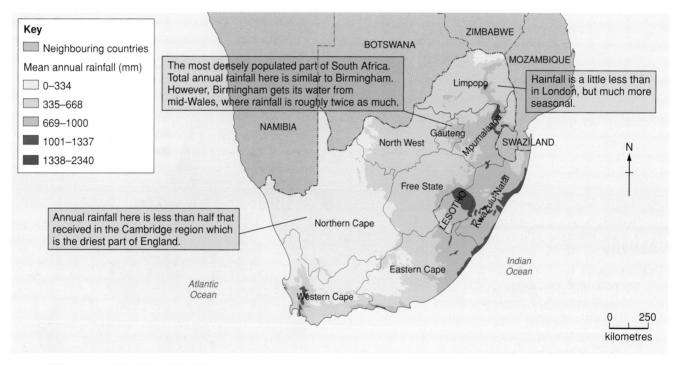

Figure 11 Average annual rainfall in South Africa

www.weathersa.co.za is the meteorological office for South Africa.

Figure 12 Rainfall (mm) for selected regions of South Africa

	Jan	Feb	Mar	Apr	May	Jun	Jul	Aug	Sep	Oct	Nov	Dec	Total
Western Cape	8	4	11	24	40	41	47	45	24	12	12	10	278
Gauteng	125	90	91	54	13	9	4	6	27	72	117	105	713

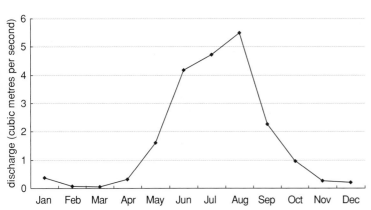

Figure 13 Hydrograph for the River Dorling, Western Cape Province, South Africa. The **catchment area** of the River Dorling before this station is 6,900 km²

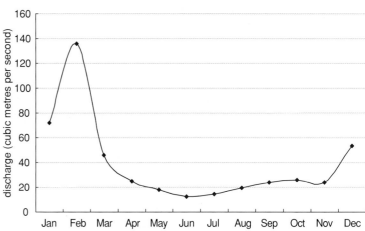

Figure 14 Hydrograph for the River Vaal, Gauteng Province, South Africa. The catchment area of the River Vaal before this station is 38,560 km²

Going Further

Activity

17 a) Use Figure 12 to draw a pair of rainfall graphs.

b) Compare your rainfall graphs with Figures 13 and 14.

c) At which times of year do these two regions face possible water shortages?

18 Suggest five reasons why families in MEDCs use more water than families in LEDCs.

19 Use Figure 15 to investigate the following questions. You should present your findings with a series of graphs.

a) Do MEDCs use more water for domestic purposes than LEDCs?

b) Do MEDCs use more water for industrial purposes than LEDCs?

20 a) Compare the water use in Iceland, Japan and South Africa.

b) Suggest reasons for the differences you have noticed.

How much water do we use?

People in More Economically Developed Countries (MEDCs) generally use more water than people in Less Economically Developed Countries (LEDCs). The average American family uses 1,304 litres of water a day whereas the average African family uses 22 litres of water a day. In **sub-Saharan Africa**, people living in urban areas are twice as likely to have access to water as people living in rural areas. In the informal settlements of Africa's cities people do not have access to piped water and cannot afford to drill a borehole. They are forced to buy water from private sellers from the back of carts. As a result, people who live in cities in LEDCs can pay up to 50 times the amount for water as people who live in cities from MEDCs.

		Water use (m² per person, 2000)			
		Domestic	**Agricultural**	**Industrial**	**Total**
MEDCs	Australia	184	941	125	1,250
	Canada	292	176	1,026	1,494
	United Kingdom	35	5	121	161
	United States	215	698	779	1,692
	Iceland	187	1	361	549
	Japan	137	435	124	696
LEDCs	Lesotho	11	5	11	27
	Somalia	2	374	0	376
	South Africa	59	257	37	353
	Turkmenistan	88	5,075	40	5,203
	Congo, Dem. Rep.	4	2	1	7
	Mali	4	605	1	610

Figure 15 Water use in selected countries

Investigating a major water management and transfer scheme

The Lesotho Highlands Water Project (LHWP) is an example of a large-scale water management scheme. There are four phases to the project, which involves the construction of six major dams in Lesotho and 200 km of tunnel systems to transfer water to areas with low water supply in the neighbouring country of South Africa. It is the largest water-transfer scheme in Africa, diverting 40 per cent of the water in the Senqu river basin in Lesotho to the Vaal river system in the Orange Free State of South Africa (see Figure 16). The River Vaal then carries the water into Gauteng Province. This is a very industrial and highly populated region of South Africa, which has a high demand for fresh water.

The project was agreed between South Africa and Lesotho in 1986. So far, only one of the four phases has been completed. The third major dam of the project, the Mohale dam, was finished in 2002.

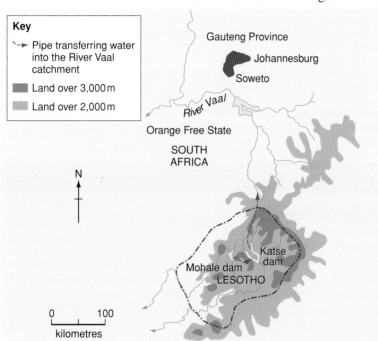

◀ **Figure 16** A map of the LHWP water management and transfer scheme

What are the advantages and disadvantages of the LHWP?

Lesotho is one of the world's poorest countries. Its **Gross National Income** per person is US$590, it has an unemployment rate of around 50 per cent and no natural resources to sell except water. The Lesotho government is hoping that the LHWP will help to develop the country. The income received from selling water through the LHWP is providing 75 per cent of the country's income.

The project is predicted to cost US$8 billion, which is being given on loan from the World Bank. The South African government will eventually have to pay this money back. The Lesotho government will receive income for the sale of its water. In the long term this could help Lesotho develop its own water management schemes.

In the short term Lesotho is still struggling with water shortages and poor sanitation. Local people have not had access to any of the water supplied by the dams since all of the water is being piped to South Africa.

But the percentage of people with a safe water supply in South Africa increased from 83 per cent to 87 per cent between 1990 and 2002. In 2002 only 76 per cent of people in Lesotho had a safe water supply and only 37 per cent had sanitation.

Most of the LHWP water is being transferred to Johannesburg in the Gauteng province of South Africa. But many residents of Johannesburg are angry because their water bills increased before receiving the improved water service. Some of these people did not even have access to basic water resources. Bills went up to fund the dam and to pay for repairs to leaking pipes.

Local people launched a campaign to halt the construction of the Mohale dam until the water pipes in Johannesburg improved. In 2000 up to 50 per cent of water was simply being wasted through leaking pipes. Despite this, construction of the Mohale dam continued ahead of schedule.

The dams will provide hydro-electric power (HEP) as well as water. The Muela dam is connected to a 72 megawatt hydro-electric power station that is providing a renewable source of cheap electricity for Lesotho. Lesotho is also benefiting from improved roads which were constructed to gain access to the dam sites.

However, many people have been displaced by the construction of the dams and the flooding of the reservoirs. The Katse dam, the first major dam of the project, completed in 1998, affected more than 20,000 people. Many of these people were relocated and given compensation but they claim the money they received was too late. They were also given training so that they could find new jobs, but the training has been criticised and most of the displaced people are still in low-income jobs.

New job opportunities have been created working on the construction of the project. About 20,000 people have moved into informal settlements to work on the dams. However, this has led to a massive increase in AIDS, prostitution and alcoholism.

The project has also destroyed thousands of hectares of grazing and arable land. Since only 9 per cent of Lesotho is considered arable, this could lead to huge problems in the nation's food supply.

The project will affect the flow of water downstream of the dams. As well as a decrease in the amount of water, it is thought that the dams will reduce the amount of sediment, oxygen levels, nutrients and even the temperature of the water. This will have negative impacts on people, wetland habitats and wildlife, including many endangered species.

▲ **Figure 17** The Mohale dam. You can see this dam on Google Earth: reference location: 29 27'29.97"S, 28 5'56.17"E

River	Senqunyane
Capacity	958 million m³
Height	145 m
Material	A concrete-faced embankment filled with 7.8 million m³ of rock
Interconnecting tunnel	To Katse (32 km long)
Water transfer capacity	10.1 m³ per second
Initial loan	US$45 million (funded to Lesotho and to be repaid to the World Bank by South Africa)
Number of affected people	7,400, many of whom lost their homes

Activity

21 Summarise the aims of the Lesotho Highlands Water Project.

22 Use the text on these pages to complete a copy of the following table. You should find more to write in some boxes than in others.

	Short-term advantages (+) and disadvantages (−) of LHWP	Long-term advantages (+) and disadvantages (−) of LHWP
Lesotho	+ ___ −	+ ___ −
South Africa	+ ___ −	+ ___ −

23 Summarise what each of the following groups of people might think about the LHWP:
a) a farmer in the Lesotho Highlands
b) a government minister in Lesotho
c) residents in Johannesburg.

24 Do you think the LHWP is an example of a good, sustainable water management project? Explain your reasons.

◀ **Figure 18** Factfile on the Mohale dam (completed 2002)

 South Africa

Activity

25 Choose five techniques shown in Figure 19. For each technique explain how it either collects rain water or recharges groundwater.

26 Explain why this type of management is sustainable.

Are there alternative ways to manage South Africa's water?

South Africa has 539 large dams, which is almost half of all the dams in Africa. But despite this, there are still a large number of South Africans without access to clean drinking water. Many of these people live in rural, remote parts of South Africa; they are too isolated to become part of the big projects such as the LHWP and they are too poor to drill boreholes to tap into groundwater supplies. Instead they have to rely on cheap, small-scale methods of rainwater harvesting.

A case study of sustainable water management on a small farm

Ma Tshepo Khumbane is a South African farmer who teaches rainwater harvesting techniques. Her management strategies are affordable and practical for families, no matter how small the farm is or how little money they have.

Rainwater harvesting can be carried out by individual households or involve whole communities. These methods of water management are not usually big enough to have negative impacts on the surrounding drainage basin so they are sustainable. They use ways that are cheap, practical and easy to maintain using appropriate technology. A number of these techniques are shown in Figure 19; they are designed to:

- collect and use rainwater, for example, by collecting water from the roof of the farm
- maintain soil moisture by encouraging as much infiltration as possible; in this way groundwater stores are recharged.

Figure 19 Rainwater harvesting techniques used by Ma Tshepo Khumbane

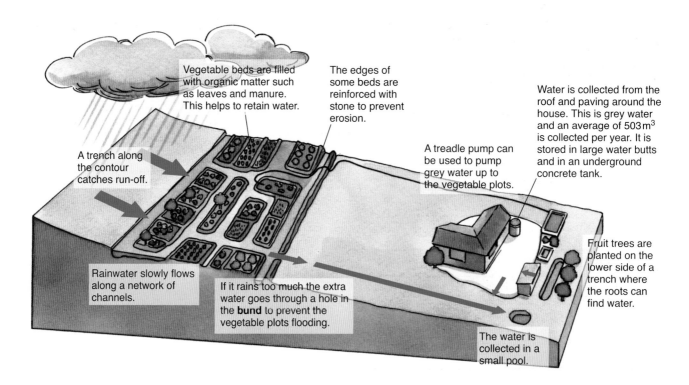

The village of Athol in Limpopo province is one community to have benefited from the teachings of Ma Tshepo Khumbane. In 1982 the community was struggling with drought and malnutrition. Despite having no regular access to water, the villagers of Athol have learned to manage their water sustainably by collecting rainwater and maintaining soil moisture. The villagers' next aim is to build a small stone dam to collect and store rainwater; this will provide a more secure water supply. They are appealing to the government to provide tractors to speed up the process.

Figure 20 Ma Tshepo Khumbane inspects vegetable growing in an earth basin. The good soil in the middle of each basin collects rainwater

Going Further

Appropriate technology

In South Africa most water is drawn from wells using hand pumps. This can be hard work for women and children. In the 1970s and 1980s money was invested in diesel pumps. These pumps abstract water much more quickly, but they are expensive to install and maintain. An engineer has to service the pump regularly and parts can be expensive.

Now there is an alternative to hand pumps and diesel pumps that is more appropriate to the level of technology and wealth in poorer South African communities. A company has invented a children's roundabout that pumps water out of a borehole. It is called a PlayPump®

water system. The children play on the roundabout and save their mothers a lot of work! There are now more than 1,200 PlayPump® systems located in South Africa, Zambia, Mozambique, Swaziland and Lesotho.

A PlayPump® water system costs US$14,000. Advertising on the billboards that surround the storage tank are available for rental and the income that is generated covers the cost of the maintenance for the system. PlayPump® systems such as the one at the Thabong nursery school in Davietown (Figure 21) are increasing access to clean drinking water and should have no long-term negative effect on the environment.

Figure 21 Roundabout waterpump at the Thabong nursery school in Davieton

Activity

27 Compare the effects of diesel pumps with the effects of hand pumps.

28 Explain the advantages of the new roundabout pumps.

29 Explain why this water management technique is more appropriate for poor communities than a diesel pump.

Chapter 5
Drought and desertification

KEY QUESTIONS

- How can a lack of rainfall and/or water deficit cause drought and desertification?
- What effect do these have on human activity?
- How can drought and desertification be managed?

Drought in Barcelona 2008

Barcelona is the capital city of Catalonia, a prosperous region of Spain. A severe water shortage in 2007–2008 forced the city to take extraordinary steps to avoid running out of water. In February 2008 a drought order was imposed. This restricted the use of water by households, for example for watering the garden or washing the car. Water use was restricted in public places such as city parks and 10 per cent of public fountains were turned off. People who broke the rules faced fines: €30 for watering gardens and €3,000 for filling swimming pools. Similar restrictions were used in the south-east of England during the drought of 2006. By May 2008 the city was so desperate that a fleet of tankers, each carrying 28 million litres of water, started to bring water into the city's port. This so-called 'water bridge' transferred water to Barcelona from Tarragona in Spain and Marseille in France.

Figure 1 One of the tankers in the so-called 'water bridge' that brought water into Barcelona in spring 2008

Figure 2 Rainfall and discharge data for R Llobregat, Barcelona (May 2007 – May 2008)

		Discharge on the River Llobregat (m³/s)	Precipitation (mm)	
			2007–2008	Average
May	2007	6.66	21	54
Jun	2007	2.50	7	37
Jul	2007	2.21	0	27
Aug	2007	7.62	71	49
Sep	2007	2.30	18	76
Oct	2007	5.86	142	86
Nov	2007	2.00	0	52
Dec	2007	1.75	13	45
Jan	2008	2.47	18	31
Feb	2008	1.92	39	39
Mar	2008	1.42	26	48
Apr	2008	3.31	28	43
May	2008	11.26	78	54

Water conflict

The Catalonian government has suggested that its long-term water supply problem could be solved if water could be transferred into the city from other regions. They have suggested two plans, shown in Figure 3. However, water is a precious resource and both plans have been vigorously opposed. The River Segre runs for part of its course along the border with Aragon and the regional government objects to the use of what it regards as its water in Catalonia.

Meanwhile Catalonia has accused Aragon of wanting to use Barcelona's drinking water in the hotels and golf courses of Aragon. Aragon has appealed to the national government. For the moment the national government has backed Aragon and Catalonia cannot go ahead with the plan. In the meantime Barcelona is counting on the construction of a new desalination plant to turn sea water into fresh water. It should open in 2009.

Figure 3 Barcelona's water supply plans

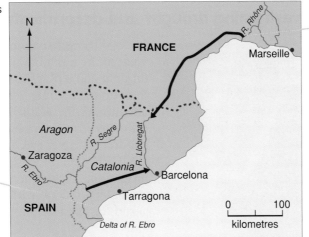

Water could be transferred from the River Rhône to Barcelona using a series of pipes and canals, but this plan is currently on hold.

Barcelona would like to transfer water from the River Segre, but this is opposed by the national government of Spain.

Figure 4 Points of view on the water shortage

The city authority is trying to make us look like criminals! Catalonia's swimming pool manufacturers are expected to lose €200m (approx £200 million) by the end of 2008. Who wants to buy a swimming pool if they can't fill it?

Building desalination plants is a big mistake. They use huge amounts of energy and therefore contribute to climate change. By building desalination plants Catalonia will actually be increasing the chance of drought. It's just not a sustainable option.

Swimming pool manufacturer

Householder

Climate expert

Protestor in France

I'm fed up with the water restrictions. I think our problem is that 70 per cent of Catalonia's water is used by farmers. A lot of them have really old irrigation systems that are leaking and they grow crops that aren't really suited to our dry climate. It's such a waste.

I belong to a protest group that opposes the plan to transfer water from France. The scheme would damage the ecosystem of the River Rhône. The people who stand to benefit most are the fat cats who own the water companies!

Activity

1 **a)** Use the data in Figure 2 to draw a series of graphs.
   b) Compare the rainfall for May 2007–2008 with the average pattern.
   c) Explain how this rainfall pattern has affected the discharge of the River Llobregat.

2 Suggest five ways that households in Barcelona could save water.

3 Use Figure 3.
   a) Describe the location of Barcelona.
   b) What is the approximate distance of each of the proposed water transfer schemes?

4 Discuss Figure 4.
   a) Suggest three other factors, apart from lack of rainfall, that have led to the water shortage.
   b) Make a list of short-term and long-term solutions to the shortage. You should find at least two of each.
   c) What do you think is the most sustainable solution to Barcelona's problem? Make sure that you justify your answer.

5 Is Aragon right to oppose Catalonia's plan? Write a letter to the Aragon government stating your point of view.

Mali

Investigating drought and desertification in Mali and Niger

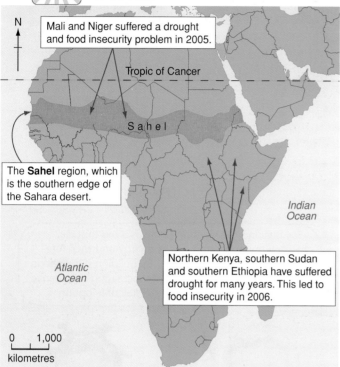

N

Mali and Niger suffered a drought and food insecurity problem in 2005.

Tropic of Cancer

S a h e l

The **Sahel** region, which is the southern edge of the Sahara desert.

Indian Ocean

Atlantic Ocean

Northern Kenya, southern Sudan and southern Ethiopia have suffered drought for many years. This led to food insecurity in 2006.

0   1,000
kilometres

▲ **Figure 5** The location of recent droughts in Africa

Figure 6 False colour satellite images. Regions where vegetation is less dense than usual (because of drought) are brown. Regions where vegetation is healthy are shown in darker green
▼

In 2004 the **subsistence** farmers of Mali and Niger were hit by a double problem: a particularly severe drought and a plague of locusts virtually destroyed their crops. By July 2005 the crisis came to the attention of the world's media. By then it was estimated that 3.3 million people (including 800,000 children) were at risk from a serious food shortage. UNICEF, already working in Niger because it has a programme of long-term aid in the country, was struggling to cope with the scale of the problem and asked for extra help to enable it to give emergency aid.

Activity

6 **a)** Give two reasons for the food crisis of 2005.
   b) Describe the effect of the drought on people.

7 Use Figure 5 to describe:
   a) the distribution of Sahel countries
   b) the location of recent droughts in Africa.

8 **a)** Compare the two images in Figure 6.
   b) Suggest how images like this could be used to provide an early warning of developing famine.

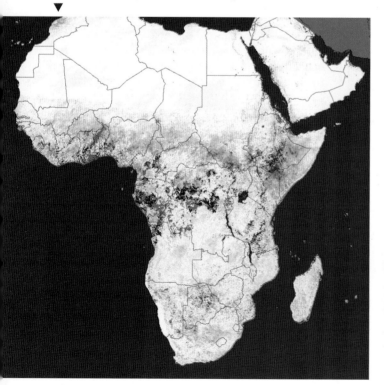

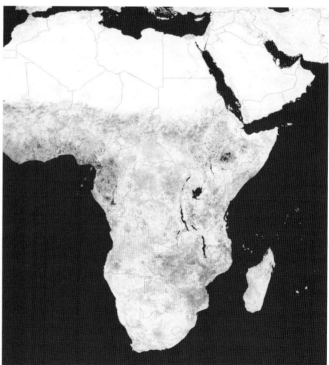

July 2004 – the drought damaged natural vegetation and crops. A famine developed over the next 9–12 months

July 2005 – in this month rainfall was better than average, helping to produce a better crop

What is desertification and how is it caused?

Rainfall in the Sahel region of Africa is extremely variable from year to year. Rainfall is lowest in the north of the region. Cattle and goat herding are possible here. Rainfall of around 600 mm per year is usual in the southern Sahel. This is sufficient for some crops to be grown.

The drought in Niger and Mali during 2004–2005 is just one of several recent water shortages in the Sahel region of Africa. This region is experiencing climate change: annual rainfall totals in most years since 1968 have been lower than in earlier years of the twentieth century. As a result, the area is becoming more arid and the crops are less reliable. There is less natural vegetation than 40 years ago so when it is windy the dry soil is easily blown away. It is as though the Sahara desert is expanding; a situation that is described as **desertification**.

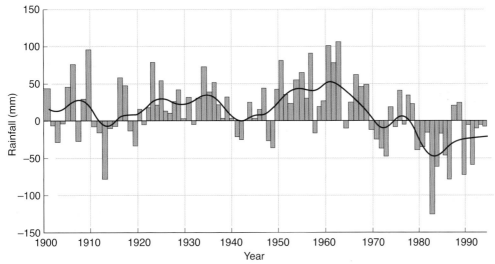

www.wateraid. org.uk
A number of Non-Governmental Organisations (NGOs), such as WaterAid, work in Mali to try to improve the amount of fresh water available.

Figure 7 Annual rainfall anomalies in Sahel countries 1900–1995. Each bar represents whether the total rainfall in each year was above or below average. The line shows the trend

---

Activity

9 Use Figure 7.
   a) How many years between 1900 and 1965 had:
      i) above-average rainfall of 50 mm or more?
      ii) below-average rainfall of –50 mm or less?
   b) How many years between 1965 and 1995 had:
      i) above-average rainfall of 50 mm or more?
      ii) below-average rainfall of –50 mm or less?
   c) Using evidence from Figure 7, compare rainfall patterns in the Sahel before 1965 with the period from 1965 to 1995.

10 Use the internet link to WaterAid, above, to research how this charity is helping to solve problems of water shortages in Africa. From the home page click on the drop-down menu under the heading 'Where we work'. Select Mali and then Ethiopia.
   a) Prepare a short report that focuses on:
      • a comparison of the water problems facing the two countries
      • how WaterAid and other NGOs are tackling problems in urban or rural areas in the two countries.
   b) Use the website to:
      • suggest how water and sanitation are linked to disease and poverty
      • explain why WaterAid thinks it is essential to involve women in their projects.

 Mali

Managing the problems of desertification in Mali and Niger

The twin problems of lack of water and soil erosion can be managed and the future of Sahel countries can be sustainable. What is needed is a combination of low-technology rainwater harvesting and soil conservation strategies, similar to those used in the drier regions of South Africa (see pages 130–31).
These include:

* tree-planting schemes
* building small rock dams
* collecting rainwater from the roofs of buildings
* building terraces on steeper slopes
* building stone lines on gentle slopes
* planting grass strips along the contours of gentle slopes.

How do bunds help?

One strategy that has been used successfully in crop-growing regions of Burkina Faso and Mali is the construction of low stone lines known as bunds. Stones are placed along the contours on gentle slopes. Sometimes the bunds are reinforced by planting tough grasses along the lines. The stones and grass encourage rainwater to infiltrate the soil and reduce the amount of rainwater that is lost by run-off. They also prevent soil **erosion**.

Activity

11 Explain how stone lines are able to:
a) reduce soil erosion
b) increase soil moisture
c) increase the amount of grain grown.

Run-off is slowed by the bund, giving more time for infiltration.

Rainwater infiltrates and recharges soil moisture.

Bunds are placed 10 to 25 m apart.

Any soil that has been eroded by run-off is trapped by the bund. Topsoil and organic matter (e.g. leaf litter) is deposited here.

Figure 8 How bunds work

Farmers report that this technique increases their yields of grain crops (sorghum and millet). Fields that have stone lines produce 30 per cent more grain than an ordinary field in a year that has poor rainfall, and twenty per cent more in a year that has average rainfall.

Going Further

Why is the Sahel becoming drier?

The reasons for desertification are complex. Some scientists believe that the region naturally experiences a cyclical climate: wetter periods are separated by drier periods that last for decades. Other scientists believe that the climate is changing as a result of human actions. Desertification could be a symptom of global warming. Alternatively, the Sahel climate may have become drier because of smoke and pollution produced in the industrial countries of Europe. Another common theory is that local people are to blame for climate change in the Sahel: population growth and overgrazing could have made the local climate drier. This theory is examined in Figure 9.

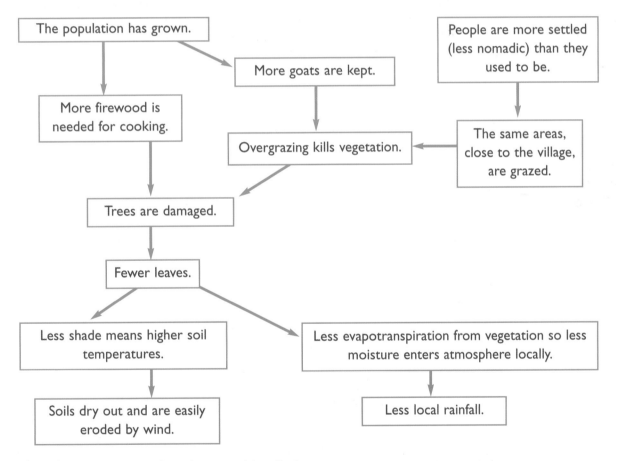

Figure 9 How population growth may have caused desertification

Activity

12 a) Explain how larger, more settled populations of people may have led to lower rainfall totals in the Sahel.

b) If Figure 9 describes the main cause of desertification, suggest how the problem could be tackled.

Chapter 6
Flood hazards

KEY QUESTIONS

✪ How can an excess of rainfall and/or water surplus cause hazards for people?

✪ What effect does this have on human activity?

✪ How can flooding be managed both in the short term and long term?

Investigating floods and flood management on the River Severn

The Environment Agency, which is responsible for giving flood warnings in the UK, estimates that around 5 million people live in areas that are at risk of flooding in England and Wales. Many of these are homes along the River Severn, Britain's longest river. How can the risk of these floods be reduced in the future? A series of floods in the last ten years (shown in Figure 1) has prompted flood defences to be built in Shrewsbury and Bewdley. These include a mixture of earth embankments, flood walls and demountable flood barriers (shown in Figure 2). These may provide short-term solutions, but are they enough to give people long-term protection from flooding?

Figure 1 Recent floods on the River Severn

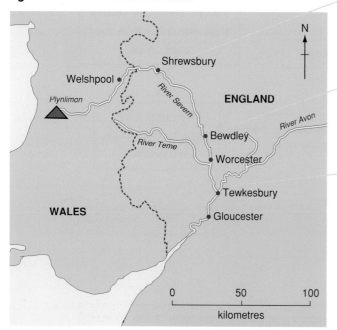

Shrewsbury. Flood damage in 1998, 2000, 2002 and 2004. The severe floods of 2000 led to the construction of flood defences completed in spring 2007.

Bewdley. Flood damage in 1998, 2000 and 2002. Flood defences (including demountable barriers in Figure 2) were completed before the February 2004 flood.

Tewkesbury is on the confluence of the River Avon and River Severn. Both Tewkesbury and **Gloucester** were badly affected by the floods in 2000 and 2007.

Figure 2 Demountable flood barriers (also known as invisible flood defences) being used in Bewdley for the first time during the February 2004 flood

Flood hydrographs

A flood hydrograph shows how a river is affected by heavy rainfall or snowmelt.

The flood hydrograph in Figure 3 shows that after two hours of rain, the river discharge starts to increase rapidly. Raindrops that fall into the river will increase the discharge very slightly. Water flowing over the ground will flow quickly into the river causing the discharge to rise. On the graph this is called the rising limb. Flooding conditions occur when:

- the ground is saturated with water
- the ground is frozen
- the surface is impermeable like tarmac
- the rainfall is so intense it cannot all soak into the ground.

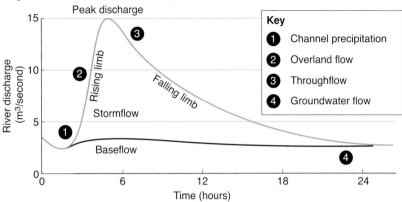

Figure 3 A flood hydrograph showing the flow of a river following a single rain event

Throughflow will occur for many hours or even days after the storm and causes the discharge to fall much more gently than it rises. Groundwater flow is slower at reaching the river and is the reason why rivers in the UK don't tend to dry up even after long periods with no rainfall.

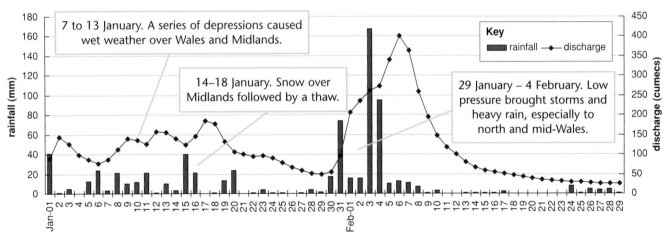

Figure 4 Flood hydrograph for the River Severn at Bewdley (January–February 2004). Rainfall data is for Capel Curig, North Wales

Activity

1 Describe the course of the River Severn.

2 Explain why rivers continue to flow even during times of low rainfall.

3 Describe and explain the changes in discharge shown in Figure 3.

4 Study Figure 4.
   a) Describe how each of the weather events described in the labels affected the flow of the river.
   b) Carefully describe the shape of the flood hydrograph between 29 January and 29 February using the terms from Figure 3.
   c) Use Figures 1 and 4 to suggest how the Environment Agency uses rainfall data from Wales to predict flood events in Bewdley.

5 **a)** Suggest why people in Bewdley may prefer demountable barriers to permanent flood walls.
   b) Discuss whether flood walls and demountable barriers are short-term or long-term solutions. Suggest some long-term solutions to flooding on the River Severn.

The effects of the summer floods, 2007

In June, July and August 2007 the UK suffered its worst floods in living memory. Flood warnings were given by the Environment Agency and weather bulletins forecast very heavy rain, but many thousands of people were caught out by the scale of the disaster. Heavy rainfall in June caused flooding in East Midlands and Yorkshire. The city of Hull was hardest hit when 17,000 homes and 1,300 businesses were affected by floodwater as storm drains failed to carry the water away quickly enough. More heavy rain in July caused flooding along the rivers Severn, Thames and Ouse. The floods caused loss of life, widespread damage to property and disruption to transport. By 1 August the floods had claimed 14 lives. A total of 55,000 homes and 6,000 businesses had been damaged by floodwater.

Figure 5 The areas affected by the summer floods of 2007

Short-term effects of the floods

People had never experienced flooding on this scale and did not expect it to affect them. Thousands of motorists were stranded as roads became impassable and motorways closed. As many as 10,000 people were stranded on the M5 motorway. In Ludlow a bridge collapsed. Rivers overflowed their banks, destroying crops that were ready for harvesting. In towns and cities the sewerage and drainage systems could not cope with the huge quantities of water. Water flowed up from manhole covers and the sewers, flooding people's houses and local businesses. People were advised to stay out of the floodwaters for fear of contamination with many complaining of sickness. In Gloucester an electricity substation was shut down, causing 40,000 people to lose electricity. The Mythe water treatment plant, near Tewkesbury, flooded, leaving 350,000 people without tap water and having to be supplied by bowsers. Schools and businesses were closed.

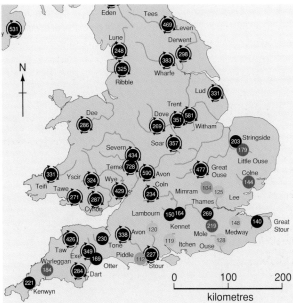

Figure 6 River discharge in June–July 2007 as a percentage of normal (200% would indicate twice the normal amount, 300% is three times etc.) ◀

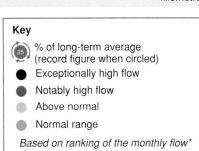

Key

% of long-term average (record figure when circled)

● Exceptionally high flow

● Notably high flow

○ Above normal

○ Normal range

Based on ranking of the monthly flow*

Figure 7 The impact of the floods in Catcliffe

Long-term effects of the floods

The disaster continued to affect people and businesses even after the floodwaters had gone down. Many people whose homes had been flooded had to stay with relatives or in caravans and hotels. Businesses had to be cleaned out and many lost orders whilst they repaired the damage. Shops were flooded and goods spoilt. Some children had to be taught in temporary classrooms without books, which had been lost in the floods. Farmers lost crops worth over £11 million. It is difficult for farmers to invest in future years without this income. One year later, in August 2008, people were still affected by the floods. A lot of houses had taken a long time to dry out, much of the repair work was unfinished and many people had still not moved back into their homes. Insurance claims were approaching £3 billion.

Activity

6 Compare the distribution of the areas affected by the floods in June and then in July.

7 Study Figure 6.
   a) How many rivers in the UK broke their record flows in July 2007?
   b) Describe the distribution of rivers that had flows of 300% or more.

8 Use evidence in the photograph to suggest how quality of life was affected by the flooding.

9 Describe the ways in which the following eight groups of people may have been affected by the floods.

local business people	school children
house owners	old-age pensioners
hotel owners	rescue services
weather forecasters	arable farmers

10 To help your revision for this case study, make a list of bullet points for short-term and long-term impacts of the flood.

What caused the 2007 floods?

The rainfall during the summer of 2007 was very unusual. Slow-moving depressions caused record-breaking rainfall on 13–15 June and again on 24–25 June. Even more rain fell on 19 and 20 July. In fact, many parts of central England had over 100 mm of rainfall on 20 July: that's more than the usual amount for the whole month. By now the ground was **saturated** with water and no more could soak in. Rivers burst their banks and drainage and sewerage systems could not cope.

Figure 8 Tewkesbury is on the confluence of the rivers Severn and Avon. The older part of the town is above the flood plain. Newer developments have been built on the flood plain and are at great risk of flooding

Figure 9 Alternative points of view on the cause of the floods

The jet stream (shown on page 88) is a westerly wind blowing high in the atmosphere. It helps to create areas of low pressure (depressions) in the North Atlantic. Often it swerves to the north of the UK during the summer and takes the areas of low pressure to the north of us. In the summer of 2007 the jet stream was much further south than usual, bringing a series of slow-moving depressions across the UK.

The problem is 'urban creep'. Over the last 60 years more and more houses have been built on the flood plains of our rivers. If flood plains are left as green fields then they act as a temporary store for the floodwater. They release water slowly back into the river as the floodwater goes down. This means that flood peaks are lower and people living further down the river are at less risk. Another problem is that a lot of people are paving over their front gardens so people can park off the road. This means more land is impermeable. Rainwater goes straight down into storm drains and into the river rather than soaking slowly into the soil.

Weather forecaster

Climate change scientist

Planner

Spokesperson for the RSPB

Ocean temperatures are gradually increasing. I believe this is direct evidence of global warming. The problem is that warmer oceans act as a heat source for the air above. The warm, moist air rises and creates a depression, and depressions bring wet and windy weather. During the summer of 2007 the North Atlantic was warmer than usual so the depressions contained much more moisture than normal.

I believe that field drains on the upland hill farms of Wales are partly responsible for the series of floods on the River Severn over the last ten years. Farmers dug the drains in the 1950s–1960s. These drains have allowed farmers to sow better grass and keep more sheep. However, the drains take rainwater off the hills quickly into the streams that feed into the River Severn.

Activity

11 Explain one physical and one human reason why people in newer developments in Tewkesbury are at risk of flooding.

12 Use Figure 9 to outline the possible causes of the floods under the headings:
Physical causes   Human causes

13 Use Figure 9. Explain fully how field drains in upland Wales and paving over gardens in cities in the Midlands could affect the flow of the River Severn. Use the following words:
infiltration   throughflow   run-off
stores   rising limb   impermeable

14 Work in a group of four to discuss the views given in Figure 9. Decide which point of view you find most convincing. Prepare a news headline and a one-minute news broadcast that focuses on the main reason for the summer flooding.

15 a) Sort the sentences in Figure 10 into a logical sequence of events.
b) Copy them out and link them together using suitable connectives to make a full explanation of the 2007 flood. Look at the Examiner's Tips panel for suitable connectives.

EXAMINER'S TIPS

Extending your explanations: The 'So what?' question I

Explain is a common command word in the GCSE Geography examination. Geographical explanations are seldom straightforward and the examiner is looking for evidence that you understand the complexity of the issue. So, to get a good mark you need to extend your answer by asking yourself the 'So what?' question. For example:

The long period of rain during June was an important reason for the flooding. *(So what?)* So the ground was saturated with water *(So what?)* which meant that when it rained again the rain could not infiltrate the soil *(So what?)*.

This 'So what?' technique will enable you to extend simple, short explanations into longer, more sophisticated lines of argument. You will need to link your shorter sentences together with connectives such as:

So…   which means that…   therefore…   leading to…   causing…

a Sea temperatures were above average.
b Soils were at their wettest in summer for over 50 years.
c Depressions were very slow-moving so rain fell for long periods.
d The ground was saturated with water from previous storms.
e Water flowed quickly as overland flow into the rivers.
f The storm drains that take rainwater off the roads could not cope with the huge quantity of water.
g There were more depressions than usual for this time of year.

The number of 'So what?' statements you provide will depend on the number of marks available for the question. Thus a question asking for **one reason** and offering **four marks** could be answered using an opening statement followed by **three** 'So what?' statements. On the other hand, a question offering the same **four marks** but asking for an explanation of **two reasons** would require **two** separate simple statements, **each** accompanied by **one** 'So what?' statement.

Figure 10 The floods were a sequence of events

Finding a sustainable solution to the flooding problem

The huge scale of the 2007 floods caused local governments and the Environment Agency to think more carefully about how flood risk can be reduced. The government report on the flood concluded that existing flood prevention measures worked well, including the use of temporary barriers, but that other factors can definitely be improved.

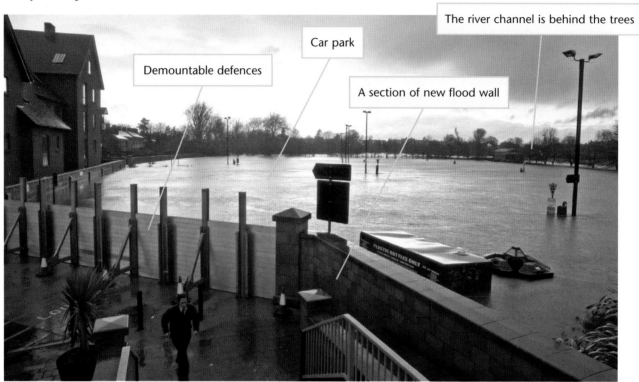

Figure 11 A total length of 700 m of flood embankments and walls has been built where the river enters the town to prevent floods in Shrewsbury. A further 155 m of river bank is protected using demountable defences like those used in Bewdley

Activity

16 You have been asked to advise Tewkesbury Council on flood prevention. What do you think should be done to prevent further floods in the town?

a) Use what you have learned in this chapter, and the points of view in Figure 12, to complete a copy of the following table:

Possible solution	Short-term benefits and problems	Long-term benefits and problems	Who might agree and disagree with this solution
Building flood defences like in Shrewsbury and Bewdley			
Restoring bogs and moorland in mid-Wales by blocking drains			
Tighter controls on building on flood plains and paving over gardens			
Allowing rivers to flow naturally and spill over onto the flood plain			

Householders should be encouraged not to pave over their gardens. Advice needs to be given so that gravel and permeable surfaces are used instead of tarmac. We also need to replace old storm drains which are too old and small to cope with heavy rainstorms. However, motorists won't like that because it will mean digging up urban roads!

Hard engineering schemes, like the flood walls and embankments in Shrewsbury, speed up the flow of water. These schemes may funnel water along to the next community living further downstream and actually increase their risk of flooding. What we need to do is to return river valleys to a more natural state. We should use flood plains as temporary water stores so that flooding can occur away from built-up areas.

Planner

Spokesperson for the RSPB

River scientist

We are involved in a scheme to restore the old peat bogs in upland Wales. Between 2006 and 2011 we are going to block a total of 90 km of old land drains on the hills close to Lake Vyrnwy. We are using bales made from heather to block the drains. This will slow down the overland flow and force water to soak back into the soil. Not only will this help reduce the risk of floods, it will also improve the moorland ecosystem and will help to protect rare birds of prey like the merlin and hen harrier.

We need to build an extra 3 million homes in the UK by 2020. Almost half of them are in the Midlands and the south of England which are the same areas hit by flooding in 2007. Some of these houses will have to be built on greenfield sites. However, we should restrict building on flood plains in the future.

Homes can be made more flood-proof with measures such as putting plug sockets higher up the walls and using yacht varnish to make wooden floors waterproof.

House builder

Resident in Shrewsbury

Government housing minister

I'm really pleased with the new flood defences. My property has flooded in the past but was protected during 2007. The Shrewsbury flood defence scheme cost £4.6 million but I think it was worth it.

Figure 12 Alternative points of view on solving the flood problem

b) Now you need to recommend your plan. What do you think should be done and why do you think your plan will work? Use the following table to plan your answer:

Key questions to ask yourself:	My answers:
Is my plan realistic, affordable and achievable?	
Which groups of people will benefit from my plan?	
How will the environment be affected?	
Why is this plan better than the alternatives?	

Chapter 7
An interdependent world of water

KEY QUESTIONS

⚙ How might long-term and short-term international co-operation improve future responses to the drought and flood risks?

 River Mekong

The risk of flood and drought in Cambodia

Many rivers cross from one country into another on their long journey to the sea. The River Mekong, for example, flows through six countries between its source in Yunan province in China and its mouth in the South China Sea. Each country relies on the river for water supply and for food. For example, fishermen in Cambodia catch about 2 million tonnes of fish a year from the river. It is thought that no other country on Earth relies so much on wild protein in its diet. But the fishermen in Cambodia are unhappy. They say that they catch fewer fish each year and that the fish that are caught are smaller. They blame a series of dams recently built in China.

Cambodia, in south-east Asia, has a tropical climate with a seasonal pattern of rainfall. Spring has low rainfall and drought and food shortages are possible. Then late summer is dominated by low pressure that usually brings heavy rainfall known as the **monsoon**. This can cause flooding on the River Mekong. The worst floods in recent years in Cambodia were in 2000 when 347 people were killed, 80 per cent of these were children. However, seasonal floods deposit fertile silt onto the flood plain and many farmers rely on these floods to water their rice crops. About 80 per cent of the rice production in the countries of the lower Mekong basin relies on these natural flood events.

Key
~ R Mekong
▨ Drainage basin

0   500
kilometres

Figure 1 The location of the River Mekong and its river basin

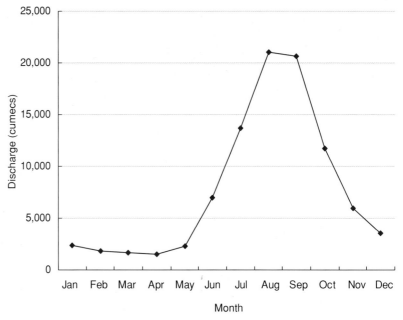

Figure 2 Hydrograph for the River Mekong, Cambodia
(discharge in cubic metres per second)

Disaster	Date	Number affected (thousands)	People killed	Damage US$ (thousands)
Drought	June 1994	5,000		100,000
Flood	September 1996	1,310	59	3,542
Epidemic	April 1999	no data	56	
Flood	August 1999	536	7	500
Flood	October 1999	124		
Flood	July 2000	3,448	347	160,000
Flood	August 2001	1,669	56	15,000
Drought	January 2002	650		38,000
Flood	August 2002	1,470	29	100
Epidemic	February 2005	no data	7	
Drought	April 2005	600		
Flood	September 2005	no data	16	
Flood	August 2006	33	5	
Epidemic	July 2007	no data	182	

Figure 3 Disasters affecting Cambodia (1994–2007)

Figure 4 The River Mekong in this photo is brown because it is full of sediment. Many boatmen have noticed that sediment banks in the river are increasing in size. Some larger boats, such as ferries, are struggling to cross the river without running aground. Are dams in China responsible for this change?

Activity

1 Name the six countries that share the River Mekong.

2 Describe the pattern of river discharge on the River Mekong in Cambodia.

3 'Low to medium-sized floods are beneficial to living conditions in the region. Floods of higher magnitude cause devastation.' Explain the beginning of this government report.

4 Analyse the data in Figure 3.
   a) Total the number of people affected by each type of disaster. Which one has affected most people?
   b) How many people have been killed in floods since 1994 and what has been their economic cost?
   c) How does this compare with the numbers for other disasters?
   d) Plot a bar graph for the numbers affected by all disasters with time on the horizontal axis. Does your graph show any pattern?

Are dams the answer or the problem?

Dams certainly have benefits. The dams in China have been built to generate hydro-electric power (HEP) to feed power into China's fast-growing economy. Dams also reduce the risk of flooding. The dams built on the Mekong have evened out its flow and should reduce the size of the annual floods suffered in Cambodia and Vietnam. However, dams also have disadvantages. For example, the building of the Manwan dam (completed in 1993) displaced 25,000 people in China when their homes were flooded. So large dam projects create conflict between people who benefit and people who lose out when they are built. And dams on international rivers, like the Mekong, can create conflict between the different countries that are dependent on the water. Building a dam in one country alters the flow of water causing problems for people who live further downstream. So as more water is used in China, less arrives in Cambodia and farmers are fearful that there will be insufficient water for a good rice harvest.

The Cambodian government feels that, as the country that is furthest downstream, it is most vulnerable to changes made to the river by other countries. It feels that river management upstream is affecting the frequency of floods, rates of sediment deposition and the fish population. The dams prevent migration and the number of fish making their annual journey downstream has been cut. The fishermen need the seasonal rise and fall in the river's flow because the fish spread out into the lakes and ponds of the flood plain during the flood season, where they are caught. The massive dams are evening out the seasonal ups and downs in the Mekong's pattern of discharge and reducing the overall size of the flood.

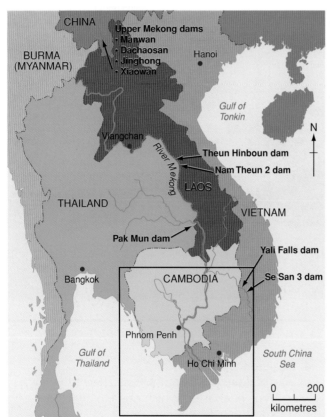

◄ **Figure 5** Major dam projects built or under construction on the River Mekong (the area of Figure 6 is shown by the box)

▼ **Figure 6** Flooding in Cambodia and Vietnam on the Mekong in 2004. 30,000 people had to leave their homes during the floods, which lasted for 59 days

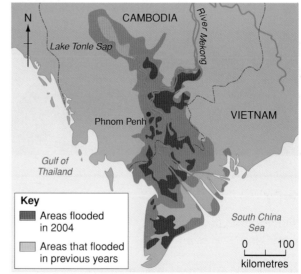

How should the river be managed in the future?

Only Phnom Penh is protected by flood embankments. Most other towns are unprotected and rural families live in houses built on stilts. The government is having to consider a range of options in order to reduce the risk of both drought and flood.

a) Fund a flood control centre to collect data and issue forecasts

b) Assess flood risks in each community

c) Produce advice to householders on how to protect themselves

d) Build flood walls and embankments

e) Build small dams to hold back floodwater

f) Better land use planning so that homes are not built on flood plains

g) Start to talk to neighbouring governments about river management

h) Set up an annual flood conference where guests are invited from neighbouring countries

i) Assist neighbouring countries with aid during emergencies

Figure 7 Strategies used in Cambodia since 2005 to reduce flood and drought risk

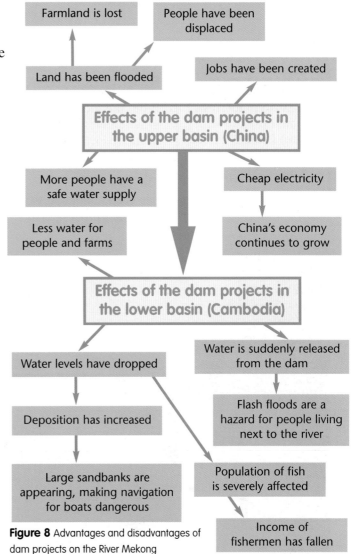

Figure 8 Advantages and disadvantages of dam projects on the River Mekong

Activity

5 Use Figures 5 and 6 to describe the location (see page 148) of the:
  a) Pak Mun dam
  b) mouth of the Mekong.

6 Describe the distribution (see page 25) of the dams on the Mekong River and its tributaries.

7 a) Describe the location of the floods in 2004.
  b) Suggest how building more dams in the future might reduce the risk of flooding.

8 Study Figures 5 and 8.
  a) What are the advantages of building more dams on the Mekong?
  b) Explain why some countries benefit from these dams more than others.

c) Do you think Thailand should complete the Pak Mun dam? Explain the advantages and disadvantages that this dam is likely to create.

9 Discuss Figure 7.
  a) Sort the strategies into short-term and long-term responses.
  b) How many of these do you think will help Cambodia deal with the international dimension of its problem?
  c) Suggest how international co-operation between the six countries on the Mekong could reduce the risk of flooding:
     i) in the short term
     ii) in the long term.

Chapter 8
Landform processes

KEY QUESTIONS

☼ How do processes contribute to the development of distinctive landforms?

☼ What landforms are produced?

River processes

From the moment water begins to flow over the surface of the land in a channel, gravity gives it the power to erode the landscape. Erosion changes the landscape as the river flows from its upland **source** to its **mouth**. The gravitational energy also enables the river to transport material or **load** downstream.

The photo in Figure 1 was taken 5 km from the source of the stream. The photo has been annotated to show the main features of an upland river valley. There are two main processes that produce these features: **weathering**, the breaking up of rock, and erosion, the wearing away of the landscape as soil and rock are loosened and move downhill.

Near the source of the river, the steep gradient gives the river energy to erode and transport a large quantity of material as its load. As the river erodes downwards, it wears away its channel and produces a narrow valley with steep V-shaped sides.

The erosive power of the river depends on four processes at work:

1 **Hydraulic action** – water crashes into gaps in the soil and rock, compressing the air and forcing particles apart.
2 **Abrasion** – the flow picks up rocks from the bed that smash against the bank.
3 **Corrosion** – the water dissolves minerals in the rocks.
4 **Attrition** – where eroded rocks smash against one another, wearing them down into more rounded particles.

The **sediment** in the stream is large and angular compared with further down the river's course. The load of the stream is carried in four ways:

1 **Solution** – minerals from the rocks are dissolved in the water.
2 **Suspension** – the smallest clay-sized particles are easily carried by the stream.
3 **Saltation** – larger particles that bounce along the bottom of the riverbed.
4 **Traction** – the largest material is dragged along the bed of the river.

Figure 1 Ashes Valley, Little Stretton, Shropshire. This stream is one of the most studied in Britain, with more than 40,000 students visiting it every year

Photo labels: Interlocking spurs; V-shaped valley sides; Deep valley; Narrow valley floor; Small meanders; Narrow stream; Large angular boulders

Activity

1 Draw four sketches to illustrate the ways that a river transports material.

2 Study Figure 1. Explain how two of the features annotated in the photo were formed.

The River Valency is a short river that flows in a steep V-shaped valley into the sea at Boscastle, Cornwall. Normally a small river like this has only a little erosive power. Its steep-sided valley was probably cut at the end of the last ice age when the river would have been swollen with melting ice. One litre of water weighs a kilogram, so you can imagine how a river that is in flood has much more erosive power than usual. When the Valency flooded in August 2004 it had enough energy to pick up and carry away over 70 cars and damage several stone buildings. Engineering works carried out between 2006 and 2008 are designed to prevent future floods.

Figure 2 An intense rainstorm caused severe floods in Boscastle, Cornwall, in August 2004

Figure 3 Engineering work on the river at Boscastle in 2007

Activity

3 A student has collected sediment data from two sites in Ashes Valley and put it into a table (Figure 4).
   a) Use the information in Figure 4 to draw a graph to compare the sediment size for the two sites.
   b) Describe how the size of sediment changes downstream in Ashes Valley.
   c) Explain the process that causes sediment size to change.

4 Why is Ashes Valley such a good place for geography students to visit?

5 The bridge in Figures 2 and 3 is the same. Describe the engineering work and suggest why it is being carried out.

Site 1 Upstream			Site 2 Downstream		
Left bank	Middle	Right bank	Left bank	Middle	Right bank
16.1	22.0	10.1	7.8	11.1	2.4
10.4	10.5	10.4	7.6	2.1	6.1
22.0	9.0	3.0	3.6	7.0	1.8
6.5	3.6	1.5	1.5	1.3	10.6
12.0	7.9	6.4	1.4	2.7	6.0
7.4	2.1	6.0	2.2	5.1	2.0
7.4	3.5	1.6	9.0	1.1	6.7
6.5	8.9	3.8	0.9	1.3	2.1
11.0	8.4	5.4	4.3	2.0	4.7

Figure 4 Sediment size (cm) from two sites in Ashes Valley, Little Stretton

How do meanders form?

A **meander** is a bend in the river. At a river meander both the forces of erosion and **deposition** are at work. The river flows faster on the outside of a bend so has more power to erode the banks. On the inside of the bend water flow is slower. The river loses the power to transport the sediment it is carrying so material is quickly dropped. In this way the river deposits its load on the inside of the bend. The material is sorted with the larger stones falling first, then the sand-sized particles and finally the finest silt and clays, called **alluvium**. Study any river meander closely and this pattern of rock size is always seen on the beach on the inside of the bend.

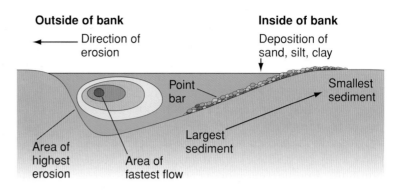

Figure 5 Processes at work on a river meander

Figure 6 Features of river meanders on the River Severn at Ironbridge

Meanders are not fixed features of the landscape; they move across the river's valley floor. As a river erodes its outer bank the meander gets larger. Eventually erosion on the outside of the bend will cause a **cut-off** at the neck of the meander, shortening the course of the river. The river channel becomes straighter and steeper. This causes erosion to begin again and new meanders are formed.

Activity

6 Study Figure 5.
   a) Suggest why the area of fastest flow is in the deepest part of the river.
   b) Explain why deposition and erosion occur on opposite banks.

7 Use Figure 6 and the text to draw a series of diagrams showing how meanders are formed and change over time.

How do waterfalls form?

Gullfoss Waterfall is located in central southern Iceland, 100 km east of the capital Reykjavik. It is where the River Hvítá drops a total of 31 m in two steps. The River Hvítá is formed from **meltwater** from spectacular glaciers flowing from the country's ice sheets. This large quantity of water cascades over the falls and has great erosive power.

Figure 7 Gullfoss Waterfall. Both steps of the falls can clearly be seen from this viewpoint

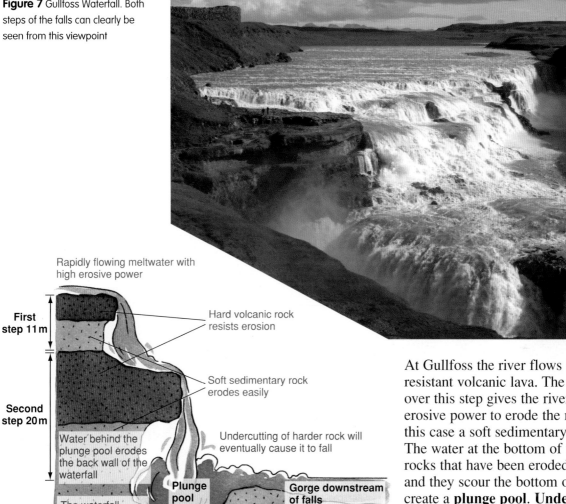

Figure 8 Features, causes and processes producing the waterfall at Gullfoss

At Gullfoss the river flows over a highly resistant volcanic lava. The water flowing over this step gives the river much greater erosive power to erode the rock below, in this case a soft sedimentary sandstone. The water at the bottom of the falls hits rocks that have been eroded from above and they scour the bottom of the falls to create a **plunge pool**. **Undercutting** occurs where the base of the waterfall is worn away, causing the top of the falls to become unstable. Eventually the overhanging rocks will fracture and the rocks will fall into the plunge pool. The waterfall at Gullfoss retreats upstream an average of 30 cm a year. Below the waterfall is a **gorge**. This is 3 km long with a depth of between 40 m and 70 m. All the rock from this gorge has been transported downstream by the River Hvítá!

Activity

8 Imagine you have visited the Gullfoss falls as a tourist. Write a postcard describing this landform to a friend.

9 Explain how the process of waterfall formation will create a gorge.

Coastal erosion: processes and landforms

The processes of coastal erosion are the same as those that cause river erosion:

- **Hydraulic action** – water crashes into lines of weakness in the cliff, pushing air further into the gap and forcing the rock apart.
- **Abrasion** – waves use rocks and pebbles as ammunition against the cliff to wear it away.
- **Corrosion** – minerals in the rock dissolve in the water.
- **Attrition** – eroded rocks smash against one another and are worn down into smaller, more rounded pieces.

Eroding hard rock cliffs

On a cliff composed of hard rock such as granite, limestone or chalk, abrasion is a relatively slow process. Hydraulic action is the dominant erosional process. This process relies on any weaknesses in the rock caused by bedding planes, faults and joints. It opens up gaps in the cliff for further erosion to take place. Corrosion also occurs, but more slowly, and is more significant in limestone and chalk cliffs.

Waves will erode the base of the cliff by undercutting it to produce a **wave-cut notch**. The cliff will eventually be undermined, causing a rockfall onto the beach. (This is similar to the way in which a waterfall moves upstream to create a gorge.) As the cliff retreats, a gently sloping area is left behind; this is called a **wave-cut platform**.

Figure 9 Wave-cut platform on the Dorset coast

Figure 10 Old Harry stack, Studland peninsula, Dorset coast

On a coast where the rock is heavily faulted by earth movements or has bedding planes, more spectacular coastal landforms are produced. Erosion starts by punching a hole in the cliff to form a **cave**. This erodes further – many caves have large rocks in them ideal for abrasion. If the cave is in a narrow headland, waves can attack from both sides to form an **arch**. Eventually the top of the arch will become unstable and fall, leaving behind a **stack**. The stack will reduce in height leaving a **stump**, all that is left as the cliff line retreats.

Eroding clay cliffs with soft rock

On a cliff composed of soft rock such as clay, abrasion is the dominant erosion process. The rock quickly crumbles as it is hit by the power of the waves carrying pebbles from the beach. Hydraulic action adds to the fast erosion rates. Corrosion also occurs but it is not so important as the other processes are so rapid.

Clay cliffs also suffer from **rotational cliff slumping**. Rain seeps through the upper layers in the cliff to the clay below and the cliff becomes unstable as wave attack erodes the base. The cliff slumps towards the beach as the clay layer slumps. These types of cliff are very unstable and are dangerous to walk across.

Figure 11 Rotational cliff slumping at Naish Farm, near Barton-on-Sea, Dorset

Activity

10 Study Figure 10. Explain in detail how Old Harry stack on the far right of the photograph was formed. Include all the following terms in your description:

fetch wave attack prevailing winds chalk bedding planes joints fault lines abrasion hydraulic action erosion cave arch stack

11 Use the internet to search for an image of 'The green bridge of Wales'. Print a copy, describe its location and then annotate the image to show how the bridge was formed.

12 You could use Old Harry Rocks as a case study of a coastal landform. However, sometimes an exam question will ask you how it affects people as well as to explain how it was formed. Look closely again at Figure 10. Explain how the footpath going out along the headland has been formed and how the landform might affect people.

13 Compare the erosion of hard cliffs with that of softer clay cliffs.

Coastal depositional processes and landforms

The coastline of the British Isles is constantly changing as the processes of coastal erosion, **transport** and deposition take place. Land is disappearing into the sea on the Yorkshire coast at nearly 2 m a year. In other places land is being created: sediment constantly arrives as rivers transport their load to the sea and as material is eroded from coasts. Waves transport this sediment along the coast where it is then deposited to create new land.

Transporting beach sediment: longshore drift

Material moves along the beach by a process called **longshore drift**. Waves nearly always hit a beach at an angle, not straight on. Sediment on the beach is therefore pushed diagonally across the beach by each wave. When the water from the wave drains back to the sea it does so straight down the beach, pulling the sediment straight back with it. There is, therefore, a movement of sediment along the beach in the same direction as the waves that hit it. On some days sediment moves in one direction but when the wind direction changes it moves in another direction. Over the course of a year, the movement of sediment – that is, the direction of longshore drift – will depend on the direction of the **prevailing wind**. On the south coast of Britain the prevailing wind is from the south-west. Longshore drift therefore transports the beach material along the coast from west to east, as seen in the example of Chesil Beach in Figures 12 and 13.

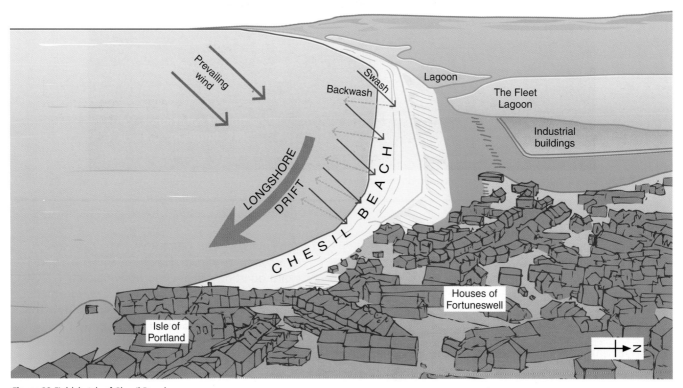

Figure 12 Fieldsketch of Chesil Beach

Coastal depositional landforms

A **spit** is the name given to the narrow stretch of land created when longshore drift carries sediment across the mouth of a river. Salt marshes often develop on the landward side of the spit as the river deposits mud in the calm water found there.

A **tombolo** is where a stretch of land is created by longshore drift connecting the coast to an island. The most famous example in Britain is Chesil Beach, which joins the island of Portland to the Dorset coast. It stretches for more than 15 km in a south-easterly direction. The beach is up to 200 m wide and has a maximum height of 14 m. Trapped behind the beach is a **lagoon**, known as The Fleet. Look closely at the sediment on the beach and you will see it is perfectly sorted by longshore drift.

When longshore drift moves material to stretch right across a river's mouth a **bar** forms. At Slapton Ley in Devon water passes under the bar to reach the sea. The Slapton Ley beach and lagoon is a nature reserve.

Figure 13 Chesil Beach looking north-west from Fortuneswell, Isle of Portland

Activity

14 Study Figures 12 and 13.
   a) Create your own case study of a coastal landform by using the information on Chesil Beach. It should include:
   - a description of the landform
   - an explanation of how it was formed (don't forget to mention longshore drift)
   - the advantages and disadvantages to the people of the area
   - effects on groups of people such as birdwatchers, golfers, holiday makers, local teenagers working in the cafés, local business owners.
   b) Compare your case study with that of a river landform, Gullfoss Waterfall (see page 153).

15 Draw a diagram to explain the process of longshore drift. Include two arrows: one for the swash – the direction a wave travels up the beach; and one for the backwash – the direction that the water takes as it returns to the sea.

16 Find Spurn Head in an atlas. This is Britain's longest spit and is on the East coast. In which direction do you think longshore drift carries the beach sediment along this stretch of coast? Explain your answer.

17 Look closely at Figure 13. How would you study the movement of pebbles along Chesil Beach? Write a hypothesis, a description of how you would do the study and what equipment you would need.

KEY QUESTIONS

- ✪ In what ways do natural processes and their landforms affect human activity?

- ✪ In what ways does human activity affect natural processes and their landforms?

- ✪ How and why do conflicts arise from the use of landforms?

- ✪ How might conflicting interests be managed to ensure a sustainable short-term and longer-term future for the landform?

RiverFun

RiverRafting on the Hvítá river right next door to Geysir in Iceland.

Rafting

Trip difficulty:

■ ■ ■ ■ ■

2 out of 5 - Easy

Guaranteed departures: Everyday at 12:30 from Reykjavík and 14:00 from Drumbó basecamp. Available from the 1st of June to the 1st of September.

The Hvítá river is a beautiful and fun river a one hour drive from Reykjavík and 10 minutes from the Geysir hot springs. For over 20 years the RiverFun rafting trip has been Iceland's most popular adventure activity and its reputation is well deserved. The river has a perfectly balanced mix of serene canyons and adrenaline pumping waves and rapids. As we pass through the magnificent Brúarhlöð canyon participants have the option of jumping from a cliff into the river, who can resist going glacial river swimming so near the Arctic circle?

No one should leave Iceland without experiencing the power that its rivers contain and lay eyes on the scenic canyons of Hvítá river.

Details:

Price: 6.590 ISK per person. With pick-up 9.590 ISK per person. Included: sauna after the trip and soup and bread before leaving. Pick-up from Reykjavík at 12:30. Distance from Reykjavik: 100 km. Duration of trip: 3/7 hours. Available: May to September (dep. on weather). Age limit: 12 years. Bring with you: a warm sweater, bathing suit and a towel.

Figure 1 A brochure for rafting on the River Hvítá in the gorge below Gullfoss waterfall.
The activity costs about £50 (or £80 including pick-up from Reykjavik)

How does Gullfoss waterfall and gorge affect people?

The waterfall at Gullfoss is one of Iceland's major tourist attractions with more than 300,000 visitors a year. Gullfoss and nearby Geyser are just one hour from Reykjavik and form part of the 'Golden Tour'. Visitors to the waterfall contribute to the local economy by:

- visiting the large café and gift shop on site
- paying £45 for a day excursion from Reykjavik
- staying overnight in one of many local hotels and guesthouses.

This creates employment for the local people of the area, who in turn spend their wages on local services. Each Krona spent by tourists creates up to 5 Krona in the economy. This is called the multiplier effect.

The site is promoted by the Icelandic Government across the world to encourage tourism.

The peak of the tourist season is in July and August; this means that employment is only seasonal. Jobs in tourism are often poorly paid. The waterfall at Gullfoss is over-used compared with other sites in Iceland and this 'tourist honeypot' creates problems of parking, litter and footpath erosion around the site.

Activity

1 Describe the advantages and disadvantages of the effects of these tourists on the local area and across all of Iceland.

2 Use Figure 1.
   a) Suggest why people want to take part in this kind of activity.
   b) Work in pairs to make a list of ten words that describe how people might be affected by experiencing this landscape.

3 Use Figure 2, and remind yourself of Iceland's climate (page 92–93).
   a) Suggest why nightlife and day excursions (coach trips to places like Gullfoss) are more popular in winter.
   b) Suggest why whale watching and boat trips are more popular in summer.
   c) List the leisure activities that are linked to landscape.

4 Explain fully why it is important for Iceland's government to protect the country's dramatic landscape.

Figure 2 Main leisure activities of tourists to Iceland

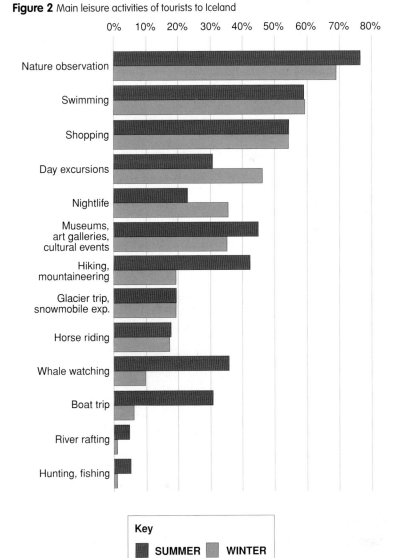

Key
■ SUMMER ■ WINTER

Controlling the mighty Mississippi

Floods on the River Mississippi are naturally occurring events. Major floods have happened in these years: 1849, 1850, 1882, 1912, 1913, 1927, 1937, 1993, 2005 and 2008. The 2005 flood was caused by Hurricane Katrina; the other floods were caused by high rainfall events.

The Mississippi flows across a wide flood plain on most of its journey to the sea, over which it naturally floods. Sandbanks are constantly shifting in its channel as sediment is deposited at times of low flow and eroded during floods. The river erodes sideways across its flood plain. Meanders increase in size before cut-offs at the neck of the meander cause the channel to change position.

It is estimated that more than 400 million tonnes of sediment is carried out of the river's mouth every year. These deposits of silt form a **delta**.

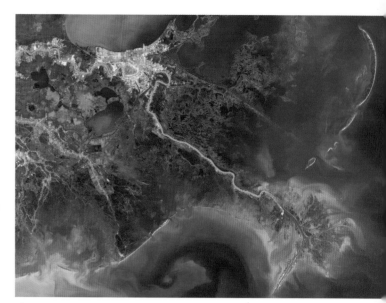

Figure 3 River management means that less sediment is deposited in the delta of the river

How is the River Mississippi controlled?

The task of controlling the Mississippi is the responsibility of the United States Army Corps of Engineers. It has straightened the Mississippi by more than 250 km. This helps to reduce flooding and allows ships to travel quickly upstream to inland ports. River management should also allow safe use of the flood plain for housing and industry.

River engineering or river management techniques that have been used to control the flow of the river include:

- Levees – natural banks which are increased in height artificially. These hold the flow in.
- **Floodways** – alternative channels built to carry water at times of flood.
- Channel improvement – which involves river straightening; **revetments** (concreting the banks); dredging; **wing dikes** (walls built into the river channel).
- Reservoir construction – to store flood waters.
- **Soft engineering** – planting of trees and creation of wetlands to slow down the flow of flood water.

Figure 4 River straightening and concrete banking (revetments) built by the United States Army Corps of Engineers

The great debate

River management is difficult and expensive, and floods continue to occur on the Mississippi. Some scientists believe that although flood prevention measures stop smaller floods, they can make larger floods worse. There is evidence that soft engineering is a better way to control flooding. By recreating wetlands the environment is returned to nature, species diversity increases and areas are becoming tourist hotspots. The floods of 2008 add weight to the argument that levees, revetments and wing dikes may not be a *sustainable* way of controlling the Mississippi.

Furthermore, the revetments (concrete riverbanks) that have been used to straighten the river have led to a reduction in river erosion and so less sediment is carried in the river. As a result, less deposition now happens at the mouth of the river, causing coastal retreat and the loss of local wildlife habitats on the river delta.

Activity

5 Make a sketch of Figure 3. Include these labels:
   levee   revetment   straightened channel

6 Outline the arguments for and against management of the River Mississippi.

7 Do you think the United States Corps of Engineers has been successful at controlling the Mississippi? Justify your decision.

8 Construct a flood hydrograph for Figure 5 to show the highest ever flow in 1993 in the Mississippi and then answer the following questions:
   a) What date was the highest ever flow on the Mississippi at St Louis?
   b) Describe how the water levels changed from 1 June to 31 August.
   c) How long did the people of St Louis have to prepare for the flood?
   d) What would you have done if you lived in St Louis at the time?

Date	June	July	August
1	25.30	32.00	49.50
2	24.80	32.50	48.50
3	24.50	34.50	48.00
4	24.20	36.30	47.20
5	24.20	37.10	46.60
6	24.30	37.90	46.60
7	25.70	38.60	45.70
8	28.50	40.30	44.50
9	29.40	41.40	43.40
10	29.60	42.30	42.30
11	29.40	42.80	41.20
12	29.30	43.00	40.60
13	29.10	42.80	39.90
14	28.80	42.80	39.90
15	28.30	43.30	39.70
16	28.00	44.20	39.10
17	27.80	45.40	38.60
18	27.80	46.50	37.50
19	27.90	46.80	36.90
20	27.50	46.90	36.00
21	27.80	47.00	35.10
22	27.70	46.90	34.80
23	27.60	46.60	33.80
24	28.20	46.50	33.50
25	28.50	46.50	33.30
26	30.00	46.40	32.90
27	31.20	46.00	32.50
28	31.00	45.90	32.50
29	31.80	46.00	32.00
30	32.00	46.90	31.70
31		48.40	31.10

Figure 5 Table of flow heights for the Mississippi River at St Louis, summer 1993

Managing coastal processes

The UK coastline is a battleground. Erosion threatens many sections of coast and coastal communities expect the government to help protect them. For example, an engineer's report suggested that the coastline between Aberdyfi (grid ref. 6195 in Figure 6) and Tywyn to the north-west will be permanently flooded by the year 2050 unless urgent repairs are carried out to the groynes and sea wall. Large parts of this coastline are protected by wooden **groynes**. These structures trap thick layers of sediment that absorb wave energy and reduce rates of erosion. However, in both Aberdyfi and Borth the coastal defence is old and needs repair. Local councils have three main options:

1 Do nothing and allow gradual erosion. This would be an option if the land has low value because building sea defences can be very expensive.

2 Use hard engineering such as timber or rock groynes and concrete sea walls. New groynes cost at least £200,000 each and sea walls cost about £5,000 per metre. Sea-level rise means that such defences need to be constantly maintained, and will eventually need to be replaced with larger structures. For this reason hard engineering is usually only used where the land that is being protected is particularly valuable.

3 Use soft engineering techniques such as beach nourishment where sand is taken from the sea bed and used to thicken the level of the beach. In this way people copy the effects of natural landforms. For example, the sand dunes at Twyni Bach (grid ref. 6094) provide a natural defence to the mouth of the estuary, the golf course and the caravan site behind them.

Should a surfing reef be built?

Ceredigion County Council and the Welsh Assembly Government are currently discussing funding for the construction of a 'surfing reef' to run parallel to Borth beach. This project would be part of Borth's new coastal defence system costing £7 million. The reef would be constructed from 700 tonnes of sandbags positioned 300 m out to sea. It would create higher waves but also deflect waves coming at an angle to the beach so that they hit the shoreline straight on.

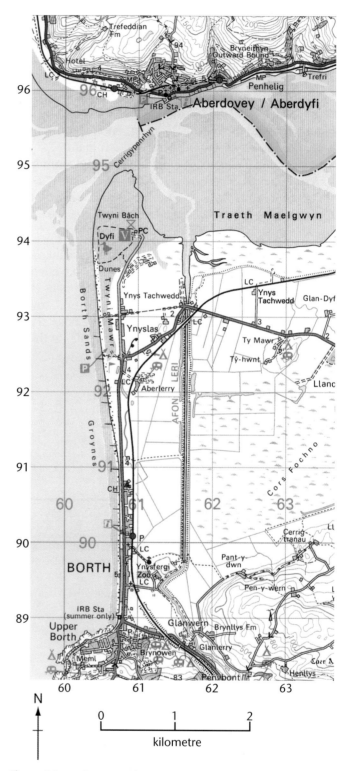

Figure 6 Extract from an Ordnance Survey map of Borth. Scale 1:50,000 Sheet 135

Ray Quant, Borth councillor, has given the surfing reef his backing, claiming environmental as well as tourism benefits: 'I am convinced that this option should be accepted by the council because it will do so much for the town as well as help with coastal protection.'

Martyn Sayer, who runs Stormriders surf shop in Aberystwyth, is another big fan of the scheme: 'It is a good natural sea defence and it would improve waves for surfers. You'll have a boomerang-shaped device underwater making the waves stand up. You normally have to go out and go looking for the sandbars but with the reef you could be out there surfing straight away. It would be the first one in England or Wales; I am sure it would attract surfers from all over the world wanting to try it out.'

Duncan from Machynlleth says a reef would bring several benefits: 'A curved artificial reef would make the waves stand up and straighten (great for surfers) and stop the drift of pebbles away from Borth where they are currently protecting the town. Also a side benefit would be a great nursery area for juvenile fish, crustaceans and other sea wildlife. So all round a great idea! I look forward to hearing if it is given the go ahead. Also to counter the "safe bathing for others" – the waves would be breaking further out and the shore waters would therefore be calmer. That's the whole idea – protect Borth from the waves! Also as an economic boon – have you seen the ghost town of Borth through the winter? The swell will be there all year, cold weather doesn't put off surfers!'

Figure 7 Opinions of the scheme taken from a web page discussion group. Viewpoints taken from www.walesonline.co.uk

Julie from Warwickshire supports the plans for an artificial reef: 'I have been visiting Borth regularly for the last three years and I love the place. The people are warm and friendly and the beaches at both Borth and Ynyslas are fantastic. I would welcome an artificial reef to the town. The residents rely so much on tourism and give fully of their time to ensure that we have a good holiday. My only concern is the parking and being able to drive down the street in one go … and not constantly having to pull over.'

Graham Hesp from Birmingham has this to say: 'With the Government and the Environment Agency now favouring natural erosion rather than building huge new coastal defences, it is pleasing to hear of people applying some lateral thinking to the obvious problems at Borth.

'However, a great deal of research will need to take place to consider the inevitable environmental impact upon Ynyslas and the Dyfi Estuary. Work undertaken by private land owners further up the coast, between Barmouth and Morfa Dyffryn, has caused a frightening change to the nature of the beach and shoreline. Whilst I applaud the thinking behind the Borth reef, I fear that the impact elsewhere will unfortunately cause it to sink before they can surf.'

Anne Wells from Warrington raises several concerns about the proposals for an artificial reef: 'I have just become aware, through the internet, of plans to create an artificial reef at Borth which could attract "thousands of surfers". We have enjoyed peaceful holidays at Borth for a number of years after initially living there for a year in 1974/5 while my husband did an MA at Aberystwyth.

'I would question how Borth could possibly accommodate all these surfers both in terms of car parking, overnight accommodation and the congestion that they could cause to the one narrow street that serves the town. Also how would the new type of waves affect ordinary swimmers of all ages on what is a beautiful safe beach for bathing?'

Activity

9 Use Figure 6 to provide five pieces of map evidence that suggest that this coastline is worth protecting.

10 Read the viewpoints of the people in Figure 7 and fill in your own copy of the table below.

	Advantages	Disadvantages
Environmental effects		
Economic effects		

11 Using your knowledge of coastal processes and landforms, explain how reducing the transport of beach material by longshore drift will affect places such as Ynyslas to the north of Borth beach.

12 Would you allow the artificial reef at Borth to be constructed? Write a detailed report to the Borth Town Council outlining the reasons for your decision. You must include both sides of the argument. Use the information from Figure 7 to help you.

Going Further

Coastal protection in Lyme Regis, Dorset

Lyme Regis is a popular tourist resort on the Jurassic Coast of Dorset. It is a World Heritage Site and the soft cliffs are a magnet for fossil hunters. The sea wall, The Cobb, was built in the thirteenth century to provide shelter for the town and create a safe harbour. It is now one of the town's most famous and popular tourist attractions.

The coast at Lyme is one of the most unstable and actively eroding stretches of coastline in Britain. The soft rocks of the cliffs are particularly prone to rotational cliff slumping. A number of destructive landslides and collapses in the sea wall have happened and action was needed to save homes, businesses and even the lives of local people.

Recent coastal management in Lyme Regis

Phase I included a new sea wall and promenade in the east of the town at the mouth of the River Lim. It was completed in 1995. Urgent stabilisation work was needed in several locations, including the slopes above the beach, in 2003–2004.

Phase 2 of the coastal management scheme for Lyme Regis will cost £17 million and include:

- adding extra sand and shingle to the beaches
- extension of The Cobb at Beacon Rocks
- realignment of North Wall Rockery
- building two concrete jetties either end of the main beach
- renewing the sea wall
- cliff stabilisation works
- Cobb Road improvements and general landscape design.

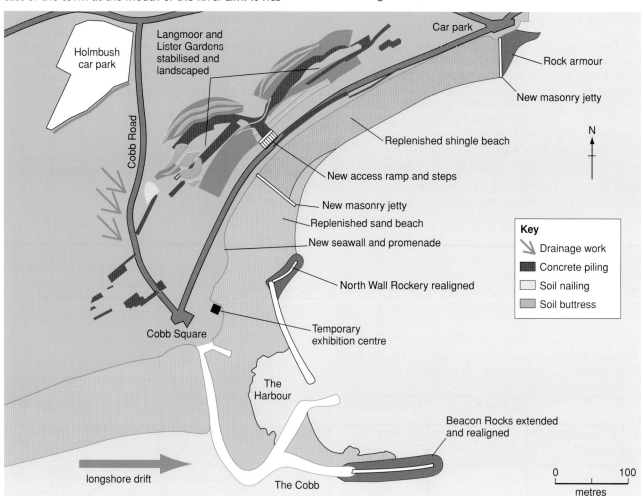

Figure 8 Phase 2 coastal management at Lyme Regis

Apart from greater cliff stability, the advantages of the Phase 2 scheme will also:

- allow a bigger sand and shingle beach, and access along the beach even at high tide, which will protect the sea wall

- increase shelter from rough seas in the harbour and bay

- produce a new promenade along the beach front at Cart Road

- improve access to the town via Cobb Road.

Figure 9 Starved beach at Lyme Regis

The coastal cliffs that provide spectacular views and abundant fossils are among the most unstable stretches of coastline in the country – and Lyme Regis sits right on top of them.

This diagram shows a simplified cross-section of the land at Lyme Regis and the processes that make it unstable.

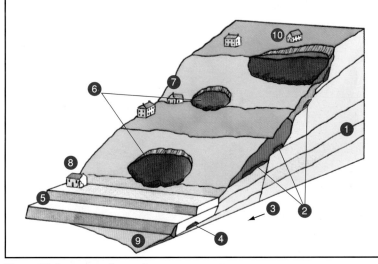

1. The rock deep below the town is made up of strong layers of limestone with shale in between. This bedrock is stable and solid.

2. On top of the bedrock there are unstable slippery clays, green sand, plus other muddy and sandy material. This moves over the strong limestone layers below to form landslides.

3. The layers slope down towards the sea, making it easier for the unstable top layer to move during wet weather.

4. The sea eats away at the bottom of landslides and undermines the land. This prevents a toe or plug forming – and means that the unstable material keeps moving.

5. Coastal defences built to protect the town have been undermined by the sea.

6. Localised shallow land slips take place in areas of weakness – usually in arc shapes.

7. Buildings subside as the land moves.

8. Property becomes damaged due to movement of the land behind.

9. The beach is depleted, offering little protection against the sea.

10. Houses under threat as the landslide expands inland.

Figure 10 The causes of coastal erosion at Lyme Regis

Activity

13 Copy the outline of the coast at Lyme Regis from Figure 8. Try to be as accurate as possible. Add the following information to your map:
- direction of prevailing wind – south-west
- direction of greatest fetch – south-west
- direction of longshore drift.

14 In what ways has the building of the original Cobb affected the natural coastal processes, the tourist beach and the cliffs of Lyme Regis?

15 Describe how the new extension of The Cobb at Beacon Rocks and the realignment of the North Wall Rockery affect the coastal landforms of the area.

16 Write a report to West Dorset District Council commenting on the short- and long-term effects of the scheme for residents, local businesses, tourists and harbour users. It should also include whether you think the plan is sustainable and whether the £17 million investment is value for money.

Chapter 10 Integrated case study: Managing weather hazards in Australia

Drought and forest fires

Between 2002 and 2008 Australia suffered the worst drought in recorded history. The long period of dry weather caused severe water shortages. These were particularly worrying in the south-east of the country which is supplied with water by the Murray-Darling river system. Scientists claimed that this was the worst drought for a hundred years, possibly even a thousand years. The extreme weather also created an increased risk of forest fires, some of which threatened suburban areas of Australia's cities.

In this exercise you will examine:

- What is the structure of the eucalypt forest?
- How is this ecosystem managed?
- What caused this extreme weather?
- How were people and ecosystems affected?
- How can the risk of forest fires be reduced?

Your decision ...

How can this suburb be made a safer place to live?

Figure 1 The forest fires of January 2003

Ecosystems and climate in Australia

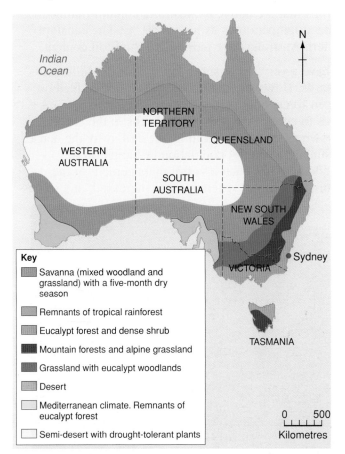

Figure 2 Ecosystems in Australia

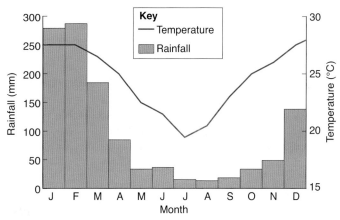

Figure 3 Climate graph for Queensland

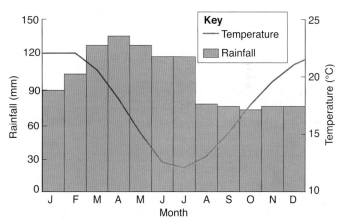

Figure 4 Climate graph for Sydney

Activity

1 Use Figure 2 and an atlas. Copy and complete the following sentences.

The remnants of tropical rainforest are mainly in the state of .... which is in the .... part of Australia. The eucalypt forest ecosystem is in the states of .... and ....

2 Describe the location of Sydney.

3 Look at the climate charts, Figure 3 and Figure 4.
   a) Copy and complete the table on the right.
   b) Give four differences between the climate of Sydney and that of Queensland.

	Queensland	Sydney
Highest temp. (°C)		
Lowest temp. (°C)		
Temp. range (°C)		
Total annual rainfall (mm)		

4 Describe the climate of the eucalypt forest ecosystem.

5 a) Compare the climate pattern of Sydney to that of Queensland.
   b) Suggest why the rainforest in Queensland grows well all year. Use evidence from the graph.

Forest fires in the eucalypt forests

Many species of trees and shrubs that are native to Australia contain flammable oil and resins. These oils ignite at temperatures as low as 60 °C. The eucalypt forests that grow in south-eastern Australia have particularly high oil content.

Unmanaged eucalypt forests have a very dense shrub layer. This dense forest is good for insects, birds and lizards. However, kangaroos and wallabies feed on grasslands, so need a more open forest with plenty of grass. In the past, aboriginal people lit small fires to control the growth of shrubs in the eucalypt forests. This management, known as 'firestick' farming, cleared away the dense undergrowth and helped to maintain a healthy population of kangaroo for hunting. Over the last 100 years there has been less fire management of the eucalypt forests. So, the amount of shrubby vegetation has increased, and so has the risk of a big fire breaking out and spreading uncontrollably through the forest.

Figure 5 Wet tropical rainforests of north-east Queensland

Figure 6 Eucalypt forests grow on the hills surrounding Sydney and Canberra

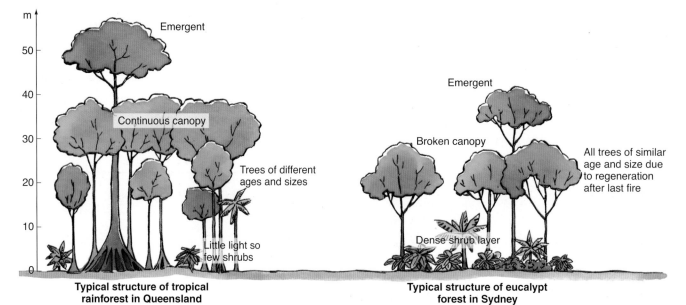

Typical structure of tropical rainforest in Queensland

Typical structure of eucalypt forest in Sydney

Figure 7 Comparing the structure of the rainforest and eucalypt forests

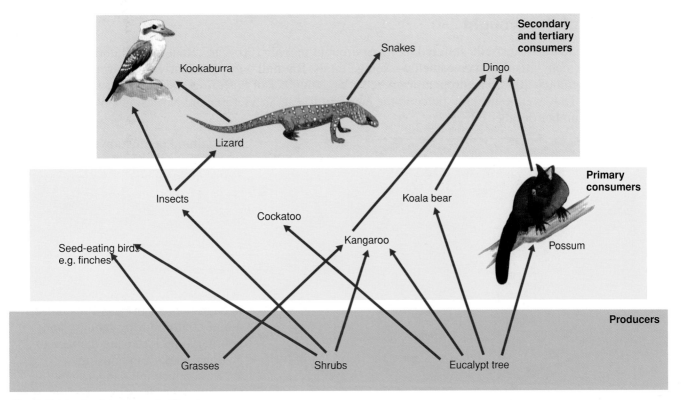

Figure 8 A food web in the eucalypt forest

Activity

6 Study Figures 5, 6 and 7. Copy and complete the following table.

	Rainforest, Queensland	Eucalypt forest, New South Wales
Height of canopy		
Density of the canopy	Forms a continuous canopy	
Age and size of trees	Variety of ages and sizes	
Amount of open space on forest floor		

7 Explain how the structure of the rainforest will help:
a) protect the soil from erosion
b) maintain a continuous water supply.

8 Suggest ways in which the following groups of people might see the forest ecosystems in Sydney or Queensland as a resource.
tourists   **scientists**
timber companies **aboriginal people**

9 Study Figure 8.
a) Describe one food chain in the eucalypt forest.

b) Explain what would happen to other parts of the food web if there were no kangaroos in the forest.
c) Explain what would happen to this ecosystem if there were no 'firestick' farming. Describe the effect on:
i) the structure of the forest
ii) the food web.

10 Study Figures 5, 6 and 7. Write a paragraph comparing the structure of the rainforest in Queensland with the structure of the eucalypt forest.

The effects of the drought

Between 2002 and 2008 Australia suffered its worst drought in over 100 years. Rain did fall during this six-year period, but many months received below-average totals. Rainfall was particularly low during 2002–2003 and again during 2005–2007. The drought triggered a large number of bush fires, especially in January and February 2003. They were especially fierce in the eucalypt forests in Victoria and New South Wales. The drought had a number of other effects:

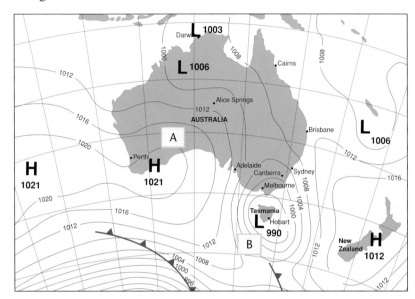

Figure 9 A weather chart of 7 January 2003: a large number of fires were burning in New South Wales and Victoria on this day

- Agricultural production for 2002-0303 was 30 per cent less than normal. Farm production fell again in 2006, causing major economic problems.
- Approximately 70,000 jobs were lost during 2002–2003, mainly in wholesale, retailing, transport and food processing.
- The drought caused soils to dry out. Winds created massive dust storms.
- A large number of bush fires burned out of control during January and February 2003, causing damage to National Parks and housing.
- Water supplies fell dangerously low. Cities faced severe water restrictions in 2003, 2006 and 2007.

Figure 10 A satellite image of south-eastern Australia, January 2003. The red dots show forest fires

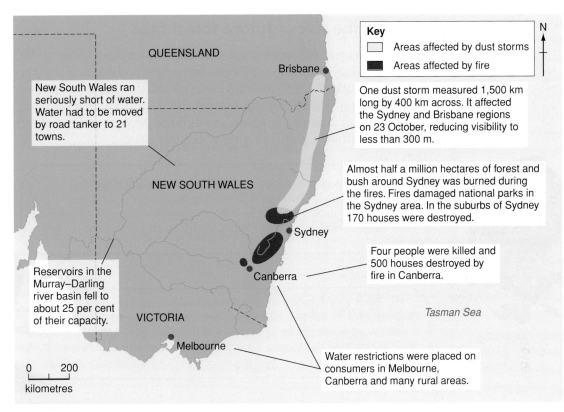

Figure 11 The effects of the drought in Victoria and New South Wales in 2003

Activity

11 Look at Figure 9.
  a) What is the name of the weather system shown at A?
  b) Describe the kind of weather associated with this weather system in the summer months.
  c) Explain how this weather system can cause a weather hazard.
  d) What is the name of the weather system shown at B?
  e) Describe and explain how this weather system is likely to bring changeable weather to Tasmania.

Group affected	Impacts of the drought
Home owners	1 2
Farmers	1 2
Other businesses	1
Government	1

12 a) Use the text and Figure 11 to complete a table showing the main impacts of the drought.
  b) Suggest how the water shortages would have affected businesses, fire fighters and home owners in the region.

13 Use Figure 10. Describe the distribution of the forest fires.

14 a) Use Figure 9. Describe and explain the wind direction over Sydney on 4 January 2003.
  b) Study Figure 10. Could this satellite image have been taken on 4 January 2003? Explain your decision.
  c) Suggest how the emergency services might use images such as Figures 9 and 10 to plan their reaction to the forest fires.

Reducing the risk of future forest fires

The forest fires of 2003 started a debate about the management of Australia's forests. Managing the eucalypt forests by controlled burning is one possible way to reduce the risk of fire. Controlled fires clear away the fallen branches and scrub vegetation. This technique reduces the risk of big fires breaking out and spreading out of control. However, the different groups who use the eucalypt forests have different points of view about this issue.

Aboriginal representative

We are proud of our culture and tradition of 'firestick' farming (controlled fires). These small fires clear away areas of scrub and encourage the growth of grasses. This management creates a range of habitats ideal for different native animals such as kangaroos.

Tourism is an essential part of the New South Wales economy. Tourists want to visit natural, undisturbed, unburned forests. They don't want to see smoke or evidence of fire damage. They also want access to all our forests. Controlled fires would restrict access for tourists.

Hotel owner

National Park ranger

We are not opposed to the use of controlled burning to reduce shrubs and leaf litter. However, we believe that our national parks should be wild places and that these management techniques should be avoided wherever possible. I don't think that the national parks can be blamed for the fires. Most of the 2003 fires started in privately owned forests and spread into the national parks, not the other way around!

Controlled burning causes smoke pollution. Smoke is a terrible nuisance and a health hazard. If they are going to manage the forests by burning them, then they can only do it when the weather conditions are just right. It can only be done when the ground is wet, or the fire could spread. Also, there must be no wind or the smoke blows into the suburbs.

Home owner in suburbs of Sydney

Private landowner of a forest

Privately owned forests are run as a business. They should be cleared of all shrubs and leaf litter. This reduces the risk of uncontrolled forest fires. It also makes it easier for our cattle to graze in the forest, and allows logging lorries to get in and out of the forest easily.

Figure 12 Opinions about managing the eucalypt forests

Alternative strategies	Explanation
I Urban planners could control the growth of suburban Sydney	Sydney has grown rapidly and sprawled into the forests. Wealthy residents enjoy living in the suburbs close to the forests but their homes are at risk from fire. Planners could restrict new suburban development in forest areas.
2 The Australian government should make more effort to reduce carbon dioxide emissions	The 2002–2003 drought may have been made hotter and drier by climate change. If Australia reduced its greenhouse emissions, the chances of another severe drought and fires would be reduced. Australian home owners might have to reduce their energy use by, for example, reducing the amount of air-conditioning used.

Figure 13 Alternative strategies to reduce the risk of fire

Your decision

15 Use the opinions in Figure 12. Copy and complete the following table.

	Arguments for controlled burning	Arguments against controlled burning
Economic		Burning is hazardous and expensive
Environmental		
Social (how different groups might be affected)		Smoke pollution will cause health problems for residents in the suburbs

16 Study Figure 13. Discuss these alternative strategies. Suggest how you think each of the following groups of people might respond to these ideas:
- house builders
- members of Sydney's fire brigade
- energy suppliers
- estate agents
- Australia's government.

17 Describe and justify your own plan for reducing the risk of future forest fires in the Sydney area (some advice is given in the exam technique on page 256).

Chapter 11
Problem-solving exercise

Managing the coastal environment in Essex

The coastline of Essex is one stretch of the UK coastline that is vulnerable to erosion and the risk of flooding due to sea-level rise. In this chapter, you will look at the arguments for and against various coastal management strategies. Then you will prepare a plan to manage the Essex coastline near Walton-on-the-Naze.

Your enquiry ...

What processes affect this coastline?

Why have these coastal defences been built here?

Is the land valuable?

Are there alternative, cheaper or more effective ways of managing this coastline?

Your decision ...

How should this stretch of coastline be managed in the future?

Figure 1 Sea defences under threat of erosion at Walton-on-the-Naze, Essex

Part A: what coastal processes affect the Essex coastline?

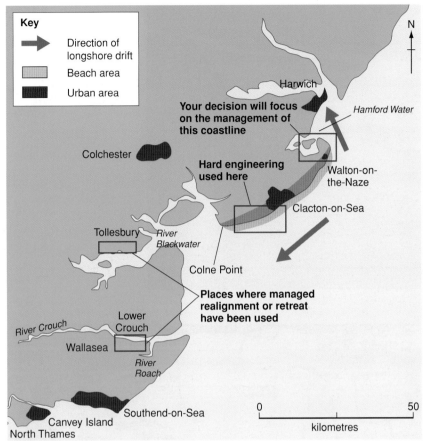

Figure 2 Location of the enquiry on the Essex coast

The Essex coastline is in serious danger of coastal erosion and flooding. The coastline is sinking and sea levels are rising due to climate change. The combined effect is that the sea along this coastline is rising at between 4 mm and 6 mm per year.

The rivers that flow through Essex deposit mud in their estuaries and on the mud flats and salt marshes of this coast. These mud flats absorb wave energy and provide a natural defence against coastal floods. Over the last 500 years people have built earth embankments to further protect this coastline from erosion, and some salt marshes have been drained and converted to farmland. The question is: what should be done in the future? Should the earth embankments be strengthened to keep out the rising sea? Or should farmland be flooded to recreate the natural buffer of salt marshes and mud flats?

Activity

1 Use Figure 2. Describe:
   a) the location of Hamford Water
   b) the location of Colne Point
   c) the direction of longshore drift between Walton-on-the-Naze and Colne Point.

2 Use Figure 3. Complete the following:

   In 1998 the largest salt marsh was in the ………. estuary. This salt marsh covered an area of ….. hectares. The salt marsh that is likely to lose most land by erosion is …….. By 2050 there will be only two salt marshes larger than 400 hectares each. These are …… and …….

3 Describe three different ways that the sea can erode the coastline.

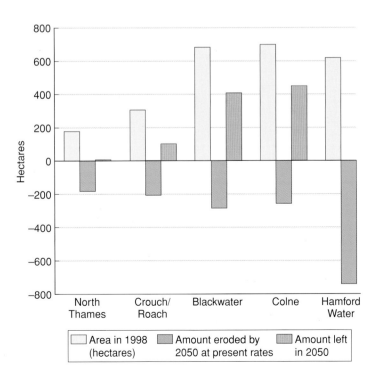

Figure 3 Predicted future erosion of salt marsh in Essex estuaries

Figure 4 Coastal landform at Sandy Point, near Point Clear, Essex

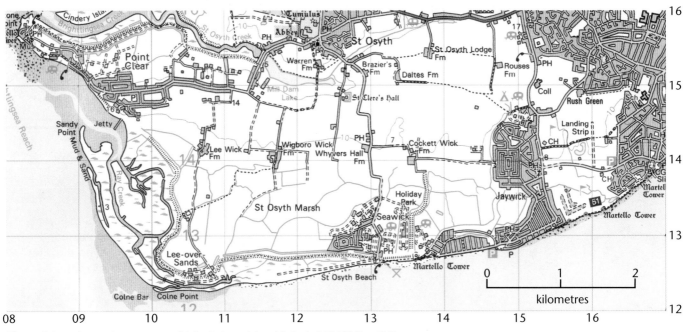

Figure 5 An Ordnance Survey extract of Colne Point and Jaywick. Scale 1:50,000 Sheet 169

Activity

4 a) Identify the landform shown in Figure 4.
b) Explain how this landform has been created by the process of longshore drift. You could use diagrams to help.

5 Study Figure 5.
a) Give a four-figure grid reference for Sandy Point.
b) What is the straight-line distance from Colne Point (100123) to the car park in Jaywick (147128)?

c) Give three pieces of map evidence to suggest that this coastline is used by tourists.

6 Use the Ordnance Survey extract, Figure 5.
a) Give a six-figure grid reference for the road junction at A on Figure 6.
b) Suggest what can be seen at B on Figure 6.

Part B: what coastal management strategies are available?

There are three coastal management strategies being used to protect the salt marshes and beaches of the Essex coastline:

- hard engineering such as building sea walls and rock groynes
- managed realignment – also known as managed retreat
- sediment nourishment of salt marshes and mud flats.

Hard engineering

Sea defences such as timber or rock groynes and concrete sea walls can be built to protect the coast from erosion. New fish-tailed groynes and an artificial reef have recently been built at Jaywick, and they can be seen in Figure 6. Hard engineering is expensive. Groynes cost at least £200,000 each and sea walls cost about £5,000 per metre. Sea-level rise means that such defences would need to be constantly maintained, strengthened and eventually replaced with larger structures. For this reason hard engineering is usually used only where the land that is being protected is particularly valuable. Hard engineering can also disrupt the natural coastal processes, causing problems at a neighbouring stretch of coastline.

Figure 6 An aerial photograph of Jaywick and its hard-engineering sea defences

Activity

7 Compare the width of the beach at C on Figures 5 and 6. What does this suggest about the success or otherwise of the hard engineering?

8 Use Figure 6.
   a) State the direction of longshore drift.

b) Explain how you can tell from the evidence in the photograph.

c) Suggest how the fish-tail groynes might affect coastal processes at Colne Point.

9 Make a sketch of Figure 6. Annotate it to show how the hard engineering has protected this stretch of coastline.

Sediment nourishment

Extra sediment is taken from the sea bed and dumped either in the estuary or on top of the mud flats. This extra sediment reduces the energy of the waves, providing a natural barrier to erosion. This method has very few negative effects unless too much sediment is placed on the mud flat. If this happens then molluscs that live in the mud can be killed and the food chain damaged.

Managed realignment

This is a controversial management technique because it allows land to be flooded by the sea (see Figure 7). Sections of the old earth embankments are breached. This means that holes are made to allow the high tide to flood farmland. The invading sea water deposits mud, recreating mud flats and salt marshes that act as a natural buffer against erosion. These new salt marshes absorb wave energy and create a new habitat suitable for wading birds.

This technique has already been used near Tollesbury on the River Blackwater, and at Wallasea (see Figure 2 on page 175). Not everyone is convinced that this is a good strategy because no one can be sure what long-term effects realignment of the coast might have on coastal processes.

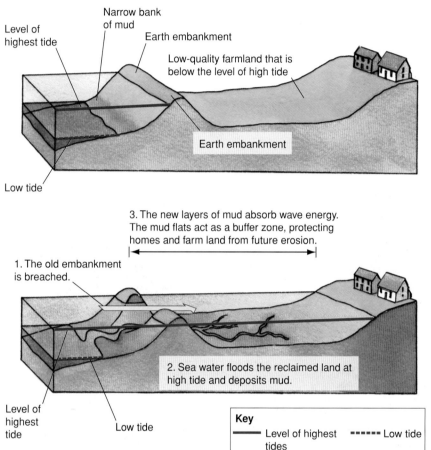

Figure 7 How managed realignment protects the coast

Activity

10 Use the information in part B. Copy and complete the following table.
Make sure you describe and explain each advantage and disadvantage.

	Advantages	**Disadvantages**
Hard engineering	Valuable homes are protected and local residents feel reassured.	
Sediment nourishment		The process has to be repeated in a few years because …
Managed realignment		Loss of reclaimed land. Some people would object to this because …

Part C: how should this stretch of coastline be managed in the future?

The Government believes that managed realignment is the most sustainable strategy for many parts of the Essex coastline. But not everyone agrees. The residents of Walton-on-the-Naze are concerned about the poor state of repair of their sea wall and groynes. They would like them to be repaired so that the erosion of the cliffs (known as 'the Naze') is slowed. Four points of view are explained below:

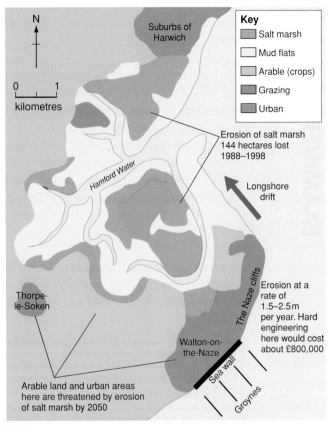

Figure 8 The coastal processes affecting the Naze and Hamford Water

Local geologist

It's not only our town that is under threat. Erosion is damaging the local areas of natural beauty that attract visitors to the town. The cliffs themselves are a tourist attraction and a Site of Special Scientific Interest (SSSI) due to over 50 million years of geological history and the large number of fossils they contain. We should protect this natural heritage from the sea using hard engineering.

Government (DEFRA) spokesperson

The cost of maintaining the sea defences along many parts of the Essex coast is greater than the benefits of those defences. The land is poor-quality farmland. It doesn't make sense to keep paying for the maintenance of structures like groynes.

The only way that we can guarantee the protection of the Naze is with groynes. They trap sand and build up a beach which will then absorb the energy of the waves and protect the cliffs. We know that this works because the Victorians used them; the groynes they built not only slowed the rate of erosion but actually caused deposition, creating new land! But the wooden groynes have rotted away and the sand has been washed away leaving the cliffs very vulnerable. With nothing to protect them they're just being lost to the sea. This is very bad news for us.

Local resident

County council spokesperson

The erosion of the cliffs at the Naze supplies sediment which is then moved northwards into Hamford Water by longshore drift. As sea levels rise it is very important that the mud flats of Hamford Water continue to be supplied with fresh sediment. These mud flats act as a natural barrier to wave energy that would otherwise cause flood damage and loss of land in the estuary.

Activity

11 Which of the three options would you choose to manage the coastline at Walton-on-the-Naze? You must justify your choice of option and may use diagrams to help.

EXAMINER'S TIPS

Getting the best mark for part C of this problem-solving exercise II

Part C is your opportunity to suggest how this section of the Essex coastline should be managed (see question 11 on page 179).

Step 1

The first thing to do is to decide which of the three options has most advantages and fewest disadvantages. Are you going to recommend:

- hard engineering: maintain the existing line of the coast by building bigger, stronger sea defences at Walton-on-the-Naze and protect the local community
- sediment nourishment: depositing new sediment on the beaches at Walton-on-the-Naze and in the estuary of Hamford Water
- managed retreat: allowing the existing defences around Hamford Water to be breached and creating new mud flats that will make a buffer zone. This would protect a large area from future floods.

Step 2

In order to get a high mark, you will need to justify your plan. This means explaining why you think your plan will be successful. Make a copy of the following table and evaluate your plan by completing the comments.

Key questions to ask yourself	Comments
How will my plan affect coastal processes on neighbouring sections of coastline?	
Is this plan sustainable? What are the long-term benefits or problems?	
Why is this option better than the two options I rejected?	

Tip

Consider how your plan will affect different communities. Coastal management schemes can have benefits for some communities while others feel their needs are being ignored. In order to get a good mark for this problem-solving exercise you need to consider the impact of your scheme on different communities.

For example, suppose you suggest strengthening the old sea wall and repairing the groynes at Walton-on-the-Naze.

Strengthening the sea wall at Walton-on-the-Naze would benefit the local residents because … (consider how the residents would feel). It might also cause local house prices to … because …. Local businesses such as guesthouses would benefit because ….

By repairing the damaged wooden groynes … (consider the effect of depositon on the beach here, and also the rate of erosion of the Naze cliffs). This would also benefit the local community because … (consider the effect on rates of erosion and how this might reduce the risk of flooding).

However, by repairing the groynes at the Naze the amount of sediment transported northwards by longshore drift would be reduced. This means less sediment would be deposited in Hamford Water and rates of erosion of the salt marsh and mud flats here would accelerate. This would affect farming communities in this area by ….

To conclude this justification you would need to explain why you think the needs of one community outweigh the needs of another.

The Big Picture

This theme is about the global economy. Flows of people, ideas, money and goods are making an increasingly complex global web of interdependence that links together people and places from distant continents. We call this process **globalisation**.

Example: local people demonstrating about the falling water levels in their wells after this soft-drinks company opened a bottling plant in Kerala, India.

Example: avocados grown in Mexico will be flown to a UK supermarket. This improves customer choice but **food air miles** have an impact on carbon emissions.

Multi-national companies: Large companies open branches in several different countries throughout the world.

Trade: Improved technology and cheap aviation fuel mean that fresh food can be flown from distant places to our supermarkets.

The factors that drive globalisation

Ideas and communication: The growth of communication technology such as the internet, mobile phones and satellite television has vastly improved global interdependence.

Culture: Certain styles of music, television and film are now shown around the world.

Example: films made in Hollywood, USA, advertised in an Asian street. But will local styles of music and entertainment survive?

Example: African countries that have few telephone landlines have used mobile technology to leapfrog the problem.

Chapter 1
Patterns of employment

KEY QUESTIONS

- How and why do patterns of employment structure vary between regions and countries and over time?
- How might changing technology affect employment structures and opportunities?

How do we classify and record employment?

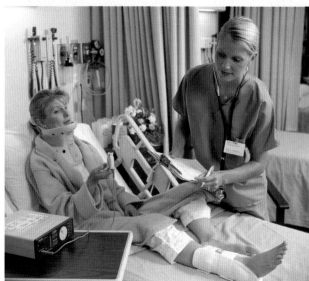

Figure 1 Images of work in twenty-first-century Europe

Primary, secondary and tertiary sectors

The usual way to classify employment is to sort all economic activities into one of three sectors of the economy. The three sectors are:

- **Primary sector**. This sector of the economy produces raw materials such as a food crop, timber or mineral. Occupations in fishing, farming, forestry and mining are all examples of primary economic activities.
- **Secondary sector**. The secondary sector is involved in processing and manufacturing. Food processing, the textile and clothing industry and the manufacture of microchips are all examples of secondary occupations.
- **Tertiary sector**. This sector provides services to other industries or to individual consumers like you and me. Employment in a school, shop, office or hospital are all examples of tertiary occupations.

The number of people working in the primary, secondary and tertiary sectors of the economy is known as the **employment structure** of that region or country. The primary sector is the world's largest employer. On a global scale, 43 per cent of the world's 3 billion workers have occupations in agriculture.

Employment structure varies considerably from one country to another. In the poorest LEDCs, such as Mali, most jobs are in the primary sector and are **labour intensive**. This means that work is still done by hand rather than using labour-saving machines. Wealthier LEDCs such as Malaysia have smaller primary sectors and much larger secondary sectors. MEDCs have even fewer people employed in the primary sector.

In Europe less than 5 per cent of people are employed in primary economic activities, and in the UK this figure is less than 2 per cent.

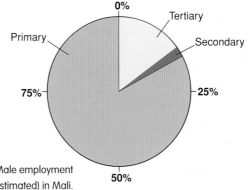

Figure 2 Male employment structure (estimated) in Mali. Source: World Bank

	UK		Malaysia		Romania	
Male employment	**1980**	**2005**	**1980**	**2005**	**1980**	**2005**
Primary	3	2	34	16	22	31
Secondary	48	33	26	35	52	35
Tertiary	49	65	40	49	26	34
Female employment	**1980**	**2005**	**1980**	**2005**	**1980**	**2005**
Primary	1	1	44	11	39	33
Secondary	23	9	20	27	34	25
Tertiary	76	90	36	62	27	42

Figure 3 Changing employment structure (figures show percentage employed in each sector). Source: World Bank

Activity

1 Study the jobs shown in Figure 1.
   a) Sort these jobs into the primary, secondary or tertiary sectors.
   b) Sort each of the jobs into the private or public sectors.

2 Study Figure 2. What percentage of Mali's population works in each sector of the economy?

3 Use Figure 3.
   a) Choose a suitable graphical technique to illustrate all the data.
   b) Describe the main similarities and differences you see between:
      i) how employment has changed between 1980 and 2005
      ii) patterns of employment in MEDCs and LEDCs
      iii) male and female employment.

Public and private sectors of the economy

Employment can be recorded as being in either the public sector or private sector.

- People working in the **public sector** are employed by the national, regional or local government. A wide range of jobs that provide a service is available including doctors, nurses, teachers, planners, social workers, soldiers, refuse collectors.

- People working in the **private sector** are either **self-employed** or they work for a larger company or organisation that is not owned by the government. The private sector provides a wide range of jobs on the land (such as farming and forestry), in construction (design, engineering and building), in **manufacturing** and in services (offices, shops, and leisure and tourism).

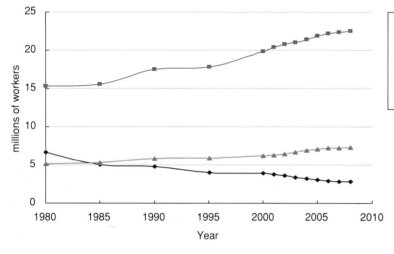

Figure 4 Changing UK employment in manufacturing and services (millions of workers). Source: Office of National Statistics

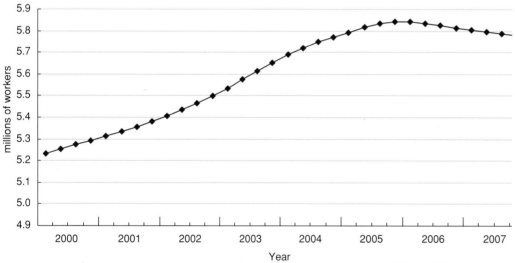

Figure 5 Changing job totals in UK public sector jobs (millions)

Activity

4 Use Figure 4.
 a) Describe the trend in manufacturing and identify the five-year period in which most jobs were lost.
 b) Compare the trends in service jobs and administration, education and health. Comment on the similarities and any differences.

 c) Suggest three reasons for the changes you have identified.

5 Use Figure 5 to describe the trend in public service employment.

How is technology changing the way we work?

The world of work is changing fast. The government believes that as many as seven out of ten children who are starting primary school today will eventually work in jobs that haven't been invented yet! Find that hard to believe? Just consider some of the jobs that we take for granted today. For example, when you surf the web you are viewing pages designed by web designers: a job that didn't exist in the 1980s. Figure 6 shows another example of how technology is changing the workplace.

Figure 6 A computer-generated image (CGI) from *King Kong*. An example of one of thousands of new jobs created by computing

Technological change is having a massive impact on all sectors of the economy. **Mechanisation**, which is the increased use of machines to replace human labour, has been a major cause of job losses on many European farms and factories. At the same time, new computer and communication technology is creating new jobs in some service industries. For example, the growth of some of the world's fastest-growing businesses is connected directly to growth in the internet. Google™, the search engine, and eBay, the online auction site, have grown rapidly since the mid-1990s as a direct result of the increased internet access of consumers like you and me.

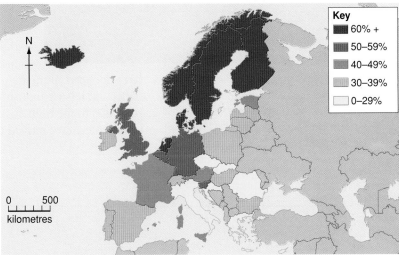

Figure 7 Percentage of the population of Europe with internet access (2007).

Figure 8 The growth of retail sales over the internet in the UK

Year	% UK households with broadband connection	% of all UK retail sales made online	£ billions spent on online purchases
2003	11	1.5	9.2
2004	16	2.3	18.1
2005	32	4.1	21.4
2006	44	6.0	no data
2007	57	7.0	no data

Activity

6 a) Study Figure 8 and suggest an enquiry question or hypothesis linking the three sets of data.

b) Choose a suitable technique to graph the data.

c) Comment on the pattern shown on your graph. Explain what it shows.

d) Use the available data to make an estimate of the value of online purchases in 2006 and 2007.

7 a) Working with a partner, suggest a list of jobs that you think might be associated with each of the following industries:
  i)   fashion
  ii) the film industry
  iii) travel and tourism.

b) Now imagine you could go back in time to 1990, a time before most people had mobile phones, powerful graphics on their computers, or access to the internet. Suggest how some of the jobs you have identified would have been different without this modern technology.

8 Look at Figure 7.
  a) Describe the distribution (see page 25) of internet access in Europe.
  b) Suggest reasons for the pattern that you see.

West Midlands, UK

Investigating the changing employment structure of the West Midlands

Figure 9 An image of work in the mid-twentieth century. C.W. Brown painted scenes of coal mines and iron works in North Staffordshire. This one is dated 1947

From the 1950s through to the 1980s, the West Midlands was regarded as the home of UK manufacturing. However, since then, the West Midlands has seen a massive decline in the number of manufacturing jobs. At the same time, the number of people working in jobs that provide a service, such as the health service, retailing, banking, and leisure and tourism, has increased. This shift in employment is known as **de-industrialisation**.

The most obvious effect of this change is in the industrial landscape: just compare the images of North Staffordshire in Figures 9 and 10. The so-called 'heavy industries' of steel making, engineering and mining, which employed tens of thousands of (mainly) men, have declined. In many places they have been replaced by out-of-town retail parks and leisure industries. The decline of manufacturing since 1980 has been due to the high costs of both labour and production in the UK. Companies have moved to other regions of the world where costs are lower.

Figure 10 An image of work in the twenty-first century. This retail park occupies the same space as C.W. Brown's painting (Figure 9)

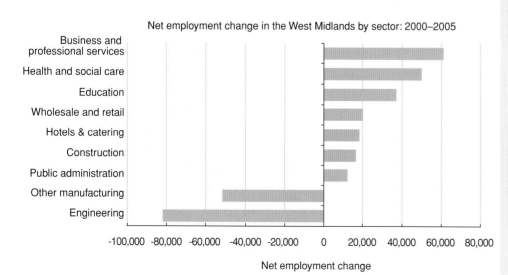

Net employment change in the West Midlands by sector: 2000–2005

Net employment change

Figure 11 Jobs gained or lost in the West Midlands, 2000–05. Source: West Midlands Regional Observatory

Activity

9 a) State whether the industries shown in Figures 9 and 10 belong to the primary, secondary or tertiary sectors.

b) What does this tell you about how jobs changed between 1947 and 2006 in North Staffordshire?

10 Study Figures 9 and 10. Compare the two images using these headings: **Landscape Pollution Job opportunities**.

What is the knowledge economy?

A recent development in the way we record employment is to identify jobs in the **knowledge economy**. These jobs require high levels of education or training. This sector of the economy includes:

- Manufacturing jobs:
  a) **High-tech industries** such as defence systems and medical equipment.
  b) Medium/high-tech jobs such as electronics.
- **Knowledge Intensive Service (KIS)** industries such as finance and education.

Approximately half of all workers in the UK worked in the knowledge sector of the economy. The West Midlands had fewer workers in the knowledge sector of the economy than most other regions of the UK. Figure 12 compares employment in the knowledge sector in Staffordshire, in the North of the region, with the rest of the West Midlands and the UK.

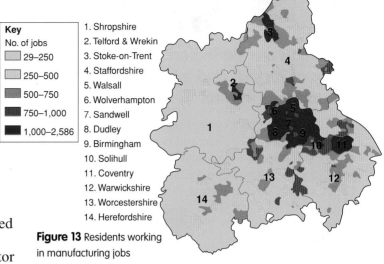

Key
No. of jobs
- 29–250
- 250–500
- 500–750
- 750–1,000
- 1,000–2,586

1. Shropshire
2. Telford & Wrekin
3. Stoke-on-Trent
4. Staffordshire
5. Walsall
6. Wolverhampton
7. Sandwell
8. Dudley
9. Birmingham
10. Solihull
11. Coventry
12. Warwickshire
13. Worcestershire
14. Herefordshire

Figure 13 Residents working in manufacturing jobs

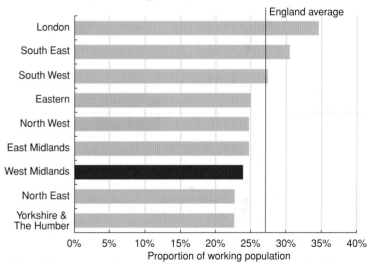

Proportion of the working age population with Level 4+ qualifications in 2006

Figure 14 Proportion of the working population with level 4 qualifications (2006). Level 4 qualifications require specialist knowledge of jobs/skills

		Staffs	**West Midlands**	**UK**
Jobs in high-tech and medium-technology manufacturing	as a % of all jobs	6.6	6.4	4.4
	% gain or loss	−39.0	−32.5	−25.0
Jobs in Knowledge Intensive Services (KIS)	as a % of all jobs	39.0	42.3	45.9
	% gain or loss	18.8	18.2	19.0

Figure 12 Percentage of jobs in the knowledge economy in Staffordshire

Activity

11 Use Figure 11.
  a) How many jobs were gained or lost in each of the following sectors?
  i) engineering ii) construction iii) education.
  b) Identify the service jobs that are mainly public sector jobs. How many gains or losses were there in the public sector?

12 Use Figure 13 to describe the distribution (see page 25) of people working in manufacturing jobs in the West Midlands region.

13 Use Figure 14 to compare the skill levels of people working in the West Midlands with other regions of the UK.

14 Choose a suitable graphical technique to show the data in Figure 12.

15 Give two reasons why the employment structure in the West Midlands is changing.

16 a) Discuss the changing pattern of work and employment in the West Midlands. Consider how education and technology could change employment in the future using evidence from pages 184–7.
  b) Write two contrasting predictions for the future of this region.

Mali

Widening our definition of work: a case study of formal and informal occupations in Mali

So far we have concentrated on the **formal occupations** of the public and private sector. These are jobs that receive a regular wage and that are recognised and regulated by the state. In the poorest LEDCs such as Mali formal work is scarce, so as many as 50 per cent of people are occupied in the **informal sector** of the economy. This sector includes many types of irregular jobs as well as types of work such as household chores and childcare. Figure 18 summarises the differences between the formal and informal sectors of the economy.

Figure 15 Work in Mali: collecting water

Figure 16 Work in Mali: scaring birds from the millet crop on a smallholding

Figure 17 Work in Mali: musicians

	Informal economy		Formal economy
	Reproduction and subsistence	**Petty commodity production**	
Examples of occupations	Daily household chores like: • fetching water • collecting firewood • childcare • preparing meals. Subsistence means that a farmer with a small parcel of land produces only enough food to feed the family with no surplus to sell for cash.	Work in this sector involves the production of low-value goods or services. Examples in Mali include: 1. Growing cotton to sell to foreign buyers 2. Selling surplus fruit or vegetables on a street market, 3. Recycling scrap metal into a useful object such as a hoe or plough.	Since there are very few jobs in manufacturing, most formal economy jobs in Mali are in a service industry such as: • a shop • school • hospital or health clinic • a Non-Governmental Organisation (NGO) providing aid or advice. These occupations may be either full time or part time.
Earnings	No earnings	Low earnings and irregular payments	Regular wage
Rights	No contract. No holidays or sickness benefit. No rules to protect your health and safety at work.		Most formal occupations benefit from a contract, entitlement to holidays and sick pay, etc.
Responsibilities	It is unusual for workers to pay tax.		Workers pay tax.

Figure 18 The formal and informal sectors of the economy in Mali

Figure 19 Work in Mali: a blacksmith recycling scrap metal

Waste recycling: an example of informal work

Bamako is the capital of Mali. It has a population of at least 1.2 million and has grown quickly in recent years. The number of formal jobs available in the city has not grown as quickly as the city has, so many people find it hard to get a job with a regular salary. Consequently, many people work in the informal sector of the economy.

Typical informal jobs include working on street markets, running bars and recycling waste. Some workers collect waste, sort it and wash it. Others recycle it into useful tools and these are sold on market stalls. Organic waste is composted and sold to farmers on the outskirts of the city.

The city authorities recognise the value of the informal sector. The collection and disposal of solid waste had become a problem but has been solved by the informal sector.

There is a large market area in Bamako. All sorts of scrap metal is collected from all over the city and brought here where it is sorted and sold to specialist dealers. Everything from car parts to railways is brought here.

Some of the smaller scrap is sold simply as scrap, but a lot of it goes directly for recycling. There are workshops everywhere in this area, all making different items out of recycled metal: trunks, wheelbarrows, braziers and farming implements are just a few of the things they make.

The recycling market has been here for more than 20 years. Recycling began in the rural areas but now it has become more commercial.

Ploughs and hoes, as well as other farming implements, are made from scrap metal. Through this recycling market a car from Europe, say a Renault or a Peugeot, could end up being used to make ploughs for a poor rural farmer in the smallest, most distant village in Mali. When a car is imported it is used for as long as possible and when it can no longer be driven it's dismantled and every last piece of it is used to make something else.

Daouda Ballo, Bamako Market

Figure 20 Extract from the Cool Planet section of Oxfam's website

Activity

17 Study the photographs on these two pages.
  a) Describe whether the work shown belongs to the primary, secondary or tertiary sector of the economy.
  b) Study Figure 18 and use it to describe whether the work in each photo belongs to the informal or formal sector. You could use a table like the one to the right for your answer.

18 Use Figure 20 to explain the benefits of the informal sector.

19 Produce a chart that summarises the main differences between the formal and informal sectors.

Figure	Formal or informal?	If informal, is this an example of reproduction, subsistence or petty commodity production?	Reason
15			
16			
17			
19			

What are the costs and benefits of informal work for people and government?

Workers in the formal sector usually have a contract, which gives them some rights. They earn a regular wage, which means they can save and plan ahead. Regular wage earners find it easier to borrow money and pay rent for housing. This sector is regulated by the state, so most employees will pay some tax. The government can then use this money to improve quality of life by investing in health and education.

But many people in Mali work in the informal sector of the economy. Earnings in this sector are low and irregular. This means that informal workers find it very hard to save, borrow money, or pay rent. That's why many people in African cities live in shanty towns (or informal settlements). Furthermore, the informal sector is not regulated by the state, so the government does not earn any tax from it. In this respect the informal sector can be seen as a problem for LEDCs like Mali, one of the world's ten poorest countries that need to invest heavily in better health and education.

However, governments of poor countries like Mali would find it hard to create enough formal-sector jobs for the number of children leaving education each year (see Figure 21). During the 1990s, the informal sector created 90 per cent of all new jobs in African countries. If people didn't take up informal work they would be unemployed.

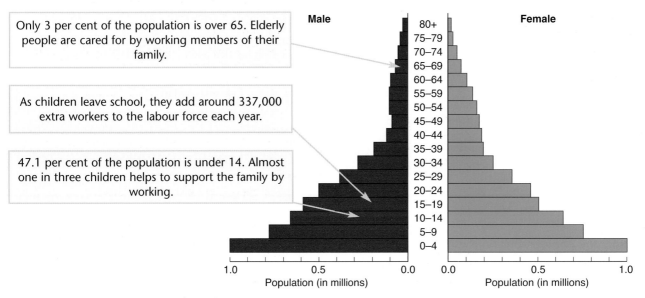

Only 3 per cent of the population is over 65. Elderly people are cared for by working members of their family.

As children leave school, they add around 337,000 extra workers to the labour force each year.

47.1 per cent of the population is under 14. Almost one in three children helps to support the family by working.

Figure 21 Population pyramid for Mali

Activity

20 Study Figure 21.
   a) Compare the percentage of under 15s to the percentage of over 65s.
   b) Explain how this population structure creates both benefits and challenges for the government of Mali.

Figure 22 African women spend a lot of time doing work that does not contribute directly to family or state income

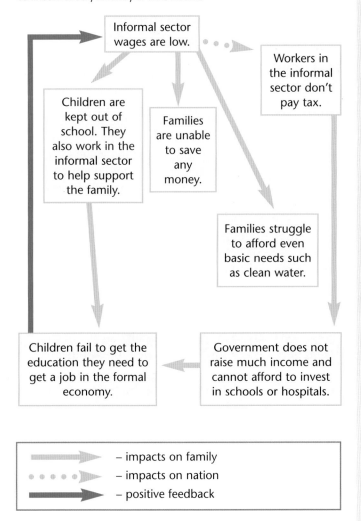

Informal sector wages are low.

Workers in the informal sector don't pay tax.

Children are kept out of school. They also work in the informal sector to help support the family.

Families are unable to save any money.

Families struggle to afford even basic needs such as clean water.

Children fail to get the education they need to get a job in the formal economy.

Government does not raise much income and cannot afford to invest in schools or hospitals.

– impacts on family

– impacts on nation

– positive feedback

Figure 23 The informal sector and the national economy

Long working days are the norm for women in the **Sahel**. Women work up to a total of 16 hours per day in the growing season, of which about half is spent on agricultural work. Time allocation studies from Burkina Faso and Mali show women working one to three hours a day more than men. In rural areas, the lack of basic services such as reliable water supplies, health centres, stores (shops) and transport adds considerably to the time women must also spend on household chores. Shortage of time constrains women's attendance at activities to benefit them, the time and attention they can pay to productive activities, and visits to health facilities.

Figure 24 Extract from a World Bank report

Activity

21 Study Figures 22 and 24.
   a) Give three reasons why women in Sahel countries such as Mali have such long working days.
   b) Suggest a number of ways in which the lives of rural African women and children would be improved if they had access to a clean and safe water supply close to their home.
   c) Suggest how women in Mali might use four extra hours a day.

22 Study Figure 23. Explain carefully how a large informal sector in the economy may prevent:
   a) the LEDC from developing greater wealth in its economy
   b) the development of improved education, training and healthcare facilities.

23 Using all of the information on pages 188–91, summarise the costs and benefits of the informal economy by completing a large table like this:

	Costs	Benefits
For the government of Mali		
For individuals working in the informal sector		

Chapter 2
Development

KEY QUESTIONS

✪ What is meant by human development?

✪ What are the advantages and disadvantages of using economic indicators as measures of development?

✪ How and why are countries at different stages of human development identified?

✪ How helpful in the twenty-first century is dividing the world into Less and More Economically Developed Countries?

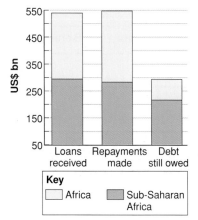

Figure 1 Coldplay performing at *Live8*, the charity concert in aid of the Make Poverty History campaign in 2005

The development gap

Almost half of the families in the world survive on an income of less than US$2 a day. More than 535 million workers live with their families in extreme poverty on less than US$1 a day. By comparison, the richest ten people in the world have more money than the combined wealth of the world's poorest 58 countries. This theme is, in part, about this gap between rich and poor. How do we measure it? Is the gap getting any smaller, and if not, why not?

The **development gap** between rich and poor countries often makes headline news. You may remember the 'Make Poverty History' campaign of 2005. The leaders of some of the world's richest nations, including the UK, discussed cancelling the **debt** owed to them by some of the world's poorest countries. For many African countries, debt has been a huge hindrance to development over the last 20 or more years. Many took out loans in the 1970s and 1980s largely from the World Bank, which is funded by wealthier countries. At that time the value of oil and other **exports** was rising, and poor countries thought that they would be able to repay their debts as their economies grew. However, in the early 1980s, the price of oil crashed. Ever since, these countries have been struggling to pay back the original loans and the interest on their debt. Critics say this money would be better invested in health, education, water and sanitation projects, which would dramatically improve quality of life. For example, Niger has been repaying an average of US$36 million of its debts each year (in the period 2001 to 2008), whereas it can afford to spend only US$27 million each year on healthcare.

Figure 2 Africa's debts, 1970 to 2002. **Sub-Saharan Africa** is the large region south of the Sahara

Figure 3 How do you see the world?

The Brandt Line

Public awareness of the development gap is not new. It was first brought into the news headlines in the Brandt Report in 1980. This report, by Willy Brandt, a German politician, drew a line on the map that separated the richer countries from the poorer ones. This map was developed to separate the More Economically Developed Countries (MEDCs) from the Less Economically Developed Countries (LEDCs). As you can see on Figure 4, the MEDCs are situated mainly in the northern hemisphere. The LEDCs are mainly in the tropics and southern hemisphere. The line loops around Australia and New Zealand to include them in the richer half of the map. This famous map draws attention to the gap between the richer North and the poorer South and is still in use today. But is it still relevant and accurate?

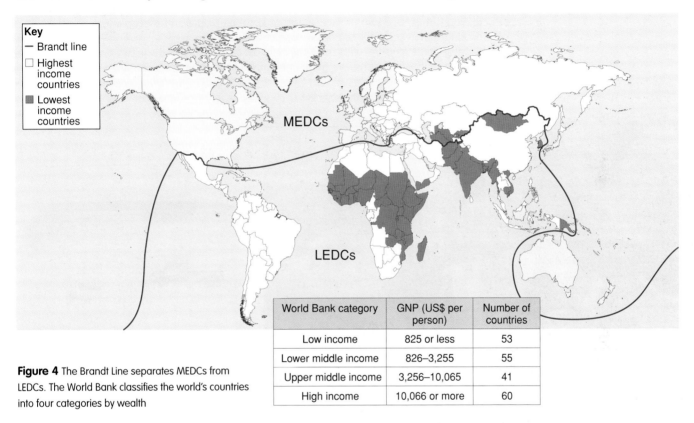

World Bank category	GNP (US$ per person)	Number of countries
Low income	825 or less	53
Lower middle income	826–3,255	55
Upper middle income	3,256–10,065	41
High income	10,066 or more	60

Figure 4 The Brandt Line separates MEDCs from LEDCs. The World Bank classifies the world's countries into four categories by wealth

Activity

1 Study Figure 2.
   a) How much money have African countries:
      i)   received in loans
      ii) repaid in debts?
   b) Explain why money is still owed. Do you think this is fair?

2 Explain how cancelling LEDCs' debt would lead to improved quality of life.

3 Discuss the cartoon, Figure 3.
   a) Describe each character: how they are dressed and what they are doing.
   b) Who do the two figures represent?
   c) Explain the actions of the larger one.

4 Use Figures 1, 2 and 3 to create a newspaper headline and the first paragraph of a news article about world poverty.

5 Use Figure 4.
   a) Describe the distribution of higher income countries.
   b) Describe the distribution of lowest income countries.

6 Use Figure 2 and any other information from this chapter to justify the view that Africa's debt should be cancelled.

What do we mean by 'development'?

One common view of development is that it can be measured economically: that increasing wealth or decreasing levels of poverty are indicators of development. We will start by considering whether or not this is helpful.

Development is...

- reducing levels of poverty
- increasing levels of wealth
- reducing the gap between the richest and poorest members of society
- creating equal status for men and women
- creating justice, freedom of speech and political participation for everyone
- ensuring that everyone is safe from conflict and terrorism
- ensuring that everyone fulfils their basic needs: food, water and shelter
- ensuring that all children have good standards of education.

Figure 5 Different ways of seeing development

Figure 6 Development is…

Figure 7 Development is…

Activity

7 Study Figure 5. Work in pairs to discuss this list.
  a) What are the advantages and disadvantages of each of these statements as a definition of development?
  b) Choose the five statements that you think give the best definition of development. Join with another pair and justify your choice.

  c) Working in a team of four, produce a joint statement that defines development. Each member of the team must contribute and agree with the statement.

8 Working on your own, explain which aspects of human development are illustrated by Figures 6 and 7. Write a caption for each figure.

Using national wealth as a measure of development

The wealth of a country is usually measured by its Gross National Product (GNP) per person. The GNP per person of a country is calculated by:

Step 1 Add up the total value of goods and services produced by people living in that country and by people abroad who are still citizens of that country.

Step 2 Divide this figure by the total number of citizens of that country.

This gives a figure which can be thought of as the average annual income for a citizen of that country. Helpfully, the World Bank and United Nations (UN) now refer to GNP as Gross National Income (GNI) per person. So for example, the average annual income (GNI or GNP) in Mali, Africa, is US$350 (or about US$1 a day). Remember, this is an average, so some people earn more than this and others earn less. In fact, 73 per cent of Mali's population earns less than US$1 a day.

Figure 8 shows the 1980 Brandt Line which divides countries into one of two categories: More Economically Developed Countries (MEDCs) to the North and Less Economically Developed Countries (LEDCs) to the South. It is also coloured to show GNP. The World Bank divides the countries of the world into four categories defined by GNP. It describes these as high income, upper middle income, lower middle income and low income countries. For the details of this classification check the details shown in the key to Figure 8.

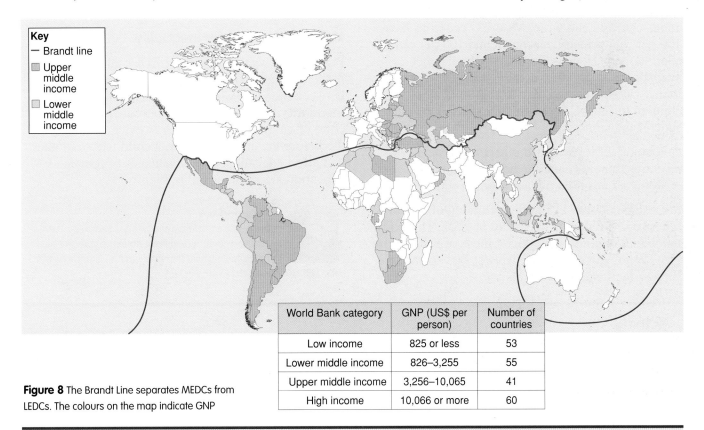

Key
— Brandt line
▨ Upper middle income
▢ Lower middle income

World Bank category	GNP (US$ per person)	Number of countries
Low income	825 or less	53
Lower middle income	826–3,255	55
Upper middle income	3,256–10,065	41
High income	10,066 or more	60

Figure 8 The Brandt Line separates MEDCs from LEDCs. The colours on the map indicate GNP

Activity

9 Study Figure 8.
  a) Describe the distribution (see page 25) of:
    i) lower middle income countries
    ii) upper middle income countries.
  b) Identify countries that have:
    i) an upper middle income but that are south of the Brandt Line
    ii) a lower middle income but that are north of the Brandt Line.

10 Study Figures 4 and 8.
  Which do you find most helpful: the two categories of the Brandt Line or the four categories defined by the World Bank?
  a) Suggest the advantages and disadvantages of each system.
  b) Do you think there is an argument to re-draw the Brandt Line? If so, where should it go?

Using education data as an indication of development

Education data is often used to describe a country's level of development. Two commonly used indicators are:

- **adult literacy** – the percentage of the adult population who can read and write; male and female literacy rates are often shown as separate data
- **primary enrolment** – the percentage of children of primary-school age who regularly attend primary school; again, enrolment for boys and for girls is often shown as separate data.

Why use education data?

In MEDCs most children attend school and most adults can read and write. Most EU countries have 100 per cent primary enrolment and 100 per cent adult literacy. However, primary school is not available to all children in many LEDCs. A poor family cannot necessarily afford to send all of its children to school. Children are expected to help support the family by:

- looking after younger brothers and sisters
- doing chores around the house or farm
- doing an informal job and earning some money.

It is estimated that 115 million children of primary-school age did not attend school in 2002. This had fallen to 93 million in 2006. Of these over half were girls. Young girls are more likely to be expected to support the family than boys.

	1990		2004	
	Male	Female	Male	Female
Sub-Saharan Africa	60	40	69	53
Middle East and North Africa	66	39	74	52
South Asia	59	34	66	42
East Asia and Pacific	88	72	93	81
Latin America and Caribbean	87	83	90	88
Russia and the countries of Eastern Europe	98	94	98	95

Figure 9 Improvements in adult literacy rate from 1990 to 2004 (%)

Investigating gender inequality

Figure 9 shows that in many LEDCs adult literacy is higher in men than in women. This difference between men and women is an example of **gender inequality** and it has serious consequences. The child of an uneducated mother is twice as likely to die before the age of one than a child whose mother had a full education. The advantages of female education are summarised in Figure 11.

www.unicef.org
is the website of the United Nations Children's Fund, a superb source of development statistics. The site has downloadable spreadsheets of data on wealth, health and education indicators.

Activity

11 Study Figure 9.
  a) Copy and complete the following statement:
  The lowest adult literacy rate in 2004 was in .... In this region female literacy improved from ... per cent in 1990 to ... per cent in 2004. Male literacy improved from ... per cent to ... per cent over the same period.
  b) Choose a style of graph to show the improvements made by any one region in the table.

12 Explain why some poor parents do not send all of their children to primary school.

13 Explain why adult literacy is not useful for describing differences between the EU countries.

14 Use Figure 11 and the model answer to extend the explanation of each of the following statements.
  An educated mother...
  - **spots the early signs of ill health in her child so...**
  - **understands the importance of a balanced diet so...**
  - **recognises the importance of a full education for her daughter so...**

15 Use Figure 9 to identify those regions that:
  a) have made the greatest developments in education
  b) face the greatest challenges of gender inequality.

EXAMINER'STIPS

Extending your explanations: The 'So what?' question II

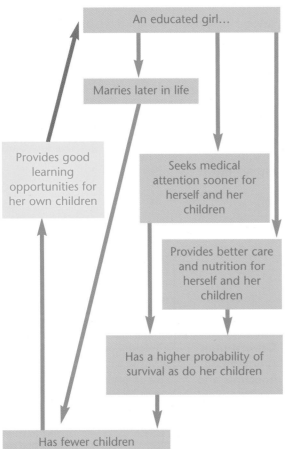

An educated girl...

↓

Marries later in life

Provides good learning opportunities for her own children

Seeks medical attention sooner for herself and her children

Provides better care and nutrition for herself and her children

Has a higher probability of survival as do her children

Has fewer children

Figure 11 The advantages of better education for girls

Figure 10 Schoolgirls taking part in a youth radio programme in Botswana

The model question and answer below show how the 'So what' question works.

Question

Study Figure 11. Explain how an educated girl can improve the standard of living of her family in later life.

Answer

An educated girl will want a good job and a career. (**So what?**) So she will marry later and have fewer children. (**So what?**) This means that she will not need to rely on her children to help support the family income. (**So what?**) So her children will complete their own education and will also have a better chance of a well-paid job when they finish secondary school or college.

On page 143, we explained the number of 'So what?' statements you provide depends on the number of marks available for the question. How many marks would the answer above be worth?

Activity

16 Make a copy of Figure 12. Use what you have learned to create extra labels for parts 3 and 4 of the diagram.

4 creating equal status for men and women

1 creating justice, freedom of speech and political participation for everyone

3 reducing poverty

Development is...

If you are unable to read it is difficult to ...

... follow the news in the newspaper

... come to informed opinions about the success of your government

... read an election ballot paper and vote

If you are unable to write it is difficult to fill in applications for loans or housing benefits

2 ensuring that everyone has their basic needs such as education and shelter

Figure 12 How does improved education lead to development?

Using health data as an indication of development

Health data is also often used to describe a country's level of development. Two commonly used indicators are:

- infant mortality rate (IMR) – the number of children who die before the age of one for every 1,000 that are born. This figure varies widely, from 270 in Sierra Leone to only three in Sweden.
- average life expectancy – the average age to which people can expect to live.

	Under-5 mortality rate		Infant mortality rate (under 1)	
	1960	2006	1960	2006
Sub-Saharan Africa	278	160	165	95
Middle East and North Africa	249	46	157	36
South Asia	244	83	148	62
East Asia and Pacific	208	29	137	23
Latin America and Caribbean	153	27	102	24
Russia and the countries of eastern Europe	112	27	83	24

Figure 13 Improving healthcare has cut infant mortality

Activity

17 Study Figure 13.
   a) Copy the following statement:
      The lowest infant mortality rate (IMR) in 2006 was in .... In this region IMR improved from ... per 1,000 in 1960 to ... per 1,000 in 2006. The highest IMR in 2006 is in the region of ....

   b) Choose a style of graph to show the improvements made by any one region in the table.

18 Make a copy of Figure 14. Working with a partner, suggest how you could complete the blank spaces in the table.

Why use health data?

A number of factors contribute to improved life expectancy and lower IMR. Increased government spending on healthcare, clean water and sanitation (sewage disposal) will all have an impact on health data. That's why this data is a useful indication of development. Around 17 million people die every year from infectious diseases such as HIV/AIDS, malaria and tuberculosis. Of these, 90 per cent are people living in LEDCs and many of these are children. Many of these deaths are preventable: improving the quality of water and providing mosquito nets would be very low-cost measures to achieve this.

	High life expectancy and low IMR might indicate that...	Low life expectancy and high IMR might indicate that...
Government spending on hospitals and clinics	a wealthy government is able to prioritise health spending	
Government spending on preventive medicine (e.g. immunisation)		lack of training facilities might result in too few medical staff
Diet		
Access to safe drinking water	most people have access to clean water in their homes	
State of sanitation		many people live in shanty housing with no proper sewage system
Standards of personal and social education in schools		

Figure 14 What health data may be telling us about a country's development

Changes to average life expectancy

Between 1960 and 2007, life expectancy increased in most countries of the world. Some of the biggest improvements were in LEDCs. For example, average life expectancy in South Asia leapt from 48 to 64 years. However, due to HIV/AIDS average life expectancy decreased in 21 countries during the 1990s. All but one of these countries is in Africa. In Zimbabwe, the average life expectancy fell by a staggering 22 years from 55 to 33.

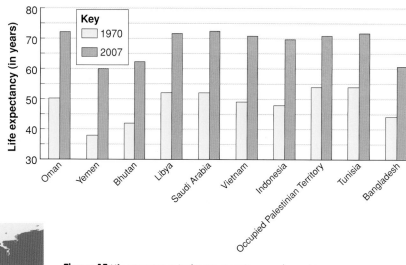

Figure 15 Life expectancy in the ten most improved countries

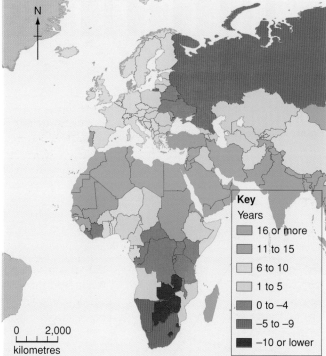

Figure 16 Increase and decrease in life expectancy, 1960 to 2003

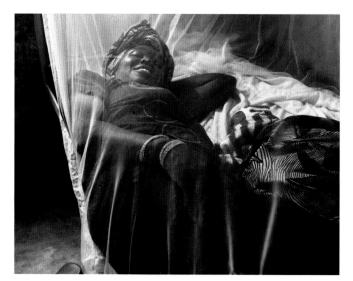

Figure 17 Deaths due to malaria can be prevented cheaply by the use of mosquito netting

Activity

19 Study Figure 15. Which country:
  a) had the highest life expectancy in 1970
  b) had the highest life expectancy in 2007
  c) made the most progress between 1970 and 2007?

20 Use Figure 16.
  a) By how much has life expectancy increased in:
    i)   Iceland
    ii) the UK
    iii) Mali
    iv) Ghana?
  b) Describe the distribution (see page 25) of countries that have:
    i) the most improved average life expectancy
    ii) the greatest decrease in average life expectancy.

21 a) Explain why people in wealthy MEDCs do not always have healthy diets.
  b) Explain what effect these diets might have on health data.

22 a) Do some research into the main causes of death in MEDCs and LEDCs.
  b) Choose one major cause of death that is easily preventable in LEDCs and explain how this issue could be solved.

23 Suggest why life expectancy has increased in some countries more than others.

Going Further

HIV/AIDS and its links to poverty

The main reason for the decline in life expectancy in Africa is the spread of HIV/AIDS. More than 15 million Africans have died from AIDS. At the end of 2007 a further 22 million Africans (including 3 million children) were infected with HIV. Not only is this causing a dramatic decrease in life expectancy, it is also the cause of a sharp rise in poverty. Figures 18 and 19 show how HIV/AIDS is linked to a vicious **cycle of poverty** because AIDS most commonly infects people of working age. Deaths among the workforce not only cause distress for families, they also reduce the earning power of the family.

However, it is possible to break out of the AIDS/poverty cycle. In Uganda, for example, HIV infection rates have fallen because the government introduced a programme of training for healthcare workers, as well as education and counselling for the public. On the other hand, HIV infection rates have risen sharply in Botswana and Zimbabwe where governments have failed to respond quickly with effective measures.

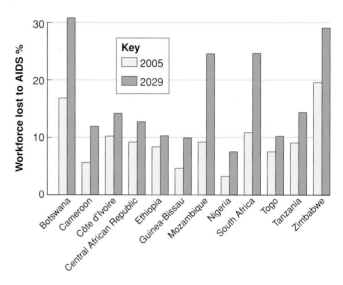

Figure 18 Workforce lost to AIDS in 2005 and estimated for 2029

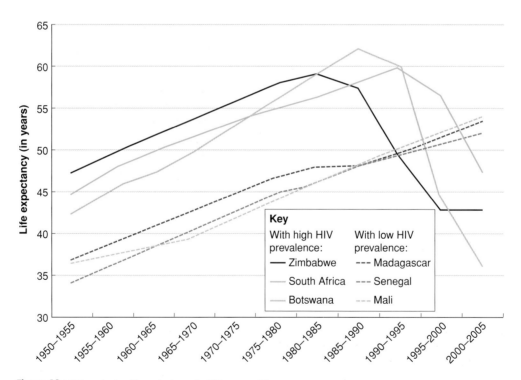

Figure 19 HIV is reducing life expectancy in African countries

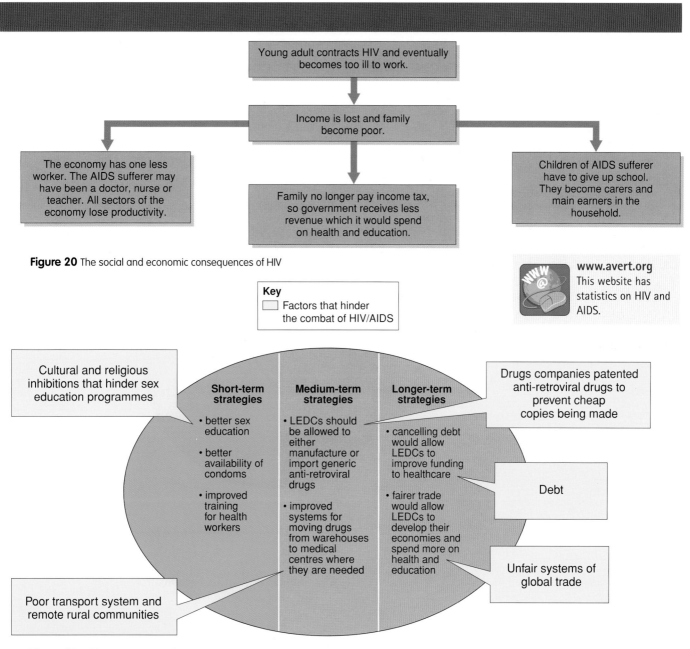

Young adult contracts HIV and eventually becomes too ill to work.

Income is lost and family become poor.

The economy has one less worker. The AIDS sufferer may have been a doctor, nurse or teacher. All sectors of the economy lose productivity.

Family no longer pay income tax, so government receives less revenue which it would spend on health and education.

Children of AIDS sufferer have to give up school. They become carers and main earners in the household.

Figure 20 The social and economic consequences of HIV

www.avert.org
This website has statistics on HIV and AIDS.

Key
☐ Factors that hinder the combat of HIV/AIDS

Cultural and religious inhibitions that hinder sex education programmes

Drugs companies patented anti-retroviral drugs to prevent cheap copies being made

Short-term strategies
- better sex education
- better availability of condoms
- improved training for health workers

Medium-term strategies
- LEDCs should be allowed to either manufacture or import generic anti-retroviral drugs
- improved systems for moving drugs from warehouses to medical centres where they are needed

Longer-term strategies
- cancelling debt would allow LEDCs to improve funding to healthcare
- fairer trade would allow LEDCs to develop their economies and spend more on health and education

Debt

Unfair systems of global trade

Poor transport system and remote rural communities

Figure 21 Tackling HIV/AIDS in Africa

Activity

24 Study Figure 19.
  a) Which country had:
   i) the highest life expectancy in 1980–1985
   ii) the lowest life expectancy in 2000–2005?
  b) Describe the trend of average life expectancy in Zimbabwe:
   i) until 1980–1985
   ii) after 1980–1985.
  c) Compare what has happened to life expectancy in South Africa with that of Mali.

25 Explain the links between HIV/AIDS and poverty. Use Figures 18 and 20 to provide evidence for your explanation.

26 Using Figure 21, explain:
  a) how various factors might prevent a government from introducing strategies to combat AIDS
  b) how the international community could help combat AIDS in Africa.

Chapter 3
An interdependent world

KEY QUESTIONS

- How are countries interdependent?
- How has changing technology contributed to an interdependent world?
- How do such links create advantages and disadvantages?

How are countries interdependent?

The world is becoming increasingly interconnected. Flows of people, ideas, money and goods make a complex global web that links people and distant places together. We call this process **globalisation**. The effect is that countries become increasingly **interdependent** on each other, which means that countries rely on each other for such things as trade, investments and information. This web of interdependence is illustrated in Figure 1.

Figure 1 Flows that link countries together and make them interdependent

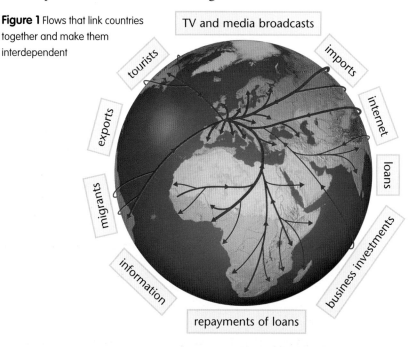

TV and media broadcasts

tourists

imports

exports

internet

migrants

loans

information

business investments

repayments of loans

 India

How interdependent is India?

India has the second-largest population in the world after China. Its population of 1,132 million people is 17 per cent (or one in six) of the global population. The Indian economy has grown quickly in recent years. As Indians gradually become wealthier they are creating new demands for products. One reason for India's economic growth is due to its interdependence in the global community. Its economy has benefited from recent technological changes and from the interdependence created by flows of people, ideas and investment.

Activity

1 Outline how India benefits from greater interdependence.

2 Use Figure 2.
   a) Compare the rise in mobile phone ownership in India and China.
   b) Compare mobile phone ownership in India and Japan.
   c) The population of China is only slightly greater than that of India. Japan has a population of only 127 million. Predict how the mobile phone market might change in the future in these three countries.

3 Using Figure 2 for ideas, create a display for your classroom that shows how India is connected to the rest of the world. You should include at least one map or graph. You could also use a search engine to find images of Indian products and brand names.

Figure 2 Examples of India's interdependence with the world economy

Rank	Forbes 2000 list (2008)	Number of companies
1	USA	598
2	Japan	259
3	United Kingdom	123
4	China (inc. Hong Kong)	109
5	France	67
6	Canada	59
7	Germany	59
8	South Korea	52
9	Australia	51
10	India	48

Rank	Country of birth of resident UK population	Population in thousands
1	India	613
2	Republic of Ireland	420
3	Poland	405
4	Pakistan	377
5	Germany	266
6	Bangladesh	205
7	South Africa	201
8	United States of America	188
9	Jamaica	166
10	Nigeria	140

Foreign investments Indian-owned multi-national companies, like Tata, are very successful in the world economy. In 2008 India was ranked 10th country in the world by Forbes 2000, which lists the location of the world's biggest 2000 companies.

Flows of people Indian migrants work in many other parts of the world, earning money and learning new skills that can be re-invested in the Indian economy. For example, 613,000 people who were born in India currently live and work in the UK.

Examples of India's interdependence with the world economy

Improved communication technologies India has excellent universities and good communication networks. It produces thousands of IT and software graduates each year. One example of India's growing demand for consumer items is the rapid growth of mobile phone ownership.

Flows of ideas and culture The Hindi movie industry based in Mumbai (known as Bollywood) produced 267 films in 2007. These films are extremely popular in South Asia and, with the growth of satellite TV, are now easily accessible in other parts of the world. Their growing popularity led to a stage show, *The Merchants of Bollywood*, which toured successfully in Europe and Australia.

Key
- China
- India
- USA
- Brazil
- Russia
- Japan

Mobile phone customers in the six largest mobile markets.

Ashwini Iyer practises her routine at a rehearsal of the production of *The Merchants of Bollywood* in Maharastra before the show moved to Europe

What has made countries interdependent?

The flows of money, people and ideas that connect the countries of the world seem to be stronger than ever. Why is this? There are three particularly important reasons for interdependence. The first is trade, which is the exchange of goods and services between countries. Trade is examined in detail in Chapter 4. The second reason is the growing influence of big multi-national companies (MNCs) such as BP, Sony, Microsoft and Nokia. These companies invest money in other countries by opening factories and offices abroad. A case study of Nokia is examined in detail in Chapter 6.

How is technology helping to make the world interdependent?

The third reason for our interconnected world is the rapid improvements in transport and communications that have occurred over the last 50 years. Advances in aircraft design, satellite technology, communications and computers have all made the world better connected. In particular, people and businesses can now communicate with each other no matter where they are in the world, as a result of improvements in satellite, internet and optical fibre technologies. Advances in communication technology and computing help MNCs run their businesses in different parts of the world more effectively. Cheaper and faster air travel has encouraged a huge increase in business travel as well as the rapid growth of tourism right around the globe.

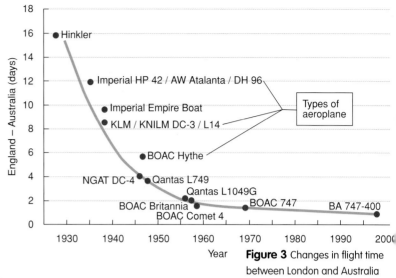

Figure 3 Changes in flight time between London and Australia

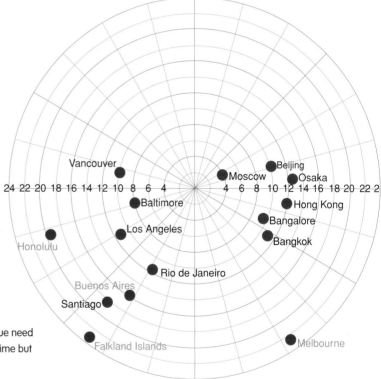

Figure 4 Flight times from London Heathrow (in hours). Place names in blue need connecting flights. The time shown for these places is the combined flight time but does not include the extra transfer time needed between flights

Activity

4 Explain how each of the following makes countries like the UK and India more interdependent:
   a) trade
   b) multi-national companies
   c) technology.

5 a) Use evidence from Figure 3 to describe how flight times to Australia have changed since 1930.

   b) Suggest how this may have created greater interdependence between Australian and UK business.

6 a) What are the flight times between:
   i)   London and Moscow
   ii) London and Osaka
   iii) London and Melbourne?

   b) Use Figure 3 to compare the flight time between London and cities in Asia with London and cities in North America and South America.

Activity

7 a) Compare the difference in times shown in Figure 3 with actual distances shown in a world atlas.

b) Explain why some places (like the Falkland Islands) still seem a long way away despite the advances in aircraft technology.

c) Suggest how this may affect the interdependence of more remote and inaccessible regions of the world. Give five examples of places from different parts of the world where you would expect interdependence to be less well developed.

Going Further

The digital divide

The internet and satellite TV give us instant access to ideas, information and the points of view of other people from across the globe. However, not everyone has access to computer technology or the information available on the internet. This inequality is known as the **digital divide**. A study carried out in the USA in 2008 found that 55 per cent of adult Americans had broadband connection to the internet. However, this figure was only 25 per cent in households where the income was lower than $20,000.

Broadband connection for African-Americans was slightly below average at 43 per cent.

At a global scale the use of computers and the internet has benefited MEDCs, but many people in LEDCs do not have access to a computer, let alone the internet. Many people in Africa in particular are not as interconnected with global society as people in Europe.

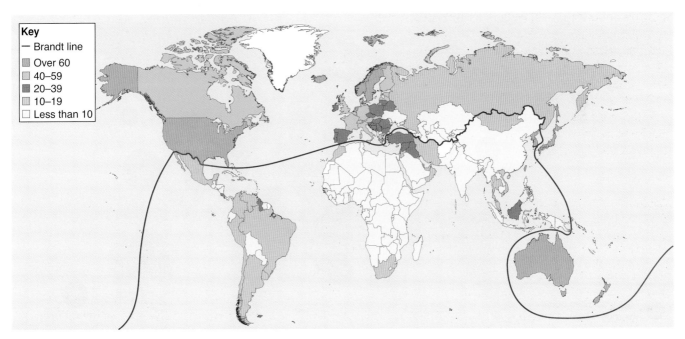

Key
— Brandt line
- Over 60
- 40–59
- 20–39
- 10–19
- Less than 10

Figure 5 The digital divide: percentage of population who have internet access. Source: UN Human Development

Activity

8 Using evidence from Figure 5, explain whether or not you think that the internet has helped all countries become more interdependent.

What are the advantages and disadvantages of interdependence?

The migration of people between countries for work or study is a major effect of interdependence. Migration has many benefits for the migrant, their family and the countries involved. Many migrants do dirty, dangerous and low-paid jobs that local people do not want to do. Others are highly skilled workers who fill jobs where there are skill shortages, for example doctors and nurses. The UK National Health Service employs thousands of health workers from India and other LEDCs. In fact, more than 11 per cent of all health workers who train in South Asia end up working in the UK.

The brain drain: investigating an ethical issue

In the period 2000 to 2005, a total of between 10,000 and 15,000 newly trained nurses joined the UK National Health Service (NHS) each year from medical schools in LEDCs. The World Health Organization (WHO) estimates that at least 12 per cent of the doctors trained in India now live and work in the UK. This is good for the NHS, which had great difficulty in this period recruiting enough staff from the UK. However, it's not so good for the health service in India and other LEDC countries, which are losing staff in a massive brain drain.

The World Bank estimates that as many as 70,000 of Africa's most highly qualified workers emigrate each year. This may be costing Africa US$4 billion a year. Another estimate suggests that only one-third of medical graduates remain in Ghana each year: the rest leave the country to find better-paid work abroad.

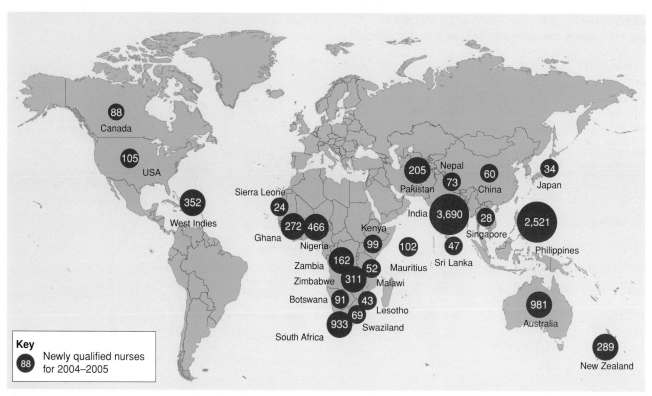

Figure 6 New admissions to the 2004–2005 nursing register who qualified overseas

The costs and benefits of the brain drain from LEDC health services:

- Staff are able to earn many times more than they would do working in hospitals in their home country.
- Staff benefit from training in the latest techniques and treatments.

- Knowledge of new medical treatments and techniques can benefit the health service in the LEDC if staff eventually return.
- The NHS would have a massive shortage of doctors and nurses if they did not recruit from abroad.
- Waiting times are reduced and patients get faster treatment because staffing levels are kept high.
- Hospitals in Africa are desperately short of trained staff. Morale is low among staff who continue to work long hours for low pay.
- The brain drain means that money spent in an LEDC on university-level education is not converted into a skilled worker who pays tax and who therefore helps to pay for the education of others.

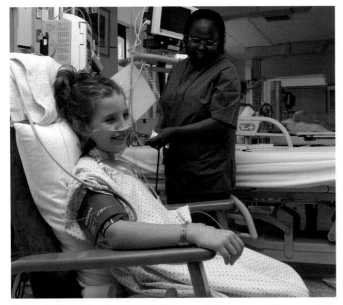

Figure 7 The NHS estimates that 43 per cent of nurses and 31 per cent of doctors starting work in the NHS were trained outside the UK (2005 figures)

Figure 8 Average annual salaries for Indian health workers in India (2008)

	Rupees	**£**
GP	190,000	2,369
Nurse	100,000	1,247
Hospital consultant	549,377	6,849
Hospital administrator	206,957	2,580

Activity

9 Use Figure 6. Describe the distribution (see page 25) of countries that supplied more than 100 nurses to the NHS. How many of these countries are LEDCs?

10 Use the internet to research average wages for health staff in the UK. Use a graph to compare your findings with the data in Figure 8.

11 Study the bullet-pointed list of costs and benefits above.
   a) Sort the bullet points into a table using these headings:

	Costs	**Benefits**
For the British NHS		
For the health service in LEDCs		
For individuals who emigrate from LEDCs to the UK		

b) Write a 200-word article in which you either strongly support or strongly oppose the migration of health workers from LEDCs.

12 Discuss the concept of interdependence that is illustrated on pages 202–207.
   a) Working with a partner, make a list of any products, brand names, companies, films and music that you associate with each of the following places:
   i) USA   ii) Australia   iii) Japan
   iv) India   v) Africa.
   b) Now combine your list with that of two of your classmates. Discuss your lists.
   c) Do you think that the UK economy relies more on other MEDCs or LEDCs? What are the advantages and disadvantages of this type of interdependence for the UK?

13 Summarise five positive and three negative impacts of interdependence.

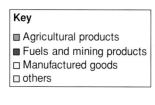

Before you finish eating breakfast this morning, you've depended on more than half the world.

Figure 1 Martin Luther King, the black American civil rights campaigner

KEY QUESTIONS

- How do international trade and aid operate?
- How effective are current international trade and aid systems in narrowing the economic gap between countries?
- How might different trade and aid systems create a more sustainable global economic system?

Speaking in the 1960s, Martin Luther King (Figure 1) reminds us that countries rely on each other for the goods and services that we all need for our daily lives. Since then, faster aircraft, larger ships, and the use of standard-sized containers for moving goods around the world have all contributed to making us rely even more on trade with other countries for our everyday needs.

Goods produced in one country and then sold abroad are exports. The goods that a country buys from abroad are **imports**. Countries also buy and sell services.

Comparing the UK and Ghana's trade

Shop in the local supermarket and you can buy a chocolate bar made from cocoa beans grown in Ghana. Ghana doesn't make much chocolate, but it does export a lot of beans and the European Union is its biggest customer. At the same time, people shopping in the supermarkets of Accra, Ghana's capital city, can buy tinned tomatoes or frozen chicken produced in the European Union. Ghana and the European Union trade with each other but, of course, they both trade with a lot of other countries as well.

Ghana imports a lot of manufactured goods whereas a lot of Ghana's exports are raw materials that haven't been processed – like cocoa beans. Later in the chapter we examine why this is. The UK, by comparison, exports a huge range of different processed and manufactured goods. One of the UK's most successful exports is TV and film. Figures 2, 3 and 4 illustrate some of these comparisons.

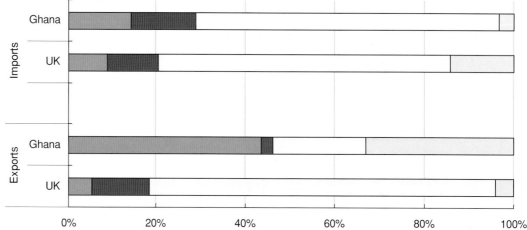

Key
- Agricultural products
- Fuels and mining products
- Manufactured goods
- others

Figure 2 Comparing the trade of Ghana and the UK by type of import and export (percentage figures)

Figure 3 Comparing the trade of Ghana and the UK by the value of their imports and exports

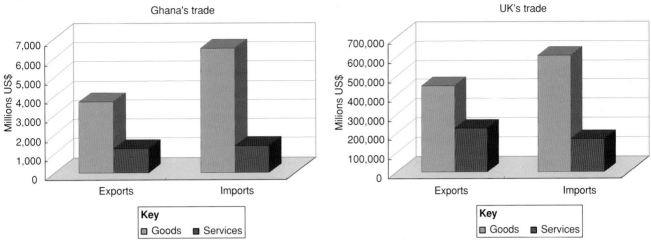

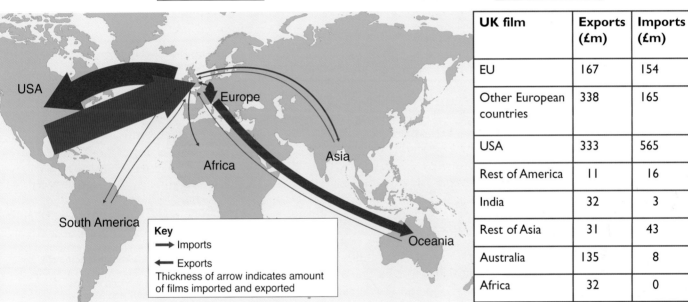

UK film	Exports (£m)	Imports (£m)
EU	167	154
Other European countries	338	165
USA	333	565
Rest of America	11	16
India	32	3
Rest of Asia	31	43
Australia	135	8
Africa	32	0

Figure 4 Imports and exports of film, 2006 (£million) between the UK and the rest of the world

Activity

1 Discuss Figure 1 with a partner. What do you think Martin Luther King meant?
  a) Make a list of all the things you have used by breakfast.
  b) Suggest which countries might export these items to the UK.
  c) Using the internet, research the main exporters of breakfast items such as coffee, tea and fresh orange juice.

2 Use Figures 2 and 3. Compare Ghana's trade with that of the UK. Pick out the main similarities and differences using connectives:

  whereas   similarly   on the other hand

3 Study Figure 4.
  a) To which regions does the UK export a greater value of film than it imports?
  b) Suggest two different advantages of the trade in film between the UK and the rest of the world.
  c) Is UK culture influenced equally by MEDCs and LEDCs? If not, why not?

Should trade be free and uncontrolled?

Free trade, or trade that takes place without any limits or control, is the aim of many countries. The advantage of free trade is that a country can export as many goods as it wants to its trade partners. This is good for the farmers and businesses who produce the exported goods and services. The disadvantage of free trade is that a country can find itself swamped by cheap imports made in countries that have lower labour costs. These cheap imports are good for consumers, but could cause jobs to be lost in similar industries within the importing country. To avoid this problem some countries protect themselves from cheap products. They can do this in one of three ways:

- Placing **quotas** that restrict the amount of these imported goods each year.
- Placing an **import duty** or tax on the imports to make them more expensive.
- Paying a **subsidy** to its own farmers and businesses so that their goods can be sold at a lower price to consumers.

The current international pattern of trade is a mixture of free trade and protected trade. This causes problems for both More Economically Developed Countries (MEDCs) and Less Economically Developed Countries (LEDCs). Figure 5 summarises three of these problems.

Farmers in the EU receive government subsidy to keep the cost of production low so that food is cheap for consumers in Europe. Some of this food is then exported to Africa.

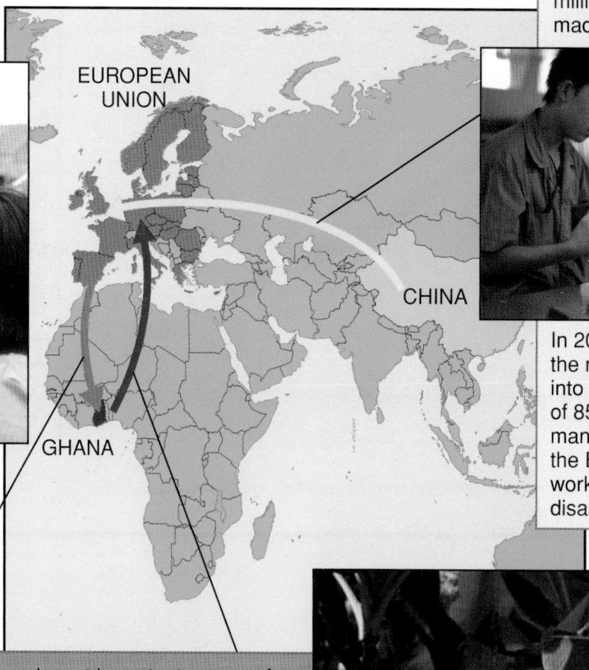

The EU imports billions of pairs of shoes from China and Vietnam. Half of the 2.5 million pairs of shoes sold in the EU were made in China.

In 2006, the EU placed a quota to restrict the number of shoes imported from Asia into Europe. It did this to protect the jobs of 850,000 people working in shoe manufacturing in Italy and elsewhere in the EU. However, the effect on low-paid workers in China and Vietnam could be disastrous.

Local farmers find it hard to sell their own tomatoes on this market in Accra, Ghana. Imports of frozen chicken, rice and tinned tomatoes (subsidised in the EU) are cheaper than local food.

Ghana's second most important source of foreign exchange comes from the export of cocoa beans. Most are sold to chocolate manufacturers in Europe and the USA.

Prices for primary commodities such as cocoa fluctuate up and down, making it hard for cocoa farmers to plan the growth of their business or even earn a decent wage. The average wage for a cocoa farmer in Ghana is just £160 a year.

EUROPEAN UNION

CHINA

GHANA

Figure 5 The problems created by the international pattern of trade

Trade blocs

Trade is made easier where partnerships have been agreed between countries. These trading partnerships are known as trade blocs. The European Union (EU) is one example of several **trade blocs** that exist around the world. Figure 6 shows two more. Each country within each bloc already has a free trade agreement with other countries in the bloc, or is working towards a free trade agreement. For example, China already has free trade agreements with some members of the Asia-Pacific Economic Co-operation (APEC) and is working towards similar partnerships with the other LEDC members of the group by 2010. However, it has no free trade partnership with the UK or with the EU. That is why the EU is able to impose the quota on imports of Chinese shoes described in Figure 5.

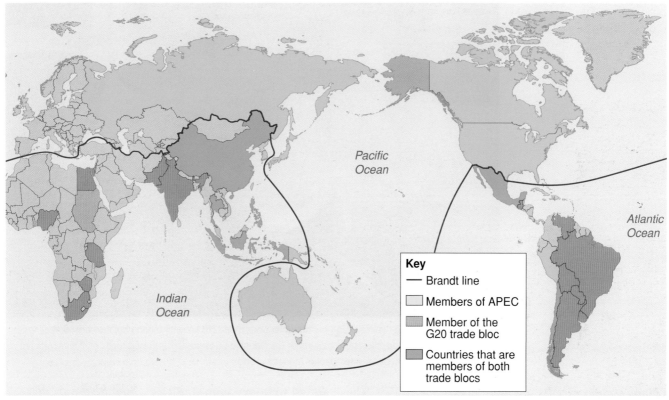

Key
— Brandt line
☐ Members of APEC
▦ Member of the G20 trade bloc
▩ Countries that are members of both trade blocs

Figure 6 Trade blocs: APEC and G20

Activity

4 Use the evidence in Figure 5 to explain the advantage of quotas and subsidies for:
   a) consumers in Europe
   b) farmers and businesses in Europe.

5 Explain the likely effect of:
   a) the EU shoe quota for workers in Vietnam
   b) the import of cheap food for farmers in Ghana.

6 Use Figure 6.
   a) Describe the distribution of APEC countries.
   b) Compare the distribution of APEC countries with that of G20 countries.

7 Explain the advantage of free trade for the LEDC countries in the G20 trade bloc.

 Ghana

A case study of Ghana and its trade

Figure 7 Joyce Oppong Kyekyeku and her daughter Doris breed chickens for a living but they are competing against cheaper imported chickens from Europe. The Ghanaian Government imposed tariffs on the imports but was forced to drop them by the International Monetary Fund

Ghana's main exports are gold, cocoa and timber. These are all **primary commodities** – raw materials that have not been processed. Ghana's imports include oil (another primary commodity) plus machinery, tools, vehicles and medical equipment – all **manufactured goods**. Ghana also earns money from abroad by attracting foreign tourists; we say that this is another way in which Ghana earns **foreign exchange**.

Like all countries, Ghana needs to trade successfully in order to create wealth and jobs. However, Ghana faces a number of problems with the international pattern of trade.

Ghana is not a member of any of the major trade blocs. For this reason it cannot rely on free trade with other countries. One of its main exports is cocoa beans. For years this product has had a relatively small tariff when it enters the EU: buyers have paid 3 per cent tax. However, the EU tariff on imports of processed cocoa products was much higher. For example, buyers of cocoa butter paid a 7.7 per cent import tax. This tariff was in place to protect the chocolate manufacturers in the EU from cheap imports of cocoa products. It made it very hard for manufacturers in Ghana to sell their cocoa products in Europe and so discouraged the growth of manufacturing.

However, things are at last beginning to improve for Ghana. In 2007 Ghana signed an Economic Partnership Agreement (EPA) with the EU. This guarantees it zero or lower tariffs on most of its exports to the EU until 2022. This includes a zero tariff on both cocoa beans and cocoa butter. So Ghana's cocoa farmers and chocolate manufacturers can now experience free trade.

Figure 8 Ghana's main imports and exports

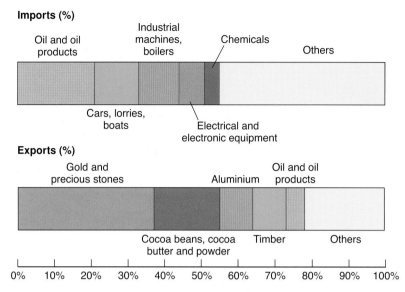

Imports (%)

Oil and oil products | Industrial machines, boilers | Chemicals | Others

Cars, lorries, boats | Electrical and electronic equipment

Exports (%)

Gold and precious stones | Aluminium | Oil and oil products

Cocoa beans, cocoa butter and powder | Timber | Others

0% 10% 20% 30% 40% 50% 60% 70% 80% 90% 100%

MAKE TRADE FAIR

Figure 9 The Make Trade Fair logo was launched by Oxfam in 2002. Oxfam is a Non-Governmental Organisation (NGO) that is drawing attention to the dumping of subsidised products in LEDCs

www.oxfam.org/en/campaigns/trade
This is the homepage of the Oxfam Trade Campaign. You'll find explanations of why the current pattern of international trade is unfair for LEDCs.

Another problem that Ghana experiences with trade is that food imported from the EU is sold so cheaply that it undercuts the cost of locally grown food. Imports of rice, chicken and tinned tomatoes are particularly cheap because the EU has subsidised the farmers who produce these goods. Any that cannot be sold in Europe are then sold cheaply in Africa: a practice known as **dumping**. Ghana tried to place import tariffs on these items but was forced to drop them as a condition of its loan from the World Bank.

Figure 10 Michael Stipe of the band REM has milk dumped on him to draw attention to the Make Trade Fair campaign. EU milk subsidies mean that European cows 'earn' US$2 a day, which is more than the daily income of a Ghanaian farmer

Activity

8 Use Figure 8 to complete the following description of Ghana's pattern of trade:

Ghana's largest export is … at 37 per cent, followed by cocoa beans which make up … per cent of Ghana's exports. Oil is the largest single import which makes up … per cent of all imports.

9 Which of Ghana's imports/exports are:
   a) primary commodities
   b) manufactured or processed goods.

10 Explain why Ghana would benefit from joining a trade bloc such as the G20.

11 Suggest how Ghana could benefit from the Make Trade Fair campaign.

12 Design a poster or leaflet featuring information about Ghana and headed 'Make Trade Fair for Ghana'.

Ghana and the cocoa trade

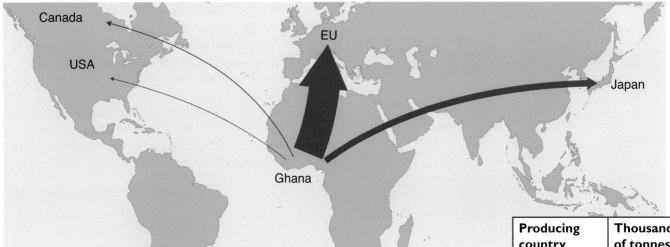

Figure 11 Typical flow of exports of cocoa from Ghana

Almost 90 per cent of all of Ghana's cocoa is grown on smallholdings: tiny farms that are smaller than 3 hectares. About 2.5 million smallholders in Ghana grow cocoa as their main crop. Most of the cocoa is sold for export; only about 5 per cent of Ghana's cocoa crop is processed into chocolate in Ghana.

Currently about 75 per cent of Ghana's cocoa beans are exported to the European Union. The main importing countries are the Netherlands, Germany, Belgium and France. The beans are ground into cocoa powder in these countries. Some of this powder is then exported to other EU countries where the chocolate is made. The main producers of chocolate are in Belgium, Germany, Ireland, the UK and Austria.

The production of cocoa beans goes up and down from year to year. Production depends on a number of factors such as weather conditions, pests and diseases. Figure 14 shows how production (supply) has fluctuated over a ten-year period. Most cocoa beans are processed into cocoa powder (known as grindings) before being used in the manufacture of chocolate. Figure 14 shows how demand for cocoa grindings has changed over the same period. When demand is higher than supply (as in 2007) the price for cocoa bean exports is high.

Producing country	Thousands of tonnes per year
Cote d'Ivoire	1610
Indonesia	574
Ghana	490
Nigeria	212
Brazil	180
Cameroon	129
Ecuador	94
Papua New Guinea	45
Dominican Rep.	44
Malaysia	43
Mexico	37
Colombia	27

Figure 12 The world's top cocoa producers, expected production in 2010

Activity

13 Use Figure 11 to complete the following statement:

All of Ghana's cocoa exports are sold in LEDCs / MEDCs. … is the largest buyer of Ghana's cocoa.

14 Use Figure 12.
a) Choose a suitable technique to illustrate the data.
b) Compare the amount of cocoa grown in Ghana with that grown in other countries.
c) If the EU imports more cocoa from other African producers, what would happen to the price of Ghana's cocoa?

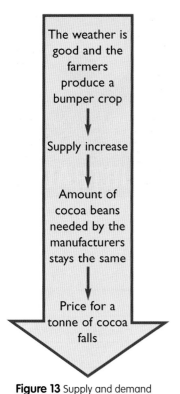

The weather is good and the farmers produce a bumper crop

↓

Supply increase

↓

Amount of cocoa beans needed by the manufacturers stays the same

↓

Price for a tonne of cocoa falls

Figure 13 Supply and demand

One major problem for cocoa growers is that the price they get for their crop is so low. The average income for a cocoa farmer is only about £160 a year. This is because of the way in which primary commodities such as cocoa beans are traded on the world market. Traders in Europe buy cocoa beans on the London Stock Exchange. They shop around and buy the beans from whichever supplier is cheapest. It's a buyer's market. If Ghana's farmers are asking too much for their beans, the buyers will shop around and buy from Côte d'Ivoire or whoever is cheapest. The price can go up or down from day to day, depending on supply and demand. Figure 12 shows that the EU buyers can purchase cocoa from a number of suppliers, but Ghana relies heavily on the EU for selling its cocoa. This fluctuating price makes it very difficult for farmers in Ghana to earn a fair wage for all of their work.

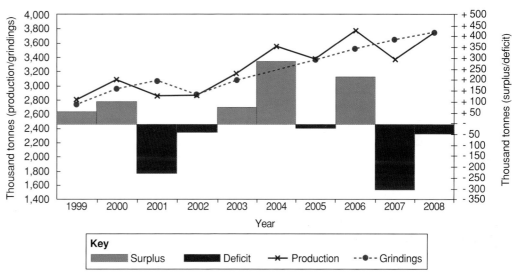

Figure 14 Production (supply) and grindings (demand) of cocoa over a ten-year period.

Activity

15 Study Figure 13. Make a similar flow chart which starts with the following statement:
A disease in many cocoa plantations means that the harvest is poor.

16 a) Describe the trend in production over the ten-year period.

b) Using your understanding of supply and demand, predict in which years the price of cocoa would have been highest and lowest.

17 Look at Figure 15. Suggest what will happen to the price of cocoa beans on the world market for each of these future scenarios.

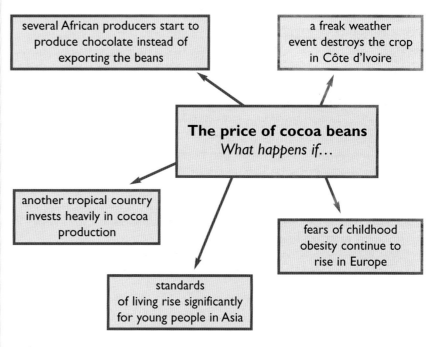

Figure 15 A futures wheel for cocoa

Fair trade

The concept of fair trade has been around for more than 30 years.
The Fairtrade Foundation was established in 1992 as an independent certification body that licenses the FAIRTRADE Mark to products that meet international standards that are set by Fairtrade Labelling Organisations International (FLO).

The FAIRTRADE Mark guarantees a better deal for farmers and workers in developing countries so that they can enjoy a better standard of living.

- The farmer receives a payment that is agreed and stable.
- The farmer also receives an additional payment called a **Fairtrade Premium**.
- One of the many aims of Fairtrade is to develop a long-term trading partnership with the producers.

Figure 17 The FAIRTRADE Mark

Figure 16 Sales of Fairtrade certified products in the UK

Estimated UK retail sales by value 1998–2007 (£ million)	1998	1999	2000	2001	2002	2003	2004	2005	2006	2007
Coffee	13.7	15.0	15.5	18.6	23.1	34.3	49.3	65.8	93.0	117.0
Tea	2.0	4.5	5.1	5.9	7.2	9.5	12.9	16.6	25.1	30.0
Chocolate/cocoa	1.0	2.3	3.6	6.0	7.0	10.9	16.5	21.9	29.7	34.0
Honey products	n/a	n/a	0.9	3.2	4.9	6.1	3.4	3.5	3.4	5.0
Bananas	n/a	n/a	7.8	14.6	17.3	24.3	30.6	47.7	65.6	150.0

The Kuapa Kokoo co-operative of cocoa farmers

Kuapa Kokoo is a co-operative of cocoa farmers in Ghana.
The co-operative sells part of its cocoa bean crop to Divine Chocolate Ltd. in the UK who make Fairtrade chocolate products such as Divine and Dubble. The main benefits of this arrangement are:

www.kuapako koogh.com is a website describing the co-operative.

- Farmers receive an extra US$150 per tonne for their cocoa which is about 10 per cent more than the usual price on the world market.
- The co-operative also receives a Premium that is then used to fund community projects such as the well in Figure 18.
- Farmers receive training to help them deal with problems such as pests or diseases that affect the cocoa crop, for example black pod.
- Members of the co-operative can borrow small amounts of money from a micro-credit bank, which is known as the Kuapa Kokoo Credit Union.
- The farmers have elected a trusted member of the village to weigh and record their cocoa beans. This makes trading more official and people more accountable.
- Kuapa Kokoo are shareholders in Divine Chocolate Ltd. Profits from the sale of chocolate bars are invested in projects in Ghana.

Activity

18 a) Use the data in Figure 16 to draw line graphs that show the changing number of sales of Fairtrade certified products in the UK.

b) Compare the trends on your graphs. Which products have been most successful? Suggest the reasons why there has been a growth in the sale of Fairtrade products.

19 Make some notes to show how Fairtrade has helped:

a) cocoa famers who belong to Kuapa Kokoo

b) the wider community.

20 Use Figure 19 to make a sketch map of Ghana. Label it using Figure 20 to show how different regions have benefited from Fairtrade.

Figure 18 The Premium is used by the producers for community projects such as this village well

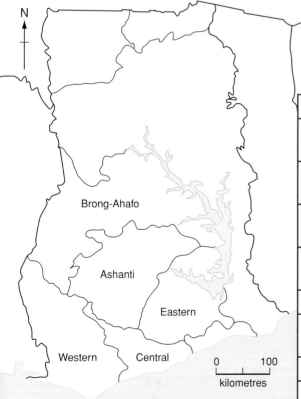

Figure 19 Where cocoa is grown in Ghana

Project	Number of projects in different regions					Total
	Western	Central	Eastern	Brong Ahafo	Ashanti	
Boreholes/ hand dug well	121	11	6	9	27	174
Women's project IGA	1	0	0	0	0	1
School/ education	0	1	1	0	2	4
Corn mills	10	4	3	2	8	27
Construction of latrines	0	0	0	0	2	2
Bridge	0	0	0	0	1	1
Total	132	16	10	11	40	209

Figure 20 How Kuapa Kokoo used the Social Premium, 1993 to 2002

Investigating different kinds of aid

The sub-Saharan countries of West Africa are some of the poorest in the world. Among these are Niger and Mali, which suffered from drought in 2005 and then flooding in 2007. Natural disasters like this, or the Boxing Day tsunami of December 2004, create massive media interest around the world. Individuals give generously to help the victims, and their money is spent by charities or Non-Governmental Organisations (NGOs) that deliver food, clean water, shelter and medical supplies. This help is described as **emergency aid**. However, emergency aid is only a small part of the total aid given by governments and NGOs such as Oxfam, ActionAid and Christian Aid. Most aid is, in fact, planned over long periods of time to tackle poverty and improve quality of life. This is known as long-term or **development aid**.

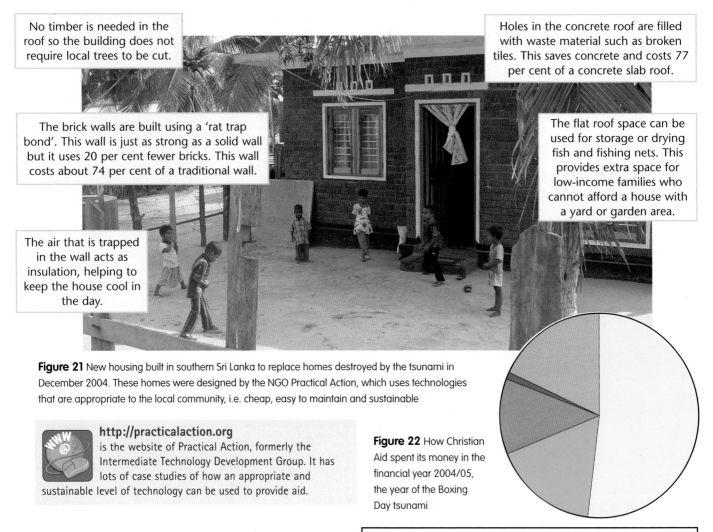

No timber is needed in the roof so the building does not require local trees to be cut.

Holes in the concrete roof are filled with waste material such as broken tiles. This saves concrete and costs 77 per cent of a concrete slab roof.

The brick walls are built using a 'rat trap bond'. This wall is just as strong as a solid wall but it uses 20 per cent fewer bricks. This wall costs about 74 per cent of a traditional wall.

The flat roof space can be used for storage or drying fish and fishing nets. This provides extra space for low-income families who cannot afford a house with a yard or garden area.

The air that is trapped in the wall acts as insulation, helping to keep the house cool in the day.

Figure 21 New housing built in southern Sri Lanka to replace homes destroyed by the tsunami in December 2004. These homes were designed by the NGO Practical Action, which uses technologies that are appropriate to the local community, i.e. cheap, easy to maintain and sustainable

http://practicalaction.org is the website of Practical Action, formerly the Intermediate Technology Development Group. It has lots of case studies of how an appropriate and sustainable level of technology can be used to provide aid.

Figure 22 How Christian Aid spent its money in the financial year 2004/05, the year of the Boxing Day tsunami

Expenditure 2004–2005 Direct charitable expenditure	£m	%
Development programmes	36.6	52
Emergencies	12.0	17
Campaigning, education and advocacy	8.6	12
Total	58.1	82
Fundraising	12.9	18
Grand total expenditure	**£71.0m**	

Key

- Over US $900
- US $650–$899
- US $400–$649
- Less than US $400

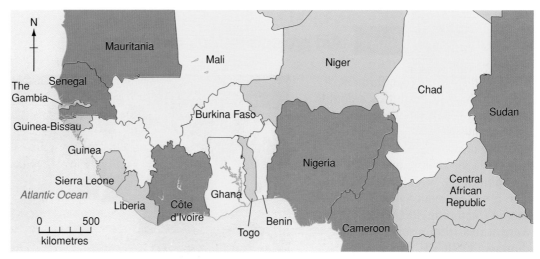

Figure 23 Gross National Income (GNI) per person 2008 for the countries of West Africa. Source: World Bank

Figure 24 Selected health indicators for Mali and Niger. Source: UNICEF

	Niger	Mali	UK
Under 5 mortality (deaths per 1,000 live births)	253	217	6
Life expectancy	58	54	79
% infants with a low birth weight	13	23	8
% population using improved (safe) drinking water	46	50	100
Maternal mortality (annual number of women who die from pregnancy-related causes per every 100,000 live births)	1800	970	8

Activity

21 Study Figure 21. Explain the benefits of this design for:
- the aid organisations that funded the reconstruction
- people who were rehoused
- the local environment.

22 Study Figure 22 and complete the following statement.

Christian Aid is an NGO that stands for …. In 2004/05 they gave … million to long-term development programmes, which is … per cent of their budget.

23 Compare the amount of money spent by Christian Aid on emergency aid and on development programmes.

24 Explain the difference between emergency aid and development aid.

25 Use Figure 23 to describe the distribution of the poorest countries in this region.

26 a) Use the data in Figure 24 to suggest why the life expectancy in Mali and Niger is so much lower than in the UK. You should be able to give at least three reasons.

b) Suggest what kind of development aid is needed in Mali and Niger to improve life expectancy.

Mali and Niger · Aid projects in Mali and Niger

In 2004, the subsistence farmers of Mali and Niger were hit by a double problem: a particularly severe drought and a plague of locusts virtually destroyed their crops. By July 2005 the crisis came to the attention of the world's media. By then it was estimated that 3.3 million people (including 800,000 children) were at risk from a serious food shortage. UNICEF, which was already working in Niger because it has a programme of long-term development aid in the country, was struggling to cope with the scale of the problem and asked for extra help to give emergency aid.

Figure 25 The food crisis in Niger

Figure 26 Location of the 2005 food crisis in Africa and percentage of population in the region who are usually undernourished

Countries affected by the 2005 food crisis are circled here.

Figure 27 Extract from UNICEF website describing the reaction to the Niger food crisis in 2005

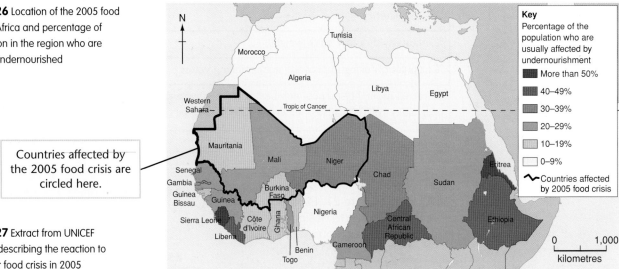

In light of this emergency, UNICEF Niger has routed an additional US$270,000 to treat 14,000 malnourished children for six months.

However, the children's agency urgently needs US$1.03 million to treat another 17,000 severely malnourished children with therapeutic food (a peanut butter based food called plumpynut and therapeutic milk) for six months, and make cereal accessible to another 163,000 people through the purchase of 641 tonnes to restock 65 cereal banks.

During the 2004 agricultural season, swarms of desert locusts consumed nearly 100 per cent of the crops in some areas. In addition, parts of the country received insufficient rainfall resulting in poor harvests and dry pasturelands, affecting both farmers and livestock breeders.

On a regular basis, UNICEF implements strategies to prevent malnutrition at the community level. Here are some examples:

- 245 cereal banks were opened in UNICEF's intervention zones to make staple grains (millet and sorghum) available. Before the harvest, when food supplies are low and hunger increases, cereal banks loan food to mothers. After harvest, the women repay their loans in cash or grain.

- UNICEF also supports 300 women's groups that promote exclusive breastfeeding and monitor children's growth in the villages. Women with malnourished children receive loans of goats to enrich their families' diets with milk and cheese.

- Twice a year, vitamin A supplements are provided to all children under the age of five. Supplementary feeding centres receive therapeutic food for severely malnourished children. This food is high in protein and fat.

Long-term development aid projects in Niger and Mali

In 2005 the UK Government gave £3 million to the World Food Programme's emergency operation to help relieve the crisis in Niger. Each £1 million was enough to feed 200,000 people for one month. In 2006 the UK Government gave a further £2 million of emergency aid to support the diet of families in Niger before the next harvest was available.

The UK Government also funds a number of long-term development projects in this region. Between 2006 and 2009 the Government spent £500,000 each year in Niger, Mali and Burkina Faso, helping to improve diet and nutrition. It is also working with the French Government in a long-term project to improve girls' education in Niger.

Oxfam is one of many Non-Governmental Organisations that provide long-term development aid to Niger and Mali. In one of its projects it is working with the Association for the Indigenous Development of the Sahel (ADESAH), a local NGO, to support primary schools for the children of **pastoral farmers** who live in the border area between western Niger and northern Mali. This nomadic community of cattle and goat herders is very poor. Many families do not feel they can afford to send their children to school, especially girls. The project supports 48 primary schools. Its successes include the following:

Figure 28 Class in Taboye school, Mali, which has received support from Oxfam and the local NGO ADESAH. It's a Millennium Development Goal to ensure that all boys and girls in the world complete their primary education

- In 2004, 4,053 pupils were enrolled in school, including 1,818 girls (44.85 per cent).
- Women are deeply involved in the management of the schools and participate physically and financially in the payment of children's school fees and in the canteen.
- The ratio of books to pupils has improved from one book for five pupils to two books for three pupils.

Activity

27 Use Figure 26 to describe the distribution (see page 25) of countries that have:
 a) between 0 and 9 per cent of the population who are undernourished
 b) more than 30 per cent of the population who are undernourished.

28 Suggest reasons why some countries in Africa are more vulnerable to food shortages than others.

29 Read the web extract in Figure 27.
 a) Give two reasons for the food crisis.
 b) Use Figure 27 to give examples of both UNICEF's emergency aid and long-term aid programmes.

30 Explain the difference between the aims of UNICEF's emergency aid and long-term strategies to prevent malnutrition.

31 Give three details that describe the group who benefit from Oxfam's project.

32 Give two facts that can be used as measures of success of this project.

33 Try to explain why Oxfam may have chosen to fund a project that gives aid to girls and women.

34 Use the internet links below to prepare a brief report on a long-term aid programme to either Mali or Niger. Include in your report:
 - how different groups of people (for example children, women, farmers) benefit from the aid
 - facts you could use to evaluate the success of the project.

www.oxfam.org.uk
www.trickleup.org
www.wateraid.org.uk
The NGOs whose websites are listed above have long-term aid projects in Mali and Niger.

Going Further

Overseas Development Aid

The UK Government funds many long-term development projects abroad. This is called **Overseas Development Aid (ODA)**. The UK Government gave £4.1 billion of ODA in the financial year 2004–2005. This rose to £6.5 billion by 2007–2008. Some of this is given directly to fund projects in Less Economically Developed Countries (LEDCs) such as Ghana.

This is known as **bi-lateral aid** because the aid passes directly from one country to a partner country. The rest of the UK's aid is pooled with money donated by the other governments of the European Union (EU). The EU then decides which projects to fund. This type of funding is known as **multi-lateral aid** because many donors are involved.

	1990	1995	2000	2002	2003
Total ODA as a percentage of national income	0.27	0.29	0.32	0.31	0.34

Figure 29 The changing pattern of the UK Government's Overseas Development Aid (ODA)

The Millennium Development Goals

The United Nations (UN) has set development targets known as the **Millennium Development Goals** (**MDGs**), which it aims to meet by 2015.

1 End extreme poverty and hunger:
  - Halve the number of people living on less than a dollar a day.
  - Halve the number who suffer from hunger.

2 Achieve universal primary education:
  - Ensure that all boys and girls complete a full course of primary schooling.

3 Promote gender equality:
  - Make it easier for girls as well as boys to access primary and secondary education.

4 Reduce child mortality:
  - Reduce by two-thirds the number of children who die before their fifth birthday.

5 Improve health for mothers:
  - Reduce by three-quarters the number of women who die in childbirth.

6 Combat AIDS, malaria and other diseases:
  - Halt and begin to reverse the spread of these killer diseases.

7 Ensure environmental sustainability:
  - Protect the environment, so that future generations can continue to benefit from it.
  - Halve the number of people without access to clean water.
  - Improve life for 100 million people who live in shanty towns by 2020.

8 Build global partnerships for development:
  - Make improvements to aid.
  - Boost freedom, justice and democracy.
  - Make it easier for the poorest people to have access to medicines.
  - Cancel some debts and reduce others.
  - Make world trade fairer.

Figure 30 Target 2015 UN Millennium Development Goals

Activity

35 Study Figure 29.
  a) Choose a suitable technique to graph the change in ODA as a percentage of national income.
  b) The United Nations has set all MEDC governments a target of giving 0.7 per cent of their wealth as ODA by 2015. Using the trend of the graph you have drawn, predict whether the UK will meet this target.

36 Study Figure 29. What has happened to the percentage of aid that is given as bi-lateral aid?

37 Can you suggest any advantages for the UK Government (or tax payer) of having more bi-lateral aid than multi-lateral aid projects?

Figure 31 UK Government ODA (£ millions)

	2005 ODA	2006 ODA	Change (£ millions)	Percentage change
Total ODA	5,923	6,851	928	15.7
of which bi-lateral	4,491	4,695	204	4.5
of which bi-lateral sub-Saharan Africa	2,071	2,912	841	40.6

Millennium Development Goal 2: DFID's aid to education

Globally, there are some 75 million primary-aged children not enrolled in school – 55 per cent (41 million) of whom are girls (UNESCO Institute of Statistics, 2008). This lack of basic education deprives young people of choices and opportunities, and makes it harder for countries in the developing world to tackle poverty and disease.

Sub-Saharan Africa accounts for more out-of-school children than any other region: 35 million, including 19 million girls (UIS). Meanwhile, across South and West Asia 18 million primary-aged children are out of school, 10 million of them girls (UIS).

But progress is being made. Global enrolment in primary education increased by over 41 million between 1999 and 2005. There are now 95 girls enrolled in school for every 100 boys, compared with 92 girls for every 100 boys in 1999. The number of primary-aged children not enrolled in school fell by over 28 million between 1999 and 2006.

DFID is spending £8.5 billion pounds over ten years to ensure that, by 2015, children everywhere, boys and girls alike, will be able to complete at least five years of quality education. Most of the money will be going to sub-Saharan Africa and South Asia.

We are working closely with the governments of poor countries to improve both the access to and the quality of schooling.

Although it's a tough target, the achievements of some countries do give grounds for optimism. In countries like Uganda and Malawi, for example, the number of children enrolling in primary school has doubled in five years and is now over 90 per cent.

Figure 32 A web extract from the UK's Department for International Development (DFID).

Activity

38 a) Choose a suitable graphical technique to display the data in Figure 31.
  b) Describe how the focus of the UK's Overseas Development Aid is changing.
  c) Suggest why the UK Government may have chosen to shift the focus of its aid.

39 Summarise the information in Figure 32 under two headings:
  a) Development challenges (outlining the problems facing children today)
  b) Progress (outlining the progress towards reaching MDG2 on education).

40 a) Study Figure 33. Which regions are:
    i)   likely to reach their target
    ii) unlikely to reach their target?
  b) Discuss why we need to set these targets.

41 Produce a 400-word newspaper article explaining:
  a) why we need to achieve the Millennium Development Goal for water and sanitation
  b) how we could achieve it.

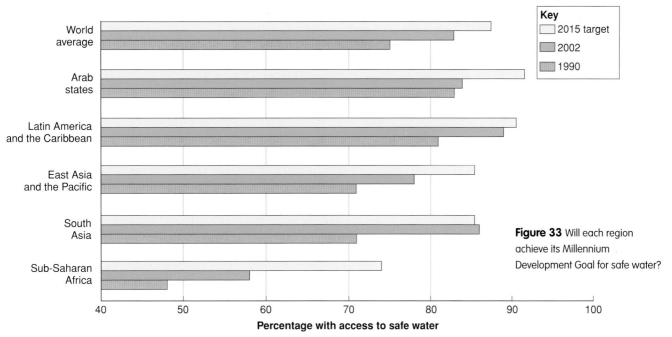

Figure 33 Will each region achieve its Millennium Development Goal for safe water?

Percentage with access to safe water

Key
- 2015 target
- 2002
- 1990

Chapter 5
Location of economic activities

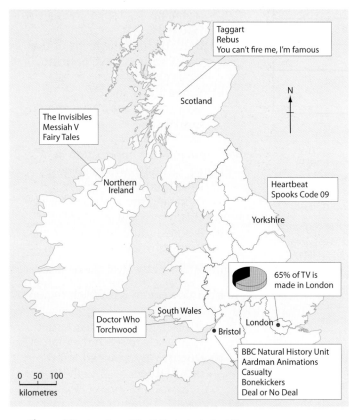

Figure 1 The location of the TV industry in the UK

Figure 2 A newspaper extract. Source: *The Guardian* 23 June 2008

KEY QUESTIONS

- Who makes decisions about the present and future location of economic activities?
- What factors influence decisions about where to locate different economic activities?
- How and why have the locations of different activities changed?

Where is UK TV and film made?

The creative industries in the UK are an important part of the service (or tertiary) sector of the economy. This sector includes jobs in TV, film, publishing, design and video game programming. It is estimated that these kinds of industries add over £100 billion to the national economy each year and employ 2 million people. There are jobs all over the country. Yorkshire, for example, is home to four of the world's top video game programming companies. However, two-thirds of the UK's TV and film is made in London. Figure 1 shows the location of some of the programmes made outside the capital.

About 7.5 million people live in London. So over 50 million people live in other parts of the UK

In other words, TV made by the big broadcasters such as the BBC or ITV

Companies who are based in London but who make television programmes that they then sell to the broadcasters like BBC or ITV

Who do you think the author means here?

The motorway that surrounds London

Some rural communities complain that too much TV (especially the news) is about urban areas. Do you think they have a point?

Why do you think the author chose these particular programmes?

A national issue

Does British TV reflect life in Britain today? London represents 12.5 per cent of the population, yet around 65 per cent of television is made in-house in London or by London-based independent production companies.

The capital is obviously the media centre of the UK, where much of the TV money is and where much of the talent gathers, but there are those who argue it would be healthier if more networked programmes were made beyond the M25. They say it would enrich our viewing, educate and entertain more, and fulfil the much-trumpeted public-service broadcasting remits of the broadcasters.

According to its charter, the BBC is supposed 'to represent the UK, its nations, regions and communities', but does it? And what about the other broadcasters?

Certainly if you poll people who live outside London they want more regional programming and more national networked programmes made regionally.

The success of the likes of *Heartbeat*, made in Yorkshire, *Doctor Who* (Cardiff), *Hollyoaks* (Liverpool) and *Casualty* (Bristol) proves that the talent and infrastructure are there outside London.

Who decides where your TV programmes are made?

The people who make decisions in the TV industry either work for one of the broadcasters (BBC, ITV, Channel 4 or Five) or they work for an independent film maker (like Aardman Animation, which makes *Shaun the Sheep*). They base their decision on where to make their programmes on a number of factors. Some of these are suggested in Figure 4. Another group of people who have a say in where TV is made is Ofcom. Ofcom is the body that keeps an eye on the TV, radio and telecoms businesses. It has to report its findings annually to the government. Ofcom believes that more of your TV programmes should be made regionally. This reflects a government aim to create jobs in the regions outside of the South East of England. Ofcom also believes that more regional TV is wanted by the consumers. They have, therefore, introduced quotas for each broadcaster. ITV should make 50 per cent of its programmes outside London. For BBC the quota is 30 per cent, Channel 4's is also 30 per cent, and Five's is 10 per cent.

Figure 3 David Tennant on the set of cult TV programme *Doctor Who*. The recent series was filmed in South Wales. Why do you think it was filmed there?

Figure 4 Factors affecting the location of the TV and film industry

Regional universities are producing creative graduates with the right skills for the industry.

Ashley Pharoah (*Life on Mars* and *Bonekickers*) chose to shoot *Bonekickers* in Bath. The city has not been used as a location for much TV before, so he thinks it makes the programme seem fresh and new.

The actor's union, Equity, claims that 40 per cent of all the UK's actors live in London.

TV producers often work to tight deadlines. They don't have time to look for talented actors or technicians outside London.

Some writers like to work from home. Russell T. Davies (*Doctor Who*) was born in Swansea and had moved back to Wales before *Doctor Who* was made in Cardiff.

One-third of TV script writers live and work in London.

People want to watch TV programmes made in their own regions featuring local people with local accents.

There is a lot of creative talent in the regions. Yorkshire, for example, is home to 100 new media companies.

The big film studios, like Pinewood (where 007 films are shot), are all on the outskirts of London, so there is a concentration of specialised film jobs there.

Ofcom is setting challenging quotas to create programmes in the regions.

Activity

1 Describe the distribution of TV production in the UK.

2 Working in pairs, discuss Figures 1 and 2.
   a) Outline the arguments for making more TV outside London.
   b) Do you think TV represents your local area or your (urban or rural) community? Explain how increased regional TV production could help your community. If you have access to ICT or a video camera, use it to make your case.

3 Identify three different groups of people who influence the decision about where TV is made.

4 Use Figure 4. Fully explain the reasons:
   a) for continuing to make TV in London
   b) for moving more production to the regions.

What factors attract business?

A large number of secondary and tertiary businesses are located in a region stretching from South Wales eastwards towards London and northwards towards Cambridge. This region is often described as the M4/M11 corridor. These businesses include many multi-national companies. Nokia, the Finnish manufacturer of mobile phones, is one such multi-national company (MNC). Nokia employs 2,000 people in the UK at three sites. Two of these are close to Cambridge and the third is in the M4 corridor. Figure 5 gives some of the reasons for this region's success in attracting industries.

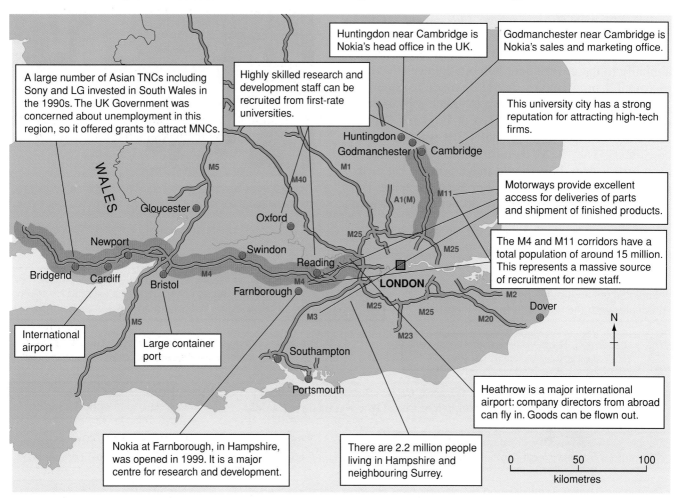

Figure 5 The location of Nokia in the UK

Activity

5 Study Figure 5.
   a) Give five reasons why MNCs might be attracted to the M4 and M11 corridors.
   b) Suggest why Nokia is located in Surrey and Cambridgeshire, rather than in South Wales.

6 a) Choose a suitable technique to graph the data in Figure 6.
   b) Suggest why these types of business are located so close to Cambridge.

7 Give six-figure grid references for:
   a) Cody Technology Park
   b) Junction 4a on the M3 motorway.

8 Use evidence from Figure 7 to explain why Nokia may have located in grid square 8355 near to Farnborough.

Figure 6 Types of business, and number owned by foreign MNCs, on Cambridge Science Park

Type of business	Number	Foreign MNCs
Biomedical	18	4
Computers and telecommunications	25	8
Technical consultants	7	2
Energy	1	0
Environmental	1	1
Financial	4	0
Industrial technologies	4	1
Other	13	4
Total	73	20

Nokia's plant at Farnborough is one of the Company's research and development centres. This is where Nokia develops and tests new products and new technologies. The staff who work here are highly skilled and have expertise in science, engineering or specialist ICT skills. Companies like Nokia often choose to locate this kind of plant close to other businesses that are conducting similar research. These companies have similar needs and are all supported by other businesses that supply specialist components or specialised technical advice and support. They therefore cluster together on specialised industrial estates that have become known as **science parks** or **technology parks**.

It's difficult to know exactly how many jobs have been created in the UK by the investment of foreign MNCs. Figure 6 suggests that one in four businesses on the famous Cambridge Science Park are foreign MNCs.

EXAMINER'S TIPS

Using evidence from OS map extracts II

Each examination will have an Ordnance Survey, or equivalent, map extract. You will almost certainly be asked a question about the map. Therefore it is important that you understand how to get the best out of a map.

Questions

Questions are likely to be of two general types:

1 Those that ask you to *read* the map. For example, 'What is found at grid reference 815555?' Answer 'A roundabout.'

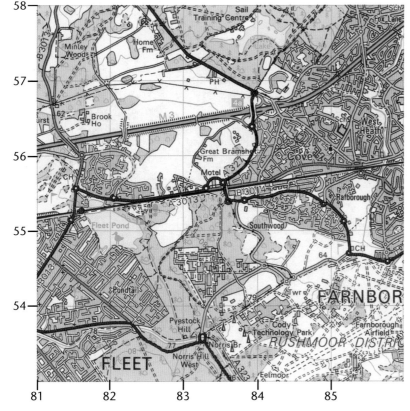

2 Those that ask you to *interpret* the map. For example, 'Use map evidence to explain how the local environment might benefit workers at the Nokia factory?' Obviously, a good answer would quote direct evidence from the map: 'The workers may appreciate the woodland views immediately south of the factory. They could use the golf courses in grid squares 8155 and 8555 and would have easy access to the factory by the motorway junction centred on grid reference 839566.'

Write two examination questions of your own for Figure 7, one asking for map reading and the other for map interpretation. Ask another member of your group to answer them.

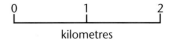

Figure 7 An Ordnance Survey extract of the Nokia site, Farnborough. Scale 1:50,000 Sheet 186. Nokia's research and development plant is in grid square 8355

227

What is the future of UK TV and film?

The TV and film industry is changing rapidly. Changing technology has allowed the number of channels to expand rapidly. Up until 1980 there were only three (terrestrial) channels in the UK. Channel 4 was added in 1982 and Five was added in 1996. Since 1994 there has been a massive increase in channels available to UK viewers via satellite or cable TV. By 2002 it was estimated that UK viewers could watch 320 different channels. Now that many more homes have broadband connections the option of watching TV on your computer means that many households can watch hundreds of different channels. This has meant a lot of extra competition for the main terrestrial channels such as BBC1 and ITV. As we have seen, these channels are expected to produce some of their programmes in the UK's regions. However, ITV has struggled in recent years to meet its Ofcom target of 50 per cent of production to be made outside London. In 2006–2007 it managed 42 per cent and in 2007–2008 it produced 44 per cent in the regions. In 2008 Ofcom announced it would reduce its target to 35 per cent. This has allowed ITV to make cuts in its regional production. In autumn 2008 ITV announced that it would be reducing the number of regional news programmes it makes from 17 down to 9. This would cause job losses and would save the company £40 million.

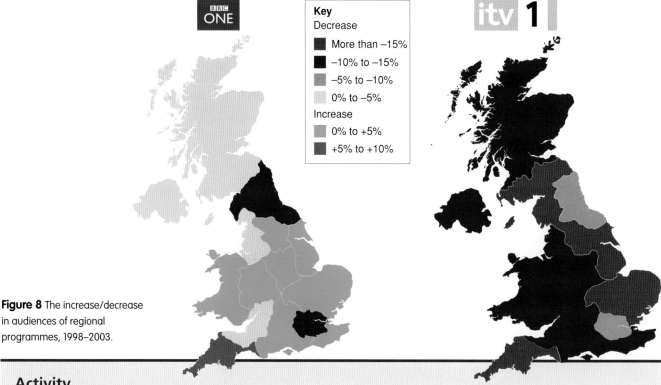

Key
Decrease
- More than −15%
- −10% to −15%
- −5% to −10%
- 0% to −5%

Increase
- 0% to +5%
- +5% to +10%

Figure 8 The increase/decrease in audiences of regional programmes, 1998–2003.

Activity

9 **a)** Describe and explain how TV is changing.
   b) Suggest how the growth of satellite or internet TV will affect TV production in the UK regions.

10 Use Figure 8 to describe the distribution of TV regions where viewing has:
   a) declined
   b) increased.

11 Use Figure 9 to outline the arguments for and against:
   a) moving more TV production to London
   b) moving all TV production to London.
   c) Suggest how these changes will affect the economy of places like Plymouth where a TV studio is likely to close.

12 **a)** Use Figure 10 to identify the main threats to the UK's creative industries.
   b) Explain what would happen in the UK if some of our creative industries decided to relocate to other parts of the globe.

Figure 9 Different points of view: should ITV move some of its production from the regions to London?

ITV manager

We have to win the battle for TV ratings. We rely on advertising to fund our TV production. Advertisers want their adverts to be seen by millions of viewers. Unfortunately, regional programmes do not get huge numbers of viewers. Nearly all of our most successful programmes, including the soaps, are made in London. In London there is a concentration of skilled people working in the TV industry so we can make more popular programmes more cheaply here. So we want to make more TV programmes in London and we believe by closing some regional studios we can save £40 million.

Regional TV producer

Our viewers want to see TV dramas and documentaries that reflect their community and culture. I believe that we can make really popular regional television, but it's almost impossible to persuade the ITV bosses to give us the peak slots in the evening. So our programmes are only shown when there are fewer viewers watching and the advertisers don't want to invest money in those programmes.

Member of National Union of Journalists

These cuts in regional TV will mean 430 people will lose their jobs. For example, ITV are planning to cut 90 jobs in the South West when the Plymouth TV studio is closed. Unless the bosses at ITV discuss their plans for the future of regional news with the union there will be industrial action.

Viewer

I would like to see more television programmes made locally. It seems to me that a lot of TV is made in London. It doesn't represent the issues or interests of people living in my part of the country. Besides, if more TV were made here it would help boost the local economy.

Figure 10 Extract from a speech by James Purnell, Secretary of State for Work and Pensions.

Making Britain the World's Creative Hub

Look at the way the creative industries have helped to transform Manchester, Gateshead or Glasgow. Over the last decade, your sectors have grown twice as fast as the overall economy. Today, they employ 2 million people – and account for a twelfth of our economy, more than in any other country.

Once we were known as the workshop of the world; but many of those industries have shrunk or disappeared. It would be a terrible day if in twenty or thirty years' time, people were saying the same about our creative industries. If they were saying, remember when we used to have the world's best advertising agencies. Or remember when Britain's television or design were the envy of the world?

That is a genuine threat. In terms of sheer volume, Bollywood is the biggest film industry in the world. China turned out over 2 million graduates last year. South Korea has one of the best online content industries in the world and a digital infrastructure of which most Western countries can only dream.

But the UK's current strength in creative industries is also a real opportunity. The UN estimates that creative industries account for 7 per cent of global GDP and are growing at 10 per cent a year. As people grow richer and become better educated, they spend more of their income on leisure activities.

So, the opportunity is clear – these markets will continue to grow, and Britain is good at them.

Chapter 6
Multi-national companies and globalisation

KEY QUESTIONS

- How do MNCs affect patterns of work and development?
- How do these companies cause positive and negative multiplier effects?

Investigating the role of multi-national companies in the global world of business

The world is increasingly interdependent: more and more places are being linked together by flows of money, ideas and goods. This process is known as globalisation. Key players in the process of globalisation have been multi-national companies (MNCs), or trans-national companies (TNCs).

Products such as soft drinks, fast food, mobile phones and clothing have global appeal and a global marketplace. The production and sale of these consumer goods is dominated by a relatively small number of manufacturers known as multi-national companies. For a company to be defined as an MNC it has to have branches in more than one country. The branches of an MNC include offices, factories and research and development (R&D) laboratories. Why do MNCs have branches located in different countries?

Figure 1 A mobile phone: a multi-national product

Activity

1 Study Figure 3 and use it complete a table like the one below:

Type of employment	Example	Place	MEDC or LEDC
Primary	1 Drilling for oil 2		
Secondary	1 Processing coltan 2	China	LEDC
Tertiary	1 2		

2 Study Figures 2 and 3 and use them to complete the following description:

Fifty-two per cent of Nokia's employees work in the continent of .... A total of ... per cent of their employees work in China and the Asia Pacific region. Many of these work in ... industries making items such as ... and .... Most of Nokia's sales are in .... Second is the Asia Pacific region with ... per cent of sales.

3 Work in pairs to structure a globalisation enquiry.
   a) Choose one of these titles: 'World in your living room' or 'World in your wardrobe'.
   b) Brainstorm all the different places you might find 'Made in...' information.
   c) Design a data collection sheet that you could use to record results from your classmates.
   d) Collect the data from at least five classmates and plot the data on a world outline map or make a large poster with photos you have collected from magazines or the internet.

4 Suggest why Nokia equips its phones with SIM cards and batteries made by a number of different manufacturers in Asia.

a) Sales by region in 2007

Key
- Europe
- Asia Pacific
- Middle East and Africa
- China
- Latin America
- North America

4%
8%
13%
39%
14%
22%

Nokia's headquarters are in Finland. Decisions about the next generation of wireless technology and communications that you will be buying are made here.

b) Employees by region in 2007

Key
- Europe
- Asia Pacific
- China
- Latin America
- North America
- Middle East and Africa

5%
4%
11%
12%
16%
52%

The plastic case of your mobile is made from crude oil. A large number of countries produce oil, but much of it comes from this region.

Figure 2 Nokia's sales (a) and employees (b) by region, December 2007

The battery for your mobile phone could also come from a number of different manufacturers. Many batteries are made in China.

Nokia has a number of branches where it conducts research and development into mobile technology. One of them is in Farnborough in the UK.

Have you got or are you going to get a TV phone? The technology for receiving television on your mobile was first developed in South Korea in 2002.

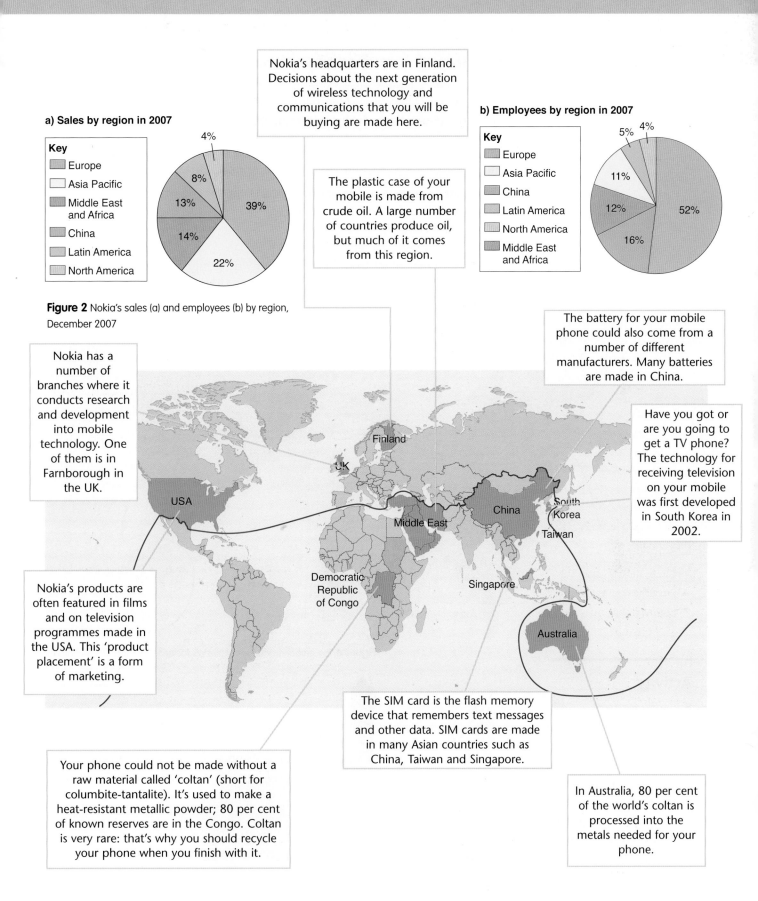

Finland

UK

USA

China

South Korea

Taiwan

Middle East

Democratic Republic of Congo

Singapore

Australia

Nokia's products are often featured in films and on television programmes made in the USA. This 'product placement' is a form of marketing.

The SIM card is the flash memory device that remembers text messages and other data. SIM cards are made in many Asian countries such as China, Taiwan and Singapore.

Your phone could not be made without a raw material called 'coltan' (short for columbite-tantalite). It's used to make a heat-resistant metallic powder; 80 per cent of known reserves are in the Congo. Coltan is very rare: that's why you should recycle your phone when you finish with it.

In Australia, 80 per cent of the world's coltan is processed into the metals needed for your phone.

Figure 3 The world in your mobile phone

Nokia

A case study of a multi-national company

Nokia is the world's largest manufacturer of mobile phones and other mobile devices. It also provides network and communication services to other businesses, improving communications. Nokia is a Finnish MNC. Its head office is in Helsinki, Finland, but it has offices and factories all around the globe. Nokia and Nokia Siemens Networks employ more than 112,000 people worldwide. Nokia has **plants** (offices, factories and laboratories) in many different countries:

- research and development laboratories (R&D) in ten countries employing 30,415 people
- factories in ten countries
- sales offices in more than 150 countries.

Why does Nokia have plants located in so many different countries?

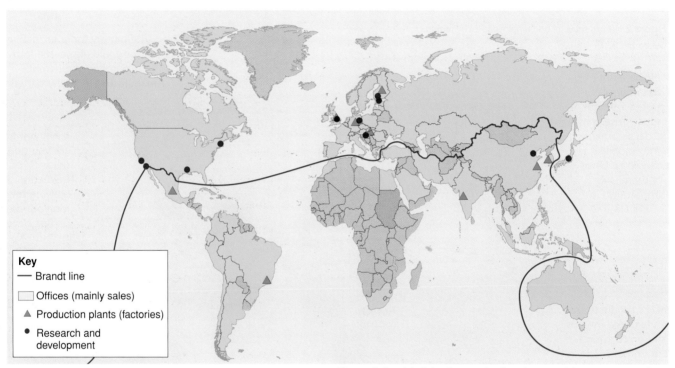

Key
— Brandt line
☐ Offices (mainly sales)
▲ Production plants (factories)
● Research and development

Figure 4 The global distribution of Nokia's factories, laboratories and offices

Activity

5 Study Figure 4.
   a) Describe the distribution (see page 25) of countries in which Nokia has production plants.
   b) Describe the distribution of countries in which Nokia has R&D laboratories.

Figure 5 Adverts for Nokia and Pepsi (another MNC) in Moscow, Russia

Locating business to minimise costs

MNCs such as Nokia have branches in many countries because they want to reduce costs. With lower costs, their profits are higher. MNCs such as Nokia keep costs low by opening factories and offices in regions of the world that have:

- low labour costs
- cheap land or building costs
- low **business rates** (the tax paid by a company).

Locating business to be close to the customer

Another reason why Nokia is constantly expanding its range of factories and offices is to be close to its customers, who are spread right across the globe. Nokia's products have massive appeal. Nokia estimates that the mobile phone market had around 2.2 billion people in 2005 and the company expects this to rise to 4 billion in 2009. Growth in mobile phone ownership and subscription has been particularly strong in Less Economically Developed Countries (LEDCs). As consumers in LEDCs have become wealthier, Nokia has expanded its business into Asia, Africa and South America. It has, therefore, opened new sales offices in many LEDCs, located closer to these new customers.

		2003	2004	2005	2006	2007
MEDCs	Finland	22,274	23,069	23,485	23,894	23,015
	UK	1,947	1,903	1,956	2,317	2,618
	USA	6,636	6,706	5,883	5,127	5,269
	Hungary	2,571	3,778	4,186	4,947	6,601
	Germany	3,486	3,522	3,610	3,887	13,926
	Italy	0	0	0	493	2,129
LEDCs	Brazil	1,497	2,640	2,184	1,960	8,527
	China	4,595	4,788	5,860	7,191	12,856
	Mexico	1,290	1,160	1,901	2,764	3,056
	India	184	591	1,609	6,494	11,491

Figure 6 Nokia's employees, 2003–07, in ten countries with most employees. Source: Nokia

		2003	2004	2005	2006	2007
MEDCs	USA	4,488	3,430	2,743	2,815	2,124
	UK	2,711	2,269	2,405	2,425	2,574
	Germany	2,297	1,730	1,982	2,060	2,641
	Russia	569	946	1,410	1,518	2,012
	Italy	1,003	884	1,160	1,394	1,792
	Spain	748	768	923	1,139	1,830
LEDCs	China	2,023	2,678	3,403	4,913	5,898
	India	1,064	1,369	2,022	2,713	3,684
	Indonesia	n.d.	n.d.	727	1,069	1,754
	Brazil	n.d.	n.d.	614	1,044	1,257

Figure 7 Nokia's sales, 2003–07 (millions of Euros), in ten countries with most sales. Source: Nokia

Activity

6 Choose two countries, one from each of the following lists:
   MEDCs: Germany, UK, USA
   LEDCs: China, India
   a) Choose a suitable technique to graph the data shown in Figures 6 and 7 for your chosen countries.
   b) Describe the trend shown on each graph.

7 Study Figures 6 and 7. Suggest two alternative reasons for:
   a) the increased sales in LEDCs
   b) the rising employment figures in LEDCs
   c) the falling employment figures in some MEDCs.

8 Study the distribution of Nokia's branches in Figure 4 again. If jobs in R&D are more specialised and highly paid than in other branches, suggest how this distribution:
   a) benefits workers in MEDCs
   b) disadvantages workers in LEDCs.

Figure 8 A Chinese worker tests mobile phones at a production plant in Ningbo, China

The advantages and disadvantages of MNC investment

When an MNC such as Nokia opens a new factory or office it can have a positive impact on local people and the local economy. Some jobs are created by the firm itself: Nokia employs 2,000 people in the UK at three sites. This is a **direct benefit** of the investment made by Nokia in the UK. These new jobs may help to stimulate extra work for other local businesses. This extra work is an **indirect benefit** of the investment made by the MNC. These benefits to the local economy are known as a **positive multiplier**.

Different jobs in different locations

Nokia employs a wide range of staff. Some are highly qualified or skilled, such as business managers or R&D staff. Other staff, such as some assembly workers or sales staff, do not require high-level qualifications or as much training. So, like many other MNCs, Nokia has chosen to locate the assembly of basic products in their range in LEDCs where wages are lower.

However, the more highly trained R&D staff tend to work in More Economically Developed Countries (MEDCs). Here, Nokia develops new products, such as hand-held devices capable of filming video, playing games and surfing the web. These devices use the latest technology and therefore need more highly trained staff to develop and produce them. These high-tech products are also aimed at wealthier consumers, usually in MEDCs, so it makes sense to make them in Europe.

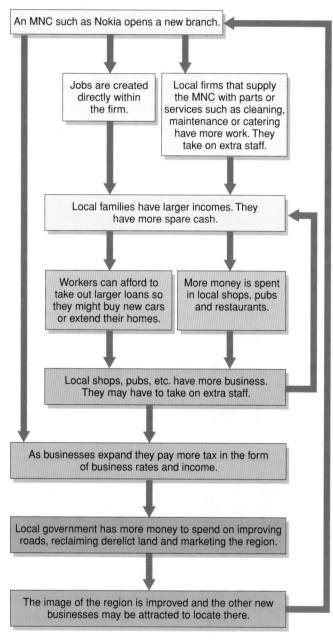

Figure 9 The positive multiplier effect

Activity

9 Explain the difference between direct and indirect benefits of MNC investment in a new factory or office.

10 Summarise the benefits of the positive multiplier under these headings:
   a) Jobs
   b) Earnings
   c) Spending
   d) Image of the region.

The advantages of new technology for Africa

The growth of mobile technology and of MNCs such as Vodacom that provide mobile networks has helped improve communications in some African countries. Many African countries have very few telephone landlines, so rural areas are often cut off. Instead of investing in landlines, countries like Tanzania have used mobile technology to leapfrog the problem. In 2001, Africa became the first region in the world where there are more mobile phone users than people using landlines.

Activity

11 Explain why Nokia continues to expand in Africa.

12 Summarise the benefits that Nokia gets from opening new branches in LEDC countries.

Figure 10 African countries that have few landlines have used mobile technology to leapfrog the problem

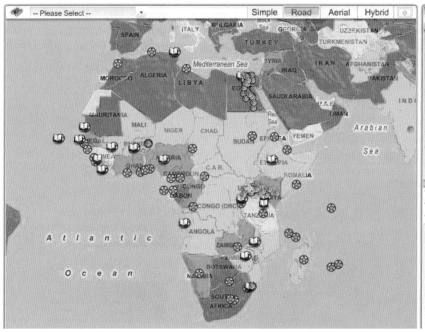

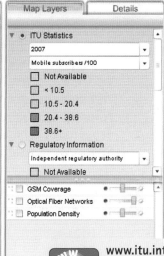

Figure 11 Mobile phone subscribers in Africa. This screenshot is from a GIS (or digital) atlas updated by the International Telecommunications Union. You can use the dialogue box (map layers) on the right of the screen to choose data for different years. The atlas then redraws the map to display the data you have chosen

www.itu.int/ITU-D/connect/gblview/index.html
This weblink takes you to ITU Global View which is the on-line atlas from which the screenshot in Figure 11 is taken.

Activity

13 Use Figure 11 to describe the distribution of African countries where the number of mobile phone subscribers is
a) below 20.4 per 100
b) above 38.6 per 100.

14 Use the weblink to view the ITU Global View atlas of Africa. Use the map layers tool to choose '% mobile coverage' and 'broadband subscribers'.
a) Describe the patterns on each map.
b) How important do you think it is for Africa's development to improve mobile and internet coverage? Explain how these technologies could help:
i) African businesses   ii) African teenagers.

Chapter 7
Economic activity and the environment

KEY QUESTIONS

- ✪ How do different economic activities damage the environment?

- ✪ What conflicts develop between damage to the environment and the creation of wealth and job opportunities?

- ✪ How could these conflicts be managed to conserve a sustainable environment?

 China

Investigating economic growth in China and its impact on the environment

Since the early 1990s China's economy has been growing rapidly. Chinese businesses and foreign multi-national companies (MNCs) have invested in new service industries and factories making everything from shoes to high-tech electronics. As China's economy has grown, the Gross National Income (GNI) or average income per person has also grown. Fewer people in China live in poverty and the standard of living for ordinary Chinese people is improving. By 2020, it is expected that the Chinese GNI per person will be similar to the GNI in the USA today. However, this development is causing a massive impact on the environment. It seems that this type of growth is unsustainable.

Local impacts

The factories and power plants that have created China's economic success are also creating a pollution problem. The burning of fossil fuels releases nitrogen dioxide (NO_2) – a pollutant that combines with moisture in the air and results in **acid rain**. Nitrogen dioxide also causes breathing and other health problems. As the Chinese have become wealthier, car ownership has increased rapidly. Cars also emit nitrogen dioxide from their exhausts. The result is a thick smog of pollution that hangs over eastern China. This smog often reaches levels that are dangerous for human health in cities such as Beijing. Research by the European Space Agency shows that **emissions** of nitrogen dioxide in China increased by 50 per cent in the period from 1995 to 2005. Chinese official figures admit that 400,000 Chinese people die every year from diseases caused by air pollution. The World Bank says that 16 of the 20 most polluted cities in the world are in China.

Figure 1 Smog in Beijing reduces visibility and causes breathing problems and eye irritations

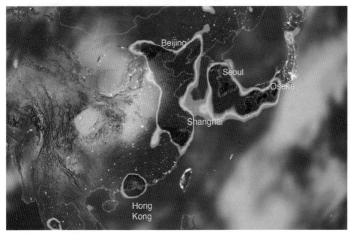

Figure 2 A false-colour satellite image of East Asia showing levels of nitrogen dioxide pollution. The brightest red colours show the highest concentrations of NO₂. Yellows and greens show lower concentrations of NO₂

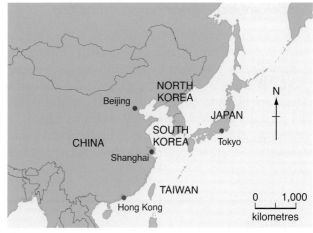

Figure 3 China and east Asia

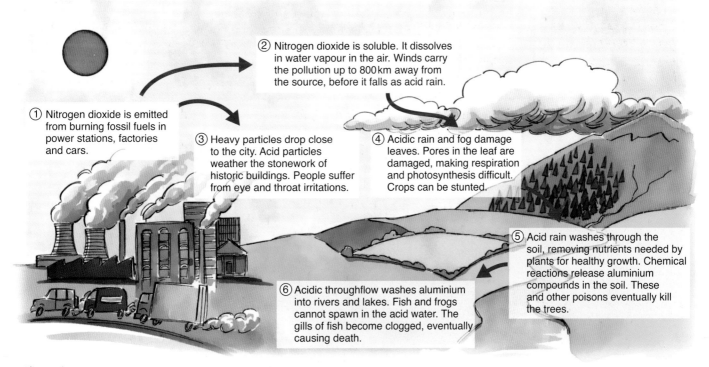

① Nitrogen dioxide is emitted from burning fossil fuels in power stations, factories and cars.

② Nitrogen dioxide is soluble. It dissolves in water vapour in the air. Winds carry the pollution up to 800 km away from the source, before it falls as acid rain.

③ Heavy particles drop close to the city. Acid particles weather the stonework of historic buildings. People suffer from eye and throat irritations.

④ Acidic rain and fog damage leaves. Pores in the leaf are damaged, making respiration and photosynthesis difficult. Crops can be stunted.

⑤ Acid rain washes through the soil, removing nutrients needed by plants for healthy growth. Chemical reactions release aluminium compounds in the soil. These and other poisons eventually kill the trees.

⑥ Acidic throughflow washes aluminium into rivers and lakes. Fish and frogs cannot spawn in the acid water. The gills of fish become clogged, eventually causing death.

Figure 4 How emissions of nitrogen dioxide lead to acid rain

Activity

1 List three sources of nitrogen dioxide pollution.

2 Use Figures 2 and 3 to describe the distribution (see page 25) of the highest concentrations of nitrogen dioxide.

3 Use Figure 4 to help explain the pollution pattern on Figure 2.

4 List the effects of acid pollution under the headings:
a) Human health
b) The environment
c) The economy.

Global impacts: greenhouse emissions

China's rapid economic development is also having consequences for the global environment. China's industrial growth requires electrical power. About 80 per cent of this is generated by burning coal and coke. This method of electricity production emits more of the greenhouse gas carbon dioxide than any other. There are plans to build another 500 coal-fired power stations to keep pace with the growing demand for energy. Many of China's other growing industries also emit a lot of greenhouse gases. The steel and cement industries are two examples. Steel and cement are both needed to build China's rapidly growing cities.

Year	Thousands of tonnes of carbon
1950	129
1960	2,202
1970	2,022
1980	12,060
1985	20,665
1990	31,136
1995	67,843
2000	83,836

Figure 5 Recent increases in emissions of carbon dioxide from China's manufacture of cement are due to massive growth of the construction industry

Activity

5 a) Use Figure 5 to draw a line graph.
   b) Describe the increase in emissions from cement making.
   c) Use the trend of this graph to predict likely emissions from this source in 2010.

6 Use Figure 6.
   a) Compare the number of people in China who have no electricity with those in:
      i) South Asia including India
      ii) Africa south of the Sahara.
   b) Explain how the development of these regions could lead to greater greenhouse gas emissions.

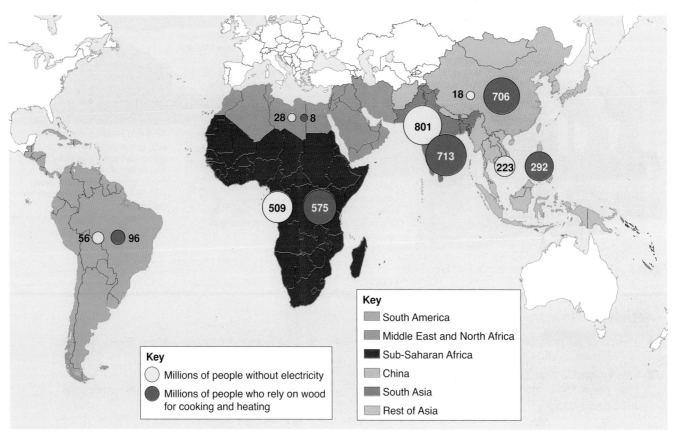

Key
- ◯ Millions of people without electricity
- ⬤ Millions of people who rely on wood for cooking and heating

Key
- South America
- Middle East and North Africa
- Sub-Saharan Africa
- China
- South Asia
- Rest of Asia

Figure 6 Global energy poverty: the number of people without electricity

Carbon is mobile in the environment: it is able to flow, or be transferred from one store to another through a series of processes such as **respiration** or solution. The flow of carbon between various stores is shown in the **carbon cycle** diagram in Figure 7. It is important to understand that some parts of the environment store carbon only for short periods of time. Others, such as fossil fuels, are able to store the carbon over much longer periods of time. These are known as **carbon sinks**.

The enhanced greenhouse effect

The greenhouse effect is a natural process of our atmosphere. Without it, the average surface temperature of the Earth would be –17 °C rather than the 15 °C we currently experience. However, human activities over the last 200 years have significantly increased the concentration of greenhouse gases in the atmosphere. Emissions of greenhouse gases throw the global carbon cycle out of balance, transferring carbon from sinks such as forests and reserves of coal into the atmosphere. With larger concentrations of greenhouse gases in the atmosphere able to absorb and trap heat, the greenhouse effect has become stronger. This is what we call the **enhanced greenhouse effect**.

Activity

7   Study Figure 7.
   a) Describe all the human actions that release carbon dioxide into the atmosphere.
   b) Give two reasons why the burning of tropical rainforests will increase the amount of carbon dioxide in the atmosphere.

8   **a)** Describe the difference in the speed of transfer of carbon in the natural part of the cycle compared to the part of the cycle affected by human action.
   b) Explain what difference this makes to the amount of carbon stored in the atmosphere compared with the long-lasting carbon sinks. Explain why this is alarming.

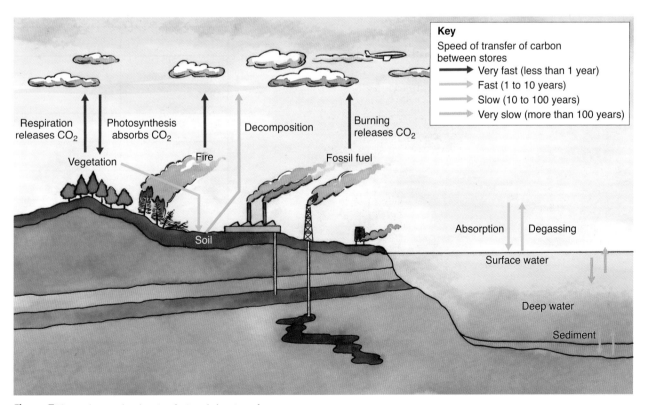

Figure 7 The carbon cycle, showing fast and slow transfers

Ecosystems are seen as a resource

The environment is viewed by people and businesses as a resource: something that can be used for our benefit. Since the Industrial Revolution, a little over 200 years ago, the world's ecosystems have been used to supply people with the things they needed:

- Rainforests and coniferous forests have supplied people with timber and other raw materials.
- Land for farming has been created by draining wetlands and destroying forests.
- Ecosystems such as mangroves and coral reefs have increasingly been used as places for tourism development.

The Millennium Ecosystem Assessment

The Millennium Ecosystem Assessment (MEA) is a scientific report into the state of the environment. Published in 2005, it took five years to write and involved the work of more than 1,360 experts from all parts of the world. The MEA concludes that the world's resources have been used to create a better standard of living for billions of people. Ecosystems have been used to supply people with a range of resources including food, clothing, energy and fresh water. However, it also warns that economic activity has done a great deal of damage to the environment (see Figure 8). One problem identified in the report is that modern fishing methods are unsustainable. More fish are caught each year than are replaced by natural reproduction. This problem was first seen in the Atlantic off the coast of Newfoundland, Canada, as shown in Figure 9.

	Millennium Ecosystem Assessment
1	Modern fishing techniques do not allow fish stocks to recover. The amount of fish in the seas is decreasing rapidly.
2	The 2 billion people who live in the world's driest areas are increasingly at risk from drought and poverty.
3	We are using up fresh water supplies at a rate that is faster than they can be replaced.
4	Climate change will cause massive problems for many ecosystems.
5	The increasing use of artificial fertilisers and burning of fossil fuels has doubled the amount of nitrogen pollution. This is causing problems in river and marine ecosystems.
6	The destruction of ecosystems (for example, forests, coral reefs and wetlands) is causing the extinction of many species at a scale that is greater than anything seen in the past.

Figure 8 The six main problems identified by the Millennium Ecosystem Assessment

Year	% of catch
1994	13
1995	10
1996	11
1997	14
1998	6
1999	8
2000	10
2001	40
2002	8
2003	22
2004	21
2005	10

Figure 10 Overfishing by European Union countries. Figures refer to the percentage of the total catch that is considered by scientists to be beyond what is safe for the fish stocks to fully recover (Source: Eurostat, Commission Services)

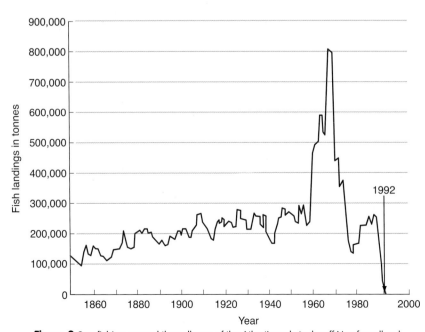

Figure 9 Overfishing caused the collapse of the Atlantic cod stocks off Newfoundland

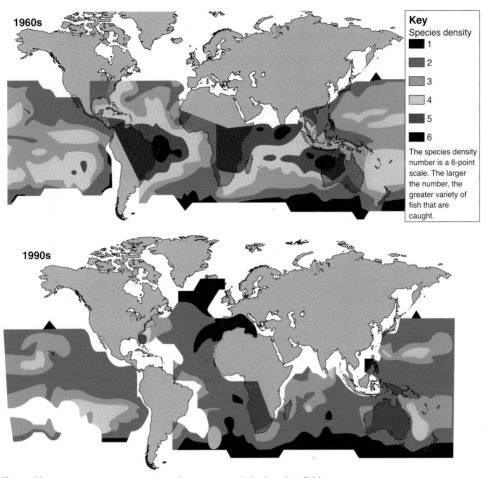

Figure 11 Changes in average number of species caught by **longline fishing**

Activity

9 Study each of the problems listed in Figure 8 by the MEA. Suggest how each of the following economic activities could have contributed to these problems.

Agriculture   **Fishing**
Mining   **Timber extraction**
Manufacturing   **Tourism**

10 Study Figure 9.
   a) Describe the trend of the cod catch:
      i)   up to 1950
      ii) after 1950.
   b) Explain what happened in the early 1990s and suggest how this affected the local fishing industry.

11 a) Choose a suitable graphical method to represent Figure 10.
   b) What conclusions do you draw from the data in Figures 9 and 10?

12 Use Figure 11 and an atlas to describe the changing distribution of fish species caught between the 1960s and 1990s.

13 Conservationists are concerned that fish stocks in the North Sea could crash due to overfishing, just like the Atlantic cod crash off Newfoundland. Suggest:
   a) two alternative strategies to protect fish stocks in the North Sea from overfishing
   b) how fishermen, boat repair yards and fishmongers would be affected by your suggestions.

Sustainable development

China's economic success has created huge wealth for some. It is also beginning to improve the standard of living and quality of life of many ordinary Chinese people. However, it is obvious that this development is also harming the environment. The current growth of China and many other countries, both More Economically Developed Countries (MEDCs) and Less Economically Developed Countries (LEDCs), is unsustainable. What China needs to do is find a way of improving the lives of people now without using up too many natural resources or polluting the environment so badly that future generations will have a lower quality of life. This would be sustainable development.

'Sustainable development is development that meets the needs of the present without compromising the ability of future generations to meet their own needs'.

Our Common Future, World Commission on Environmental Development (WCED) report 1987

Development can be described as sustainable development if:
- it improves standards of living for people today
- it uses natural resources at a rate that can be renewed. For example, trees are replanted when mature timber is felled
- businesses take responsibility for their impact on the environment. They reduce waste and pollution. They also pay the cost for cleaning up the environment if there is accidental damage such as an oil spill.

Figure 12 'Squeezing the Earth'

Country	Number of Earths needed to sustain the whole world at that level of national consumption	
USA		5.3
UK		3.1
France		3.0
Germany		2.5
Russia		2.4
Brazil		1.2
Mauritius		1.0
China		0.8
India		0.4
Malawi		0.3

Figure 13 The ecological footprint of selected countries: the number of Earths needed to support the whole world at current levels of consumption

Activity

14 Work in pairs to discuss Figure 12. Which continents are shown being squeezed? Why is this half of the world shown? What or who does the hand represent?

15 Study Figure 13.
   a) Sort these countries into LEDCs and MEDCs.
   b) Explain why one group of countries is using more of the world's resources than the other.
   c) Explain what is likely to happen to the world's resources as LEDCs continue to develop.

16 a) Study Figure 14. Choose a suitable graphical technique to represent the data.
   b) Compare the growth of the UK population to its growing ecological footprint.
   c) What conclusions do you draw from this data about development (sustainable or unsustainable) in the UK?

17 a) Study Figure 15 and calculate your own ecological footprint.
   b) Discuss and then list the factors that might increase or decrease your own ecological footprint.

18 Explain why the unsustainable use of resources by some societies will result in poverty for others.

Year	UK ecological footprint	UK population (millions)
1961	1.0	52.8
1971	1.7	55.9
1981	2.0	56.4
1991	2.5	57.4
2006	3.1	60.0

Figure 14 The UK's growing ecological footprint: number of planet Earths needed to support the UK's growing levels of consumption

1 What do you eat?

Fresh food	5
Processed food	10
Ready meals	15

2 Where was last year's holiday?

UK	10
Europe	20
Rest of world	150

3 What kind of home do you live in?

Flat	5
Terraced house	15
Detached	35

4 How do you travel?

Walk or cycle	3
Public transport	25
Car	50

5 How often do you wash?

Bath every day	20
Shower every day	4
Shower every other day	2

How much did you score?

24–49
Well done, your ecological footprint is close to the world average. Your lifestyle is sustainable. If everyone lived like you we could survive on the resources of just one planet Earth.

50–99
Your ecological footprint is similar to the European average. If everyone lived like you we would need the resources of between one and three planet Earths.

100–199
Your ecological footprint is larger than that of the average European. If everyone lived like you we would need four or more planet Earths.

200+
Your ecological footprint is similar to those living in the USA. If everyone lived like you we would need more than five planet Earths to sustain your quality of life.

Figure 15 Calculate your own ecological footprint

Chapter 8 Integrated case study: Development and trade in the Solomon Islands

 Solomon Islands

Development issues in the Solomon Islands

The Solomon Islands are a large group of islands in the Pacific Ocean. The World Bank estimates GNI (per person) to be $730, making this the poorest country in the Pacific region. The country has one of the highest malaria rates in the world and infant mortality is high. Standards of education also need to be improved and adult literacy is relatively low compared with that in other Pacific countries.

The country's economic and social development was crippled by fighting between different ethnic groups between 2000 and 2003. Since then the Australian government has provided long-term development aid of Aus$236 million a year (2008–2009). A large part of this is used to support the country's police force.

The islands are at risk from natural disasters. Cyclones are a major threat. Cyclone Zoe, which was the strongest cyclone ever recorded in the southern hemisphere, took a course through the Solomon Islands in December 2002. Australian warships were sent to give emergency aid but the islands are so remote it took several days to reach the affected areas. An earthquake and tsunami hit the western Solomon Islands on 2 April 2007. The wave affected 36,500 people, 6,300 houses were damaged and 52 people were killed. Australia, which is the nearest MEDC, offered emergency aid of Aus$6 million to provide shelter, food and clean water and prevent the spread of disease.

Activity

1 Use Figure 1 to copy and complete the following:

The Solomon Islands are located in the ...... Ocean to the ...... of Papua New Guinea. They are approximately ...... km to the north of New Caledonia. They are between the Tropic of Capricorn and the ....

www.rollbackmalaria.org/
This weblink takes you to the home page of the Roll Back Malaria campaign. The site contains lots of information about how people can combat the disease.

Figure 2 Soloman Islands: children playing in a lagoon

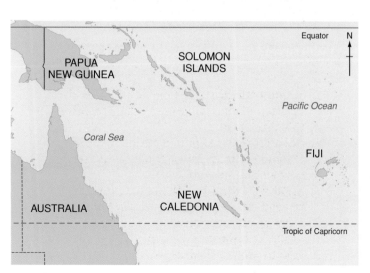

Figure 1 Location of the Solomon Islands

kilometres

Figure 3 An extract from the UNICEF website

Because populations are dispersed over multiple islands in the Pacific, efficient delivery of healthcare, education and other social services is difficult. Airfares are expensive and not always available to the most remote corners of the region; even boat service may be infrequent. The region is also linguistically diverse, necessitating multiple translations of UNICEF messages. Many islands in the region are vulnerable to natural disasters like floods, typhoons and volcanic eruptions.

Figure 4 Development data for selected Pacific region countries. Source: UNICEF

	Solomon Islands	New Zealand	Fiji
GNI US$	730	28,780	3,800
Under 5 mortality (deaths per 1,000 live births)	73	6	18
Life expectancy	63	80	69
% infants with a low birth weight	13	6	10
% population using improved (safe) drinking water	70	100	47
Maternal mortality: Annual number of women who die from pregnancy-related causes per every 100,000 live births	220	9	210
Adult literacy (% who can read and write)	76	100	96

Figure 5 Street market sign in Honiara

Activity

2 Use examples to explain the difference between emergency aid and development aid.

3 Explain how the geography of the Solomon Islands has made social development difficult.

4 Choose suitable graphical techniques to illustrate the development data in Figure 4. Use your graphs to make comparisons between the Solomon Islands and the other countries.

5 a) Suggest why the City Council chose to display the information about buying fish in this street market.

b) Adult literacy is about 76 per cent in the Solomon Islands. Explain how the poster gets around this problem.

c) Another health issue is malaria. Do some research into how people can protect themselves from malaria. Design a public health poster to show people how they can help to protect themselves.

Figure 6 Logs are tagged before being exported to Malaysia

Figure 7 A skid track to remove felled logs has been created on a slope that is far too steep. This has caused soil erosion. The loggers had promised that they would not create this kind of problem

Figure 8 Waste timber from the logging process blocking the Kahigi river. The MNC agreed not to fell trees within 50 m of any major river or 25 m of any minor stream

Work and trade

More than 80 per cent of Solomon Islanders are subsistence farmers or fishermen. This means they only produce enough food to feed their own families and do not make much profit from their work. The natural ecosystem of these mountainous islands is tropical rainforest. Many multi-national logging companies have recently bought logging rights to fell and export timber from the Solomons. Where land has been cleared of forest it has often been converted to oil palm plantations. These trees produce an oil that can be used in the production of many products including vegetable oil for cooking, soap, washing powder and bio-fuel (such as bio-diesel for cars).

Why is the forest resource so important to local communities?

The second-largest island in the Solomons is Santa Isabel. The island is heavily forested and most communities are located around the coastline. The rainforest is an important resource for villagers. They use it to gather foodstuffs such as fruit, nuts and honey. They also collect leaves, berries and bark to make custom medicine (herbal remedies). For many communities the forest is also an important source of firewood, timber for houses and boat building, palms for roofing materials, and craft materials such as vines for ropes.

Why is logging unsustainable?

The communities in the North of Santa Isabel sold logging rights to a Malaysian MNC. This meant that the land was still owned by the community, but the logging company paid the community for the right to log timber for a fixed period of time. They made various promises to protect the environment during logging. Figures 7 and 8 provide evidence that the MNC operating in Santa Isabel broke these promises. Their poor logging practices have resulted in severe soil erosion, silting up of rivers and flooding.

Commercial logging firms such as this MNC make more profit if they work quickly. They use bulldozers to reach the valuable trees. For every tree cut for its timber, it is estimated that 40 or more are destroyed by the heavy machinery. This process destroys trees that have fruit, nuts or medicinal value to the villagers. The villagers have received payments from the MNC, but this amounts to only about 1 per cent of the value of the timber.

Figure 9 Members of the Lobi Community in Morovo Lagoon use a portable sawmill to process a freshly felled log into planks. This tree was felled as part of a sustainable eco-forestry programme

Could logging be sustainable?

Logging can provide a better income for local people and not cause long-term damage to the environment. This can be achieved if:

- only a few trees are felled; if only two trees per hectare are felled every ten years, a rainforest will naturally recover
- saplings are planted to replace cut trees
- local people fell the trees and process the timber on site using small portable tools.

The Isabel Sustainable Forestry Management Project is one small example. It was funded by aid (€450,000) given by the European Union in the mid-1990s. The scheme created skilled labour for local people. Trees are carefully felled to avoid damage to trees of fruit or medicinal value. The timber is then cut into planks in the forest using a portable sawmill. This means that large machines are not needed. It also means that local people add value to the timber so more profit is retained by the village. This method of processing the timber means that the community keeps about 40 per cent of the finished value of the timber. The project was successful in protecting 17,000 hectares of forest, but the amount of timber produced has been very small.

Activity

6 Explain why the forest is a valuable resource to the communities of the Solomon Islands.

7 Use the text on this page to complete a table like this:

Effects on...	Unsustainable logging practices	Sustainable logging practices
Soils		
Rivers		
Fruit, nut and medicinal trees		

8 Imagine you could visit the communities affected by commercial logging in Santa Isabel. Discuss what they might tell you about the impact of the MNC on their lives.

9 Explain how the Isabel Sustainable Forestry Management Project is able to:
a) improve standards of living today
b) ensure decent standards of living for future generations.

Investigating the timber trade

Timber, oil palm and minerals are the Solomon Islands' main exports. Logging is a fast-growing industry. Most of the timber is exported in the round: that means that it is exported as unprocessed logs. The country is currently exporting 830,000 cubic metres of legally felled logs (plus an unknown quantity of illegally felled timber). This is estimated to be three times the sustainable rate. Many ecologists are very worried about the damaging impact that this industry is having on the Solomon Islands' fragile environment. If felling continues at this rate, most of the country's rainforest will have been destroyed by 2020.

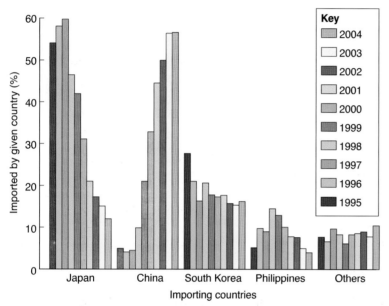

Figure 10 The destination of timber exports from Papua New Guinea and the Solomon Islands

One country importing timber from the Solomon Islands is China. China's imports of timber and forest products have grown rapidly in recent years. Softwoods from the conifer forests of East Russia make up a large part of the imports. China also imports a lot of hardwoods from tropical rainforests. Some timber imports are used in China's furniture and paper industries. A lot is used in the rapidly growing plywood industry. Plywood is used in the building industry. Demand for plywood in China has shot up as Chinese cities have experienced a massive building boom.

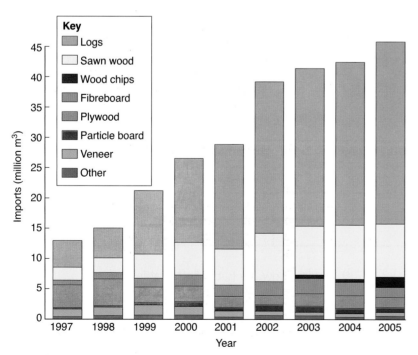

Figure 11 Imports of timber products to China, 1997 to 2005

Activity

10 Study Figure 10.
  a) Which country imported most timber in 2004?
  b) Describe what has happened to exports to Japan compared with exports to China.

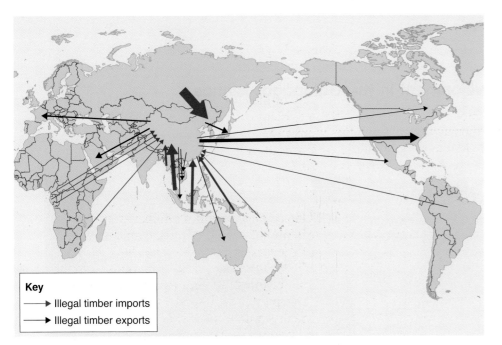

Figure 12 Illegal imports and exports of wood-based products (2005) estimated by Global Timber, a UK-based NGO

Key
→ Illegal timber imports
→ Illegal timber exports

The growth of timber imports to China is causing serious concern to some Non-Governmental Organisations (NGOs). The timber trade is unsustainable at the current rate. It is causing deforestation in many countries where logging is much more rapid than replanting schemes. It is estimated that if logging continues at this rate, the natural rainforests of Indonesia will be all gone by 2015, and the massive conifer forests of Far East Russia will have gone by 2025.

Deforestation damages wildlife habitats and often leads to problems of soil erosion. In many cases the logging companies are acting illegally. Illegal logging practices include:

- cutting trees without permission
- cutting trees close to rivers where soil erosion can then lead to flooding
- ignoring the rights of local land owners
- paying bribes to local officials
- non-payment of taxes.

	Percentage
Brazil	80
Burma (Myanmar)	90
Cambodia	100
Cameroon	50
Congo	90
Equatorial Guinea	90
Gabon	70
Indonesia	90
Liberia	100
Malaysia	60
Papua New Guinea	70
Russia	80
Solomon Islands	70

Figure 13 Percentage of imports of timber to China in 2004 that are considered to be illegal according to the NGO Global Timber

Activity

11 Use Figure 11 to estimate the import of the following products in both 1997 and 2005:
  a) Total timber imports
  b) Logs
  c) Sawn wood
  d) Plywood.

12 What does the decrease in the import of plywood tell you about China's own plywood industry?

13 Use Figure 12.
  a) From which region of the world does China import most timber illegally?
  b) Use an atlas to name the three tropical countries from which China illegally imports most timber.

14 Use a world outline map to plot the countries named in Figure 13. Use a suitable technique to show the values in Figure 13 on your map.

Investigating sustainable development in the Galapagos Islands

Your enquiry...

- How developed is Ecuador? What standard of living do people have?
- What are the main economic activities in the Galapagos Islands?
- How do these economic activities affect the natural environment?
- Is this kind of economic development sustainable?

Your decision...

How can the Galapagos Islands manage its economic development in a way that is sustainable?

Figure 1 The marine iguanas of the Galapagos depend on a clean and healthy marine ecosystem. There is a fear that the increasing population of the islands will lead to more pollution. In February 2001 the oil tanker *Jessica* ran aground and spilled fuel. It was being delivered for use by the islanders for cooking and for powering their boats

Part A: introducing Ecuador and the Galapagos Islands

Ecuador is a Less Economically Developed Country (LEDC) in South America.

It relies on the export of a number of primary commodities, as can be seen in Figure 3. Ecuador also earns money from abroad by attracting an increasing number of foreign tourists. Roughly one in six of these tourists visits the Galapagos Islands.

Much of Ecuador's trade is with the USA and the European Union. It has also formed a trading partnership with a number of other LEDCs. This trading bloc involves Ecuador, Bolivia, Colombia, Peru and Venezuela. It is known as the Andean Community of Nations (CAN in Spanish). Each country within this trading bloc has a free trade arrangement with other countries in the bloc.

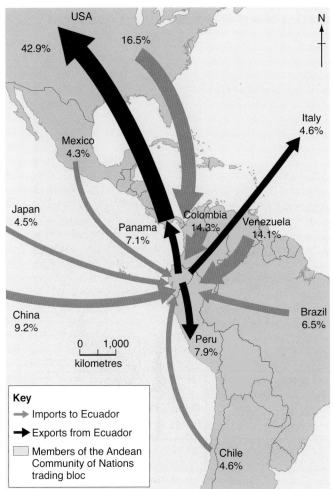

Figure 2 Ecuador's main trading partners

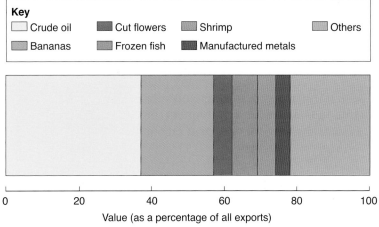

Figure 3 Ecuador's exports

Indicator	Ecuador	Average for South and Central America
Child (under 5) mortality (%) (2006)	24	27
Adult literacy (2006)	91	90
Life expectancy (2006)	75	73
Telephones per 100 population (2005)	60	61
Internet users per 100 population (2005)	7	16
GNI per capita (US$) (2006)	1,790	4,847

Figure 4 Development indicators for Ecuador

Activity

1 Use Figures 2 and 3 to complete the following statement:
Ecuador's largest export and import partner is .... It also imports goods from ... and ... in Asia. Ecuador's largest export is .... Bananas are worth ... per cent of all exports from Ecuador.

2 Use Figure 3 to give three examples of Ecuador's primary commodity exports.

3 a) Describe the distribution (see page 25) of the Andean Community of Nations trading bloc.
   b) Explain the advantages of being a member of a trading bloc.

4 a) Use Figure 4 to compare Ecuador's level of development with other South and Central American countries.
   b) Explain why it is important for the people of Ecuador that the country continues to develop its economy.

The Galapagos Islands

The Galapagos Islands are a group of volcanic islands in the Pacific Ocean that belong to Ecuador. The Galapagos Islands are world famous for their wildlife: many plants and animals here occur nowhere else on Earth. Due to their unique environment, the Galapagos have international recognition and protection. The islands, and 133,000 km^2 of the marine environment that surrounds them, have UNESCO World Heritage Site status. It is also a Biosphere Reserve and whale sanctuary.

Economic activity in the islands depends largely on fishing and tourism. Both of these activities have the potential to harm the physical environment of the islands and the surrounding marine environment.

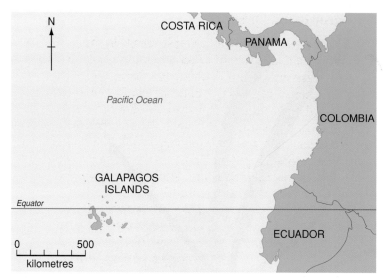

Figure 5 The location of the Galapagos Islands

primary sector   secondary sector   tertiary sector

Type of economic activity	1982		1990		2001	
	Population 2,503	**% 100**	**Population 4,759**	**% 100**	**Population 8,765**	**% 100**
Agriculture and fishing	468	18.7	786	16.5	1,491	17.0
Mining	0	0.0	2	0.0	14	0.2
Total primary		18.7		16.5		17.2
Manufacturing	109	4.4	200	4.2	503	5.7
Electricity, gas and water	11	0.4	28	0.6	43	0.5
Construction (building)	275	11.0	371	7.8	663	7.6
Total secondary		15.8		12.6		13.8
Retailing	175	7.0	553	11.6	1,416	16.2
Transport	250	10.0	716	15.0	1,342	15.3
Banking	21	0.8	63	1.3	308	3.5
Services (incl. tourism)	1,073	42.9	1,916	40.3	2,243	25.6
Other services	17	0.7	100	2.1	688	7.8
New businesses	104	4.2	24	0.5	52	0.6
Total tertiary		65.6		70.8		68.4

Figure 6 Economic activity in the Galapagos Islands

The growth of tourism

Tourism is the main form of employment in the Galapagos and the islands' main source of income. Most tourists visit from Ecuador on cruise ships. The total number of tourists is limited to avoid damage to the natural environment. But from 2007 more tourists will be visiting the islands. Twelve cruise ships a year, each with 500 passengers on board, will be allowed to dock in San Cristobal from 2007. The economic impact on the island would be huge and is expected to create a positive multiplier effect. It is estimated that the local economy could receive an extra US$20 million to US$30 million a year. Some of this will be direct investment: tourists have to pay a US$100 admission fee to enter the islands. It is argued that the islands desperately need the extra jobs that would be created by these extra visitors. There will be extra direct employment opportunities, such as tour guides. Other benefits will be indirect: for example, extra sales of fish to restaurants and to the cruise ships.

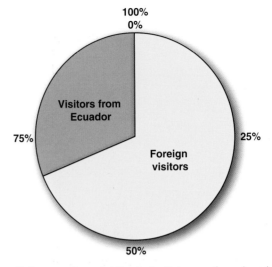

Figure 9 The percentage of visitors to the Galapagos from abroad

Year	Tourist arrivals
2000	68,865
2001	77,570
2002	82,226
2003	90,533
2004	No data
2005	122,000
2006	130,000

Figure 7 Tourist arrivals to the Galapagos. Source: Galapagos National Park

Activity

5 Describe the location (see page 252) of the Galapagos Islands.

6 Study Figure 6.
   a) Draw a graph that shows how the total numbers of people employed in both agriculture and fishing and tourism have changed over time.
   b) Describe the pattern of your graph.

7 **a)** Use Figure 7 to draw a suitable graph to show the increase in tourist arrivals to the Galapagos.
   b) What percentage of tourists are foreign visitors?

8 Define what is meant by direct and indirect economic benefits of investment.

9 Explain how allowing extra tourists to visit the islands could create a positive multiplier effect.

Figure 8 Visiting tourists are a vital resource to the economy of the Galapagos

Part B: the conflict between fishermen and the travel and tourism industry

Figure 10 The Galapagos albatross. A female lays about 25 eggs in its lifetime, but only two of these will hatch and survive. The Galapagos albatross therefore has a very low reproduction rate, which makes the natural rate of increase of its total population very slow

In 2004 fishermen from Ecuador began to demand the right to begin **longline fishing** (or longlining) in the waters around the Galapagos. Longline fishing uses a single line up to 130 km long, which is dragged behind the boat. The line contains thousands of hooks that are baited with scraps of fish and squid and are intended to catch large fish such as tuna and swordfish. However, they also catch and kill a large number of unwanted birds and animals, known as bycatch. The bycatch includes seabirds such as albatross, which swoop down on the baited hooks before they sink out of reach. They are then dragged under water and drowned. Conservation charities estimate that 300,000 seabirds are killed in this way each year around the world, as well as turtles, seals and cetaceans (whales and dolphins).

There have been violent clashes between fishermen and conservationists, who claim that the fishermen have already destroyed the local population of lobster and sea cucumber. Conservationists fear that longlining will kill seabirds, sharks, turtles and whales.

'If this situation doesn't change it will be catastrophic for the Galapagos,' says Xavier Bustamente, leader of Fundación Natura conservation group. The travel and tourism industry agrees with the conservationists on this issue. More than 100,000 tourists visit the islands every year. Tour operators believe that the special environment of the islands must remain unspoiled so that it continues to attract tourists. The International Galapagos Tour Operators Association warns that the fishing industry is worth only £6 million a year, whereas tourism to the islands earns £90 million.

Figure 11 Huge numbers of birds, turtles and whales are caught as bycatch by longline fishing

This conflict has attracted attention at a much wider scale. Ecuador's Government would like to help the fishermen because the fishermen's union was very supportive at a time when the Government was weak. However, the Government is under pressure from the United Nations Educational, Scientific and Cultural Organisation (UNESCO) to conserve the Galapagos marine environment.

UNESCO sees the Galapagos as a very rare resource that must be protected from pollution, exploitation and unsustainable development. It protects the islands and their marine ecosystems as a World Heritage Site. This recognises the 'outstanding value to humanity' of these special ecosystems.

Activity

10 Give two reasons why longline fishing off Galapagos would endanger the local albatross population.

11 The text describes four different groups of people. Each of these groups sees the resources of the Galapagos environment in a different way.
   a) List the four different groups of people.
   b) Which group/groups see the islands' ecosystems as a:
   • financial resource that should be exploited
   • vulnerable resource that needs protection
   • rare resource that has scientific and cultural value
   • resource that we should manage so that future generations will also benefit.
   c) Choose two opposing groups and carefully explain their points of view.

12 Explain why both increased fishing and increased tourism might be an unsustainable development for the Galapagos Islands.

13 Imagine you have to explain the situation in the Galapagos to intelligent aliens. Explain why the Galapagos offers 'outstanding value to humanity' and why the islands' environment should be protected for educational, scientific and cultural reasons.

Part C: time to decide. What is your plan for the sustainable development of the islands?

It's time to make your decision. How can the Galapagos Islands manage its economic development in a way that is sustainable?

Human Impact

Humans ... are an introduced and invasive species, and the islands have seen a dramatic growth in recent years. Settlers from mainland Ecuador have moved to the islands in search of a better life. This population pressure causes serious problems for conservation. With only three per cent of the islands set aside for human settlement, there is little room for people, and little for them to do except fish. Competition between local fishermen and the National Park and conservation workers has been heated and sometimes violent. Despite restrictions on new immigration, it continues.

Figure 12 Extract from the International Galapagos Tour Operators Association website

Year	Population*
1950	1,346
1962	2,391
1974	4,037
1982	6,119
1990	9,785
2001	18,640
2015*	40,000
2027*	80,000

*Population figures for 2015 and 2027 are estimates

Figure 13 Population growth in the Galapagos

Activity

14 a) Use Figure 12 to explain how the settlers from Ecuador view the Galapagos as a resource.
  b) Graph the data in Figure 13.
  c) Explain how these two figures may indicate that development in the Galapagos is unsustainable.

15 You are to advise the government of Ecuador as to how it should sustainably develop the Galapagos Islands. You should advise which one economic activity should mainly be developed. Choose from fishing, tourism and fish processing. Explain why your choice is better than the other two economic activities.

EXAMINER'S TIPS

Justifying your solution

In Section C of Paper 2 you will be asked to solve a geographical problem. You will be marked on how well you justify your solution to the problem.

Tip 1

Look carefully at the instructions. Activity 15 asks you to do three things:

- Choose an economic activity to develop.
- Explain the good points of your choice of activity.
- Explain what it is about the other two economic activities that made you decide not to develop them.

Tip 2

When explaining these good and bad points make sure that you divide them into effects on both the environment and the local people.

Tip 3

Make sure that your report looks at the short term impacts of your decision and also at your strategy's longer term sustainability.

Glossary

A

Abstraction – When people remove water from either a surface or **groundwater store**.

Acid rain – Unnaturally acidic rain caused by a high presence of certain pollutants (especially nitrogen dioxide and sulphur dioxide) in the atmosphere.

Adult literacy – The percentage of the adult population who can read and write.

Affordable homes – Houses that are either sold or rented at relatively low cost.

Air pressure – The force caused by molecules in the atmosphere pressing down on the Earth's surface.

Alluvium – Sediments deposited by a river. Alluvium may be fine grains, such as silt, or coarser sands and gravels.

Anomaly – An unexpected event or piece of data that does not follow the expected pattern or normal trend.

Anticyclone – A **high pressure** system in the atmosphere associated with dry, settled periods of **weather**.

Aquifer – A large **store** of underground water usually contained in **porous** rocks.

Arch – A landform sometimes found at the coast. Sea arches are formed by the **erosion** of weaknesses in a headland.

Atmosphere – The layer of gases surrounding the Earth. The atmosphere is one **store** in the **water cycle**.

B

Bar – A coastal landform created by the **deposition** of **sediment** across the **mouth** of river.

Bedding planes – Lines of weakness between the layers of sedimentary rock.

Bi-lateral aid – Aid that is passed directly from one country to a partner country.

Biodiversity – The variety of living things.

Biodiversity hotspot – A region with a particularly great variety of organisms. Central America (or Meso-America) is one such hotspot.

Biomes – Very large **ecosystems** (for example, tropical rainforests or deserts).

Blow-outs – Erosional hollows in a sand dune. Blow outs are caused by trampling which kills the vegetation. The wind then erodes the sand.

Brain drain – The reduction in the number of highly qualified workers due to emigration.

Brownfield sites – Development sites where older buildings are demolished or renovated before a new development takes place.

Bunds – Small stone walls that are built along contour lines to retain soil moisture and prevent soil being washed away.

Business rates – A type of tax paid by a company.

C

Canopy – The upper layer of a forest. The canopy receives most sunlight so contains many leaves, flowers and fruit.

Carbon cycle – The flow of carbon between various **stores**.

Carbon sinks – Places where carbon is stored over very long periods of time, for example, in fossil fuels.

Carbon-neutral development – Developments which do not add any extra carbon dioxide to the atmosphere. The new buildings are highly energy efficient and may use renewable technologies.

Catchment area – The area from which a river collects its water. This is also called a **drainage basin**.

Cave – A natural cavity in the rock. This landform is created by **weathering** and **erosion**.

Circular migration – The flow and return of people between rural and **urban** areas. People leave the countryside when there are few farming jobs and return at busier times of the year.

Climate – Taking **weather** readings over long periods of time, and then working out averages, patterns and trends.

Climate change – A long-term change in the annual **weather** conditions. These changes can be natural or caused by human actions.

Cloud forests – Tropical forests located in mountains where they are permanently surrounded by cloud.

Commute – When people who live in rural areas travel every day to jobs in **urban** areas.

Continentality – The climatic condition of large land masses heating up and cooling down very quickly.

Counter urbanisation – The movement of people and businesses from large cities to smaller towns and rural areas.

Cut-off – The point where river **erosion** closes the neck of a **meander** to leave an ox-bow lake.

Cycle of poverty – A theory which suggests that children of poor families find it difficult to earn higher incomes.

D

Debt – The money owed by a country.

Deforestation – The cutting down or burning of trees.

De-industrialisation – A shift in employment from **manufacturing** to jobs that provide a service.

Delta – A river landform found at the **mouth** of a river where **deposition** causes new land to be formed.

Depopulation – The loss of people due to migration and low birth rates. For example, many of the rural areas of Iceland are suffering from depopulation.

Deposition – The laying down of material in the landscape. Deposition occurs when the force that was carrying the **sediment** is reduced.

Depressions – Weather systems, associated with low air pressure, that bring changeable weather that usually includes wind and rain. The rainfall brought by depressions is also known as frontal rainfall or cyclonic rainfall.

Desertification – When the **climate** of a dry region becomes even drier. Vegetation dies or is eaten by grazing animals and the soil becomes vulnerable to soil **erosion**.

Development aid – Help which is given to tackle poverty and improve **quality of life**. Development aid is usually given to combat long-term problems such as improving education or healthcare rather than to deal with an emergency such as a famine.

Development gap – The difference in wealth between rich and poor countries.

Digital divide – The gap between those who have digital technology (usually defined by computer ownership ot internet connection) and those who do not.

Direct benefit – An immediate advantage created by an improvement in the economy. For example, a direct benefit of a new company opening a factory in a region is new jobs.

Discharge – The amount of water flowing through a river channel or out of an **aquifer**. Discharge is measured in cubic metres per second (cumecs).

Displaced – People who have lost their home because of conflict, or an environmental disaster or because their land has been used by a major development such as the creation of a new reservoir.

Diversification – Where a much wider variety of new business opportunities and jobs are created in a region.

Dumping – The practice of selling goods cheaply abroad if they cannot be sold at home. For example, tomatoes that cannot be sold in Europe are sold cheaply in Africa.

E

Economic migrant – A migrant who moves in order to find work.

Ecosystems – A community of plants and animals and the environment in which they live. Ecosystems include both living parts (for example, plants) and non-living parts (for example, air and water). Ecosystems exist at various scales from **biomes** such as rainforests to micro-scale ecosystems such as garden ponds.

Ecotourism – Small-scale tourist projects that create money for conservation as well as creating local jobs.

Emergency aid – Help that is given urgently after a natural disaster or a conflict to protect the lives of the survivors.

Emergent – The tallest trees in a forest that poke out above the **canopy**.

Emissions – Chemicals released into the atmosphere by industry, such as nitrogen dioxide.

Employment structure – The number of people working in the **primary**, **secondary** and **tertiary sectors** of the economy.

Enhanced greenhouse effect – A strengthening of the greenhouse effect caused by the release by humans of large concentrations of **greenhouse gases** into the atmosphere.

Erosion – The wearing away of the landscape. See **abrasion**, and **hydraulic action**.

Evaporation – Where water changes state from liquid into vapour.

Evapotranspiration – The combined loss of water from plants by both evaporation and transpiration.

Exports – The sale of products from one country to another.

F

Fjords – Deep-water sea inlets in the coastline of countries that have been **eroded** by ice.

Floodways – Artificial channels built to divert the flow of a river. –

Flow – The movement of a substance from one **store** to another (for example, the ways in which water moves in the **water cycle**).

Food air miles – How far the food has been transported to get from producer to consumer.

Foreign exchange – The way in which countries earn money from abroad (for example, by the sale of **exports** or by attracting foreign tourists.

Formal occupations – Jobs that receive a regular wage and which are recognised and controlled by the state.

Free trade – When countries trade without any limits to the amount of goods that can be **exported** and **imported**.

Fuel poverty – A family who cannot afford to heat their home are said to live in fuel poverty. In the UK households who spend more than 10% of their income on fuel fall into this category.

G

Gender inequality – Differences in income or **quality of life** that exist between men and women.

Global warming – The slight rise in average temperature of the Earth's atmosphere that is a sign of **climate change**.

Globalisation – Flows of people, ideas, money and goods are making an increasingly complex global web that links people and places from distant continents together.

Gorge – A steep sided, narrow valley. Gorges are often found below a **waterfall**.

Green Belts – A government policy used to prevent the spread of cities into the countryside. It is very difficult to get planning permission for new homes inside a green belt.

Greenfield sites – Plots of land which have not been used before for building.

Greenhouse gases – Gases such as carbon dioxide and methane that are able to trap heat in the atmosphere.

Gross National Income (GNI) per person – The average income in a country. It is also known as **Gross National Product (GNP) per person**. –

Groundwater flow – The **flow** of water through rocks.

Groundwater stores – Water in the ground below the water table.

Groynes – A type of coastal defence scheme consisting of low walls built into the sea. Groynes trap the **sediment** that is being moved by **longshore drift**.

H

High pressure – Values of air pressure between 1020 and 1040 millibars. High pressure systems are known as **anticyclones** and bring periods of dry settled **weather**.

High-tech industries – The use of advanced technology in **manufacturing** such as defence systems and medical equipment.

Housing tenure – The legal right to live in a house. Housing tenure is usually categorised as either rented or owner occupied.

Hydro-electric power (HEP) – Electricity generated by water flowing through turbines.

Hydrograph – A line graph showing the **discharge** of a river over time.

Hypothesis – A statement that can be proved or disproved using the available evidence.

I

Impermeable – Soil or rock which does not allow water to pass through it, such as clay.

Import duty – A tax placed on goods brought into a country to make them more expensive.

Imports – The purchase of goods from another country.

Income poverty – A household is said to be in **income poverty** if it's income is less than 60% of the contemporary UK median (average) household income.

Indigenous peoples – Tribal groups who are native to a particular place.

Indirect benefit – An advantage that has come as a result of the investment by a business but not within the business itself. For example, an indirect benefit of a new company opening a factory in a region is work for other local businesses.

Infant mortality rate (IMR) – The number of children who die before the age of one for every 1000 that are born.

Infiltration – The movement of water from the **ground surface** into the soil.

Informal sector – The sector of the economy that includes many types of irregular jobs as well as types of work such as household chores, childcare and studying.

Informal settlements – Homes where the householders have no legal rights to the land, that is, they do not have legal **housing tenure**. Informal settlements are commonly known as shanty towns and squatter settlements.

Infrastructure – The systems needed to make a region work efficiently. These include paved roads, communication facilities, power supply, water supplies and sewers.

Inner urban – The central, and usually older, part of a city.

Intercepts – When water is prevented from falling directly to the ground. For example, the **canopy** of leaves in a forest intercepts rainfall.

Interdependence – The complex patterns of trade, communication and aid, which link different countries together.

J

Joints – Cracks that form lines of weaknesses running through rock.

K

Key services – The way in which **ecosystems** provide benefits for people. For example, **mangrove forests** act as coastal buffers, soaking up wave energy during a storm and reducing the risk of **erosion** and flooding.

Knowledge economy – Jobs which require high levels of education or training.

Knowledge Intensive Service (KIS) – Industries such as finance and education.

L

Labour intensive – Work that is still done by hand rather than using labour-saving machines.

Lagoon – A shallow pond of salt water.

Less economically developed countries (LEDCs) – The countries that are to the south of the Brandt Line in Central and South America, Africa and parts of Asia. Most LEDCs have lower incomes than More Economically Developed Countries (MEDCs).

Life expectancy – The average age to which people can expect to live.

Load – The **sediment** carried by a river.

Local Development Framework – A planning document produced, after consultation with local residents and businesses, by a local authority.

Longline fishing – A fishing technique in which fish are caught on hooks on extremely long lines. The technique is criticised by conservationists for killing many species of unwanted fish as well as sea birds, turtles and sharks.

Longshore drift – A process by which beach material is moved along the coast.

Low pressure – Values of air pressure between 970 and 990 millibars. Low pressure systems are known as **cyclones** and bring periods of unsettled weather with strong winds and rain.

M

Mangrove forests – A type of tropical forest that grows in coastal regions.

Manufactured goods – Goods which have been produced in a factory or workshop.

Manufacturing – The production of goods and processed materials by the **secondary sector** of the economy.

Maritime climate – The climatic condition of land close to sea. The sea moderates temperatures meaning that there are only small variations in temperature.

Meander – A river landform. A sweeping curve or bend in the river's course.

Mechanisation – The increased use of machines to replace human labour.

Meltwater – Water flowing from a melting glacier. Meltwater rivers are seasonal with very low **discharges** in winter and very high discharges in summer.

Micro-credit – Where small loans are given to businessmen and women who are too poor to qualify for traditional bank loans.

Millennium Development Goals (MDGs) – Development targets set by the United Nations with aims to meet by 2015.

Monsoon – A **climate** type experienced in South Asia in which a seasonal pattern of wind brings a distinct wet season.

More economically developed countries (MEDCs) – The countries that are to the North of the Brandt Line in North America, Europe, northern Asia and parts of Oceania. Most MEDCs have higher incomes than Less Economically Developed Countries (LEDCs).

Mouth – The point at which a river enters a lake or the sea.

Multi-lateral aid – Funding that involves many donor countries.

Multi-national companies (MNCs) – Large businesses, such as Sony, Microsoft and McDonald's, which have branches in several countries. Multi-national companies are also known as trans-national companies.

N

Natural increase – A population increase which is due to there being more births than deaths.

Net out-migration – When more people leave the region than move in.

NIMBY – People who object to a development because they live close by and will be affected by it are said to be MIMBYs. The initials stand for 'Not in my back yard'.

Non-governmental organisation (NGO) – Non-profit-making organisations, such as Oxfam, ActionAid or WaterAid, which are independent of the government.

O

Off-grid electricity – Electricity supplied by using car batteries or photo-voltaic cells and which is not connected to the national electricity network.

Over-abstraction – When water is abstracted at a faster rate than it is recharged, leading to a **store** of water decreasing in size.

Overland flow – The **flow** of water across the **ground surface**.

Overseas Development Aid (ODA) – Government funding given to many different long-term development projects abroad.

P

Pastoral farmers – Farmers who keep grazing animals such as cattle or goats.

Percolation – A **flow** in the **water cycle**. The movement of water out of the soil and into the rocks below.

Permeable – A rock which allows water to pass though it, such as limestone.

Plant – A factory, office or laboratory.

Plunge pool – The pool of water found at the base of a **waterfall**.

Population density – The number of people per square kilometre

Porous – A rock which has many tiny gaps within it (pores) that allow it to **store** water, such as chalk and sandstone.

Positive multiplier – A positive chain of events triggered by the creation of new jobs in a region.

Poverty line – A level of income. If someone earns less than this amount they are said to be poor.

Prevailing wind – The direction in which the wind most often blows.

Primary commodities – Raw materials which have not been processed. Coal, minerals and unprocessed foodstuffs are all examples.

Primary enrolment – The percentage of children of primary school age who regularly attend primary school.

Private sector – People who are either **self-employed** or work for a larger company or organisation that is not controlled by the government.

Public sector – People employed by the national, regional or local government.

Pull factors – Reasons that attract migrants to move to a new home.

Push factors – Reasons that force people to move away from their existing home.

Q

Quality of life – A measure of the happiness and contentment of an individual or family.

Quotas – Restrictions on the amount of particular goods that can be **imported** each year.

R

Rainwater harvesting – The collection of rain water. For example, the collection and use of rain water from the roof of a house.

Recharge – Water that enters an **aquifer** and refills a **groundwater store**.

Refugees – People who are in danger and who leave their homes for their own safety. Refugees may move because of a natural disaster such as a volcanic eruption or because of conflict.

Regional Spatial Strategy – A planning document produced by each Regional Assembly in England which considers the need for such things as new housing, roads and schools.

Remittances – The return of money sent by migrant workers to support their families who have remained at home.

Renewable resource – Something useful to people that is capable of replacing itself. Water, forests and wind energy are all examples of renewable resources.

Repossession – Repossession occurs when an owner occupier who has a mortgage fails to make their regular repayments to the bank or building society. At this point they can be forced to leave the home and the bank will sell the house so that it can get its money back.

Respiration – The biological process of breathing in which living things take in the oxygen that is needed for life and expel waste gases such as carbon dioxide.

Revetments – Structures that reduce the **erosion** of coastlines and river banks.

Rotational cliff slumping – A process where soft cliffs collapse towards the sea.

Rural depopulation – When the population of a rural region decreases.

S

Sahel – The semi-arid region of North Africa to the south of the Sahara desert. The word means 'shore' in Arabic.

Sanitation – The safe disposal and treatment of sewage and waste water.

Saturated soil – When the pore spaces of a soil are full of water. In these conditions the water table comes to the surface and the ground is covered in puddles.

Savanna ecosystem – An **ecosystem** of grasslands with scattered trees and bushes, and which has a seasonal wet/dry **climate.**

Science parks – A group of industrial buildings used for research and design or high tech processes. Also known as **technology parks**.

Second homes – Houses which are used only for holidays or at weekends. Also called holiday cottages.

Security of tenure – Where people have no legal right to live in their home and could be evicted at any time.

Sediment – Material carried by a river or wave in the sea. Sediment is produced by **erosion** and varies in size from large particles such as boulders through gravel and sand down to silt and mud.

Self-employed – People who are their own boss.

Self-help – Improvement projects carried out by ordinary people rather than by businesses or governments. Many homes in **informal settlements** are improved in this way.

Social housing – Homes that are rented from a not-for-profit organisation such as a housing association or the local authority.

Social landlord – An organisation, such as a Housing Association or Local Council, which rents properties on a not-for-profit basis.

Social premium – A small payment made by **Fairtrade** companies to their suppliers, which is then used to fund community projects such as wells.

Socio-economic – A combination of social and economic factors.

Soft engineering – Alternative method of reducing floods by planting trees or allowing areas to flood naturally.

Soil store – Store in the **water cycle** between the **ground surface** and rock, composed of minerals, organic matter, air and water.

Solar footprint – The amount of the Sun's energy that heats each square metre of the Earth varies depending on latitude. Near the equator the Sun's rays hit the Earth at almost 90 degrees. The solar footprint is small and the amount of energy received per square metre is much greater than near to the poles.

Source – The place where a river starts to flow.

Spit – A coastal landform formed by the **deposition** of **sediment** in a low mound where the coastline changes direction, for example, at the **mouth** of a river.

Stack – An **erosional** landform, a pillar of rock that remains when a headland recedes.

Stakeholders – Any person or group of people who have an interest in a planning / development issue.

Standard of living – A measure of the relative wealth of individuals or families.

Store – A place where something remains for a period of time (for example, within the **water cycle** or **carbon cycle**).

Storm surge – A rise in sea level caused by unusually low air pressure (also known as a **cyclone**). A storm surge can cause devastating coastal floods.

Stump – A low pillar of rock that is left behind when a stack has been **eroded**.

Sub-Saharan Africa – Africa south of the Sahara.

Subsidy – A payment which a country makes to its own farmers and businesses so that their goods can be sold at a lower price to consumers.

Subsistence – A type of economic activity where very little money is used. In subsistence farming the farmer produces only enough food to feed the family. There is very little surplus that can be sold for cash.

Surface stores – Places where water is found on the surface such as lakes and reservoirs.

Sustainable community – A community which is designed to have minimal impacts on the environment. Such communities may make use of energy efficiency, renewable technologies and also make use of local employment and services to reduce the impacts of commuting.

Sustainable development – Making changes that improve the **quality of life** for people today but without damaging the environment so that future generations will also be able to have a reasonable quality of life.

T

Technology parks – A group of industrial buildings used for research and design or high tech processes. Also known as **science parks**.

Tele-working – Jobs where most of the working week is spent working from home. Tele-working (or tele-cottaging) has been made more widely available by the use of personal computers, mobile technology and the internet.

Temperature range – The difference between maximum and minimum temperature. A temperature range can be calculated for a single day, or for the year.

Throughflow – The **flow** of water through the soil. Part of the **water cycle**.

Tombolo – A coastal landform made by **deposition** of **sediment** joining the coast to an island.

Trade blocs – Trading partnerships between different countries. The European Union is one example.

Transpiration – Water loss from plants though pores in the leaves.

Transport – The movement of material through the landscape.

Tundra – An **ecosystem** largely found in the Arctic region. The tundra is treeless because the growing season is short and the average monthly temperature is below 10 degrees Celsius.

U

Undercutting – **Erosion** at the base of a river cliff, sea cliff or **waterfall**.

Unsustainable – At a rate that cannot be maintained.

Unsustainable development – Improving the lives of people but in a way that is using up too many natural resources and/or is polluting the environment so badly that future generations will have a lower **quality of life**.

Urban – Larger towns and cities. The United Nations definition is that urban settlements have more than 20,000 inhabitants.

Urban heat island – When a city has temperatures that are warmer than in the surrounding rural area.

Urban microclimate – The small-scale, local climate of a large city which is influenced by its buildings and traffic.

Urban population – The percentage of a country's population that lives in settlements greater than 20,000 people.

Urban sprawl – The growth of towns and cities into the countryside. Sprawl is usually considered to have negative impacts.

Urbanisation – The physical and human growth of towns and cities.

W

Water cycle – The continuous **flow** of water between the Earth's surface and the atmosphere – also called the **hydrological cycle**.

Wave-cut notch – **Undercut** slot cut into the bottom of a cliff by wave action.

Wave-cut platform – A rocky shelf in front of a cliff. The wave cut platform is caused by **erosion** and left by the retreat of the cliff.

Weathering – The breaking up of rock by the effects of the **weather** such as rainfall and temperature change.

Wilderness – Areas that have been left in a wild state. Wilderness regions are uninhabited and are not farmed. Large parts of Iceland can be described as wilderness.

Wildlife corridor – Strips of habitat which allow wild animals to migrate from one **ecosystem** to another. For example, wildlife corridors can be created by planting hedgerows and trees to connect remaining fragments of forest together.

Windward – The aspect of a slope which faces into the **prevailing wind**.

Wing dikes – Walls built into the river channel to increase river flow and thereby to deepen the river channel.

Index

018654

THOMAS TALLIS SCHOOL LIBRARY